E.P. 2
Morgan, College Algebra
MADE IN U.S.A.

COLLEGE ALGEBRA

by
FRANK M. MORGAN
Director of Clark School
Hanover, New Hampshire
Formerly Assistant Professor of Mathematics
Dartmouth College

AMERICAN BOOK COMPANY
NEW YORK CINCINNATI CHICAGO BOSTON ATLANTA DALLAS SAN FRANCISCO

E.P. 2
Morgan, College Algebra
MADE IN U.S.A.

Preface

Today there are two classes of students entering college—those with one year's preparation in algebra and those with two. Most colleges place both groups in the same section; hence, a college algebra text must be written to satisfy both groups. Moreover, very often a pupil has had no algebra for a year or two before entering college. Hence, a rapid review of elementary algebra is necessary before proceeding with the advanced work. In this text the author has tried to present this elementary work in such a manner that the pupil who remembers most of his elementary algebra will not be bored. To do this, ideas new to the pupil have been introduced. Such, for example, is the work on geometric interpretation of multiplication, division, addition, and subtraction. Note also the emphasis that has been placed on what one can do and what one cannot do to an equation and expect the resulting equation to be equivalent to the given one.

This text emphasizes accuracy of statement. Whenever assumptions are made, they are so labeled.

When it is possible to interpret an analytical result graphically, it is done. Hence, the idea of functionality is emphasized.

In order to make the pupil think while studying, questions have been interspersed throughout the text, making it read somewhat like a class discussion.

In order to add interest to the subject matter, historical notes will be found in the text. These show the pupil that the subject has had many years of growth. Throughout the text there are numerous lists of well-graded exercises. A few problems, entitled Honor Problems, have been added in order to arouse the interest of the few budding mathematical geniuses one may be fortunate enough to have in class. At the end of most chapters there is a comprehensive Mastery Test, which covers the work of the chapter and contains review problems on earlier chapters.

The college algebra text of a couple of decades ago included many topics which today are omitted in a first-year course. For example, "series" is now taught in the calculus. Tartaglia's solution of the general cubic and Ferrari's solution of the general quartic are now usually taught only in courses devoted entirely to the theory of equations. This text omits these topics.

Some of the topics included in this text may be omitted in a short course—for example, maximum and minimum of quadratic functions, which bright students enjoy, some of the harder cases of factoring, some of the proofs of the determinant theorems, etc. There is included enough work to enable any teacher to pick a course to suit the needs of his particular class.

The author wishes to thank Professor Robin Robinson of Dartmouth College, Professor T. C. Benton of Pennsylvania State College, Professor R. Beatley of Harvard University, Professor Burton Jones of Cornell University, Professor William Breckenridge formerly of Teachers College, Columbia University, and Mr. Eugene Barker of San Francisco for their helpful criticisms and suggestions.

Table of Contents

Algebraic Symbols

The following symbols are merely shorthand expressions, which we shall use extensively.

Symbol	**Meaning**
$+$	Plus, more than, added to, increased by, the sum of.
$-$	Minus, subtracted from, diminished by, the difference of.
$3 \times a$, $3 \cdot a$, $3\,a$	Three times a, a multiplied by 3, the product of 3 and a.
$\frac{x}{y}$, $x \div y$	The quotient of x divided by y or just x divided by y.
$=$	Is equal to.
$\stackrel{?}{=}$	Are the two quantities equal?
$\neq$	Is not equal to.
$\equiv$	Is identical with.
$>$	Is greater than.
$<$	Is less than.
$\geq$	Is equal to or greater than.
$\leq$	Is equal to or less than.
$\propto$	Varies as, is proportional to.

Symbol	Name	
( )	Parenthesis	These signs are used as in arithmetic to indicate that the expressions included are to be treated as a whole. Thus, $5(2 + 1)$ means 5 is to be multiplied by $2 + 1$, or 3.
{ }	Brace	
[ ]	Bracket	
—	Vinculum	

CHAPTER I

Numbers of Arithmetic

Whole numbers

One of the first things primitive man learned to do was to count, or to answer the question: How many objects are there in a given group? For this purpose he used the so-called whole numbers, or *positive integers:*

$$1, 2, 3, 4, 5, \cdots$$

For centuries these were the only numbers man needed; and even today when asked to think of a number, most people will immediately think of a positive integer, or whole number. We know that if we add or multiply any two positive integers we obtain a positive integer; whereas if we subtract or divide two positive integers, the result need not be a positive integer. Which of the following can be reduced to a positive integer: $11 + 3; 3 - 11; 8 \div 4; 4 \div 12$?

Man next asked such questions as the following: If there are A objects in one group and B objects in a second group, how many objects are there in the two groups? If there are A objects in a group and B objects are taken away, how many objects remain? If there are A objects in one group and there are B such groups, how many objects are there all together? How many groups of B objects each can be formed from a group of A objects? In answering such questions, he introduced the ideas of addition, subtraction, multiplication, and division.

If positive integers are added in any order, will the result be the same? Is $7 + 3$ the same as $3 + 7$? Is the product of two positive integers the same regardless of the order of the integers? For example, is 7×5 the same as 5×7?

Since the order in which numbers are added or in which they are multiplied does not affect the final result, we say the operations of addition and multiplication are *commutative*.

Do you think the operations of subtraction and division are commutative? Is $3 - 7$ the same as $7 - 3$? Is $8 \div 4$ the same as $4 \div 8$?

In the addition of positive integers we can group the numbers in any way we wish. For example $5 + (3 + 2)$ is the same as $(5 + 3) + 2$. This principle is also true with respect to multiplication. For example, $3 \times (5 \times 7)$, and $(3 \times 5) \times 7$ have the same value. Hence we say the operations of addition and multiplication are *associative; i.e.*, we can operate with any two numbers first and then with another number.

We also note, for example, that $3 \times (2 + 5)$ is the same as $3 \times 2 + 3 \times 5$. That is, multiplication is *distributive* with respect to addition.

In illustrating these laws we have used particular whole numbers. The laws are true, however, for all types of numbers, such as fractions, negative numbers, etc. Thus a, b, and c may stand for any numbers whatsoever, and the laws can be stated symbolically as follows:

1. $a + b = b + a$
2. $a + (b + c) = (a + b) + c$
3. $ab = ba$
4. $a(bc) = (ab)c$
5. $a(b + c) = ab + ac$

Classification of integers

Integers are often classified as being even or odd. An even integer is one that is divisible by 2, while an odd integer is one that is not divisible by 2. Is 278 even or odd? Euclid (about 300 B.C.) classified integers as composite and prime, a prime number being one that has no integral factors [1] except itself and unity. What do you think would be the definition of a composite number? Which of the following numbers do you think are prime and which composite: 7, 16, 29, 11, 42?

If two numbers have no common factor except unity, they are said to be prime to each other, or relatively prime. There exists an infinite number of prime numbers, a fact which Euclid was the first mathematician to prove.

Many theorems concerning prime numbers are rather difficult to prove. In fact, some apparently simple ones, such as finding a prime larger than a given prime or finding directly the value of the nth prime, have never been completely solved.

Fractions

Ancient man next introduced *fractions* to represent parts of the whole. However, he found their use very difficult, as is seen from a mathematical document written about 1700 B.C. by an Egyptian priest named Ahmes. In this document, which is now in the British Museum, a fraction whose numerator is not unity is always expressed as the sum of fractions with unit numerators. Thus,

$$\tfrac{2}{7} = \tfrac{1}{4} + \tfrac{1}{28}, \qquad \text{while} \qquad \tfrac{2}{99} = \tfrac{1}{66} + \tfrac{1}{198}$$

How the Egyptians reduced fractions to such sums is not known, but it is believed the results were found by trial.

EXERCISES

1. What are the prime factors of 30?

2. List all the prime numbers from 1 to 50.

3. By inspection find as many sets of three relatively prime whole numbers as you can which satisfy the relation $x^2 + y^2 = z^2$.

4. If a positive integer is a perfect square, show that it contains every prime factor at least twice. What can you say about a perfect cube? a perfect nth power?

[1] If several integers are multiplied together, the resulting number is called their *product*. Each of the several integers is called an *integral factor* of the product. Thus 2 and 3 are integral factors of 6.

Rational numbers

When a magnitude is measured and is not an exact multiple of the unit of measure, fractions must be used. These numbers are intimately associated with the idea of a ratio. Thus, in geometry, two line segments AB and CD are called *commensurable* if there exists a third segment PQ of which each of the other two is an exact multiple (Fig. 1). PQ is then called a

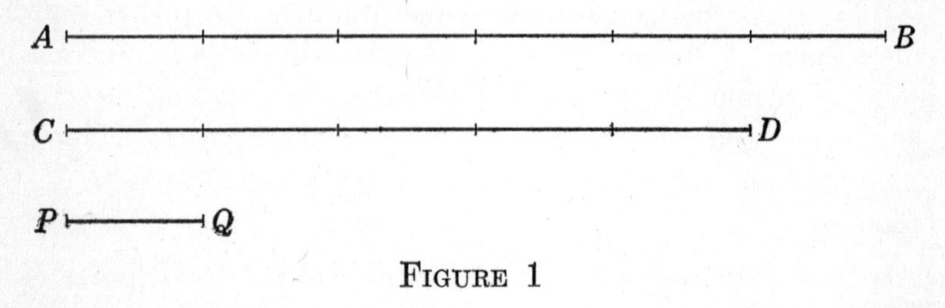

FIGURE 1

common measure of AB and CD. If AB is exactly m times PQ, and CD is exactly n times PQ, m and n being integers, we say that the ratio of AB to CD is m/n, and we write:

$$\frac{AB}{CD} = \frac{m}{n}$$

If CD is chosen as the unit of length, we have:

The measure of $$AB = \frac{m}{n}$$

A number which can be written as a fraction in which the numerator and denominator are both integers is called a *rational number*. Such numbers suffice to represent the measure of any magnitude which is commensurable with the unit of measure.

Irrational numbers

If two magnitudes have no common measure, they are called *incommensurable*. Thus we know from our study of geometry that the diagonal of a square (Fig. 2) is not commensurable with one of its sides. Hence, the length of the diagonal of a square whose side is 1 unit cannot be expressed exactly by any rational number. To meet this deficiency the so-called *irrational numbers*, such as the $\sqrt{2}$, were introduced.

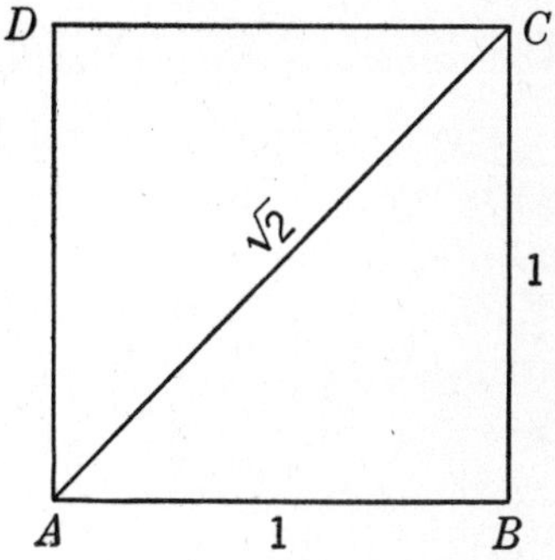

It is beyond the scope of this book to treat irrational numbers fully. But we may note that they serve to express *the ratio of pairs of incommensurable magnitudes*, and, in particular, to express *the measure of any magnitude which is incommensurable with the unit.*

D C √2 1 A 1 B

FIGURE 2

Moreover, *any irrational number may be represented approximately by a rational number with an error which is as small as we please.* This follows from the following considerations.

It is important to note that *the result of any actual direct measurement is always a rational number.* For example, in measuring a distance we use a foot rule marked into fourths, or eighths, or thirty-seconds of an inch, or else some more accurate instrument divided into hundredths or thousandths of a unit; and we always observe how many of these divisions are contained in the length to be measured. The result is, therefore, always a rational number m/n where n represents the number of parts into which the unit was divided. Any such actual measurement is, of course, an *approximation.* The greater the accuracy of the measurement (and this accuracy depends among other things on the number of divisions of the unit) the closer is the approximation. Since we may think of the unit as divided into as many divisions as we please, we may conclude that *any magnitude can be expressed by a rational number to as high a degree of accuracy as may be desired.* Thus, the length of the diagonal of a square whose side measures 1 inch is expressed approximately (in inches) by the following rational numbers:

$$1.4, \ 1.41, \ 1.414, \ 1.4142$$

These decimals are all rational approximations, increasing in accuracy as the number of decimal places increases, to the irrational number $\sqrt{2}$.

The number system of arithmetic

The (unsigned) rational and irrational numbers, together with the number zero (which is counted among the rational numbers), constitute the *number system of arithmetic.* Which of the following numbers belong to the number system of arithmetic?

$$\pi, \ -5, \ \sqrt{2}, \ -\frac{3}{\sqrt{5}}, \ -\pi^2, \ 7$$

EXERCISES

1. Is $\sqrt[3]{8}$ rational or irrational? Why?

2. Which of the following numbers are rational and which are irrational?

$$\frac{3}{5}\sqrt{9}, \qquad \sqrt{7}, \qquad \sqrt{\frac{4}{9}}, \qquad 3.273, \qquad \pi, \qquad \frac{\sqrt{3}}{\sqrt{9}}$$

3. Prove $\sqrt{2}$ is irrational. *Hint.* Assume $\sqrt{2} = \frac{a}{b}$ where a and b are relatively prime. Then $2\,b^2 = a^2$. Now show that a and b each contain the factor 2 and hence are not relatively prime, which contradicts the hypothesis.

The arithmetical scale

An arithmetical scale is a scale that starts at some point 0 and extends from 0 in *one direction.* The most familiar example of such a scale is the yardstick. Another example is the beam on a certain type of balance. In the first example the divisions of the scale represent lengths, while in the second they represent weights.

In general, the quantities represented by an arithmetical scale are expressed by the numbers of arithmetic—*i.e.*, unsigned numbers—and represent simply the magnitude or size or amount of something.

Negative numbers and zero

We learned in arithmetic that to subtract 3 from 7 means to find what number one must add to 3 in order to get 7. In other words, subtraction reduces to finding what number one must add to the subtrahend in order to produce the minuend. Obviously, there is no meaning to $3 - 7$ if we limit ourselves to positive integers. However, we do know it is possible to purchase an article for $7, pay $3 down and charge the balance of $4. To denote the fact that the $4 has been charged we may prefix a minus sign; *i.e.*, we write -4. Hence we say $3 - 7 = -4$. The number -4 is called a negative number. When negative numbers were first introduced in the fifteenth century, they were often referred to as "fictitious numbers".

If a and b are given numbers and x is such that $x + b = a$, then x is called the difference between a and b. If b is less than a, then $x = a - b$; if $b = a$, then $x = 0$, which we call zero; if b is greater than a, then $x = -(b - a)$. Thus $7 - 7 = 0$; $5 - 11 = -6$. What is the value of $5 - 8$? $3 - 3$? $0 - 4$? $4 - 0$?

The number system of algebra

Corresponding to any unsigned number x (except 0) there exist two signed numbers $+x$ and $-x$. The magnitude represented by a signed number is called the absolute value of the number, and is indicated by placing a vertical line on each side of the number. Thus, the absolute value of $+3$ and of -3 is 3; in symbols $|+3| = |-3| = 3$. Likewise, $|+a| = |-a| = a$.

If $|a|$ is greater than $|b|$, we say that a is numerically larger than b. Thus -7 is numerically larger than 2. Is 2 numerically greater than -2?

The signed numbers are called rational or irrational according as their absolute values are rational or irrational. Together the positive, negative, rational, and irrational numbers, and zero (which is neither positive nor negative and has no sign) make up the *real number system*. Any number of this system is called a *real number*. These numbers are contained in the *number system of algebra.* The number system of algebra also contains the so-called imaginary or complex numbers, which will be discussed in Chapter XIV.

A signed number represents a magnitude and one of two opposite senses. The two opposite senses are often expressed by such phrases as "to the right of", "to the left of"; "greater than", "less than"; "above", "below".

The algebraic scale

The best known example of an algebraic scale is the ordinary thermometer. What is meant by $+7°$? $-10°$?

An algebraic scale starts at an arbitrary point called the zero point or origin (0), and extends from this point in two opposite directions. In the scale pictured in Fig. 3, numbers

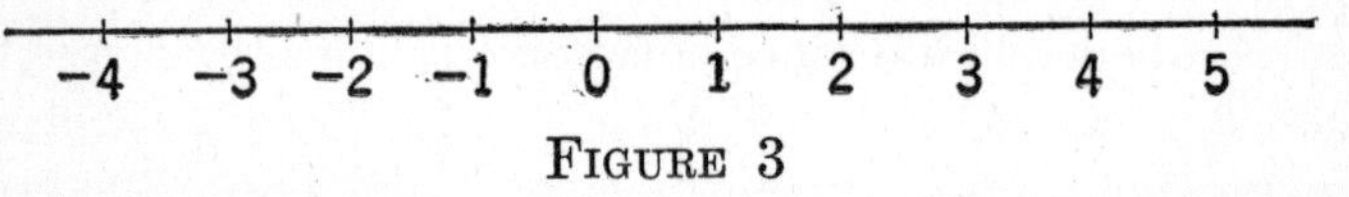

FIGURE 3

at the left of 0 are taken as negative and those at the right as positive. Hence any given number on the scale is greater than any number at its left and less than any number at its right. Thus -7 is less than -2, just as on a thermometer 7° below zero is a lower temperature than 2° below zero.

EXERCISES

1. What type of scale is used on: (a) radio dials? (b) pressure gauges? (c) ammeters?

2. What type of scale is used on a map in denoting: (a) latitude? (b) longitude?

Definitions and symbols

Before one can understand any subject it is necessary that he become familiar with certain technical words and phrases. The following words and phrases will be used extensively throughout this course.

Any expression which is formed by combining letters (or letters and numbers) by the four fundamental operations is called an *algebraic expression,* provided the letters represent numbers. Thus, $7x^2y$ and $2x - 3y - 5$ are algebraic expressions if x and y represent numbers.

The expression $4a$ means $a + a + a + a$, and the number 4 is called the *numerical coefficient* of a.

If in a product all of the factors are equal, the product is called a *power* of one of them. Thus $x \cdot x \cdot x \cdot x \cdot x$ is the fifth power of x and is written x^5. The number x is called the *base*, and the number 5, which in this case indicates how many times x is used as a factor, an *exponent*. It is not necessary for an exponent to be a positive integer. (See page 53.)

A *term* is an algebraic expression whose parts are not separated by a plus or minus sign. Thus, in the expression $5x^2 + 3xy - 7$, there are three terms, namely:

$$5x^2,\ 3xy, \text{ and } -7$$

A single term is often called a *monomial.*

Any factor of a term is called the *coefficient* of the remaining part. Thus, in $5a^2b$, 5 is the coefficient of a^2b; $5a^2$ is the coefficient of b; and $5b$ is the coefficient of a^2. The coefficient of x in the expression x, is 1.

A *binomial* is an algebraic expression consisting of two terms. For example, $2x + y$ and $a - b$ are binomials.

A *trinomial* is an algebraic expression consisting of three terms. For example, $2x + y - z$ and $a - 3b + 2c$ are trinomials.

A *polynomial* is an algebraic expression consisting of two or more terms. Is $3x + 2y$ a polynomial?

A term such as $7x^2y^3$ is said to be of the second degree in x, third degree in y, and fifth degree in x and y. What degree is $x^\alpha y^\beta$ in x? in y? in x and y?

Since $x^0 = 1$, then $k = kx^0$, and the constant k is said to be of degree zero in x. What degree is k in y? in x and y?

The *degree of a polynomial* is the degree of the term whose degree is either equal to or greater than that of any other term. Thus, $7x^2y - 3xy^3 + 2x - 7y$ is of degree 2 in x, of degree 3 in y, and of degree 4 in x and y. What degree is $x^\alpha y^\beta - 7x^\alpha - 2870$ in x? in y? in x and y?

It should be noted that any integer such as 217 is simply a shorthand way of writing $2 \times 10^2 + 1 \times 10 + 7$; *i.e.*, it is the value of the polynomial $2x^2 + x + 7$ when $x = 10$.

EXERCISES

What degree is each of the following polynomials in x? in y? in x and y?

1. $3x^2 - 2x + 1$
2. $4x^2y - 2x + 4$
3. $y^3 - 2y + 7$
4. $xy^2 + x + y - 7$
5. $x^3y^2 + 3x^2y - 7x + 2y - 3$
6. $x^5y - 3x^2y^2 - 270$
7. For any integer prove:
   a) If the last digit is even, the integer is divisible by 2.
   b) If the number formed by the last two digits is divisible by 4, the integer is divisible by 4.
   c) If the number formed by the last three digits is divisible by 8, the integer is divisible by 8.
   d) If the last digit is 0 or 5, the integer is divisible by 5.
   e) If the sum of the digits is divisible by 3 or 9, the integer is divisible by 3 or 9.

Historical note

About eleven hundred years ago an Arabian mathematician by the name of Al-Khowarizmi used the word *al-jabr* to mean transposing terms in an equation. From this word *al-jabr* has been derived our English word algebra.[1]

For many hundreds of years algebraic expressions were written out in full detail. Diophantus, who lived in Alexandria during the fourth century of the present era, did, however, introduce some symbols we use today. However, our present symbolic language has been developed mostly during the last four hundred and fifty years. For example, in 1489 was printed the first text book using the symbols + and −. It was not, however, until fifty years later that these symbols came into common use. In 1557, an Englishman by the name of Recorde introduced the symbol = for equality. He said "No two things can be more equal" [than the parts of this symbol].

[1] For a more extensive account see D. E. Smith's *History of Mathematics*, Vol. II, page 386.

CHAPTER II

The Fundamental Operations

We shall now consider the fundamental operations of addition, subtraction, multiplication, and division. We shall also interpret these operations geometrically.

Addition

In your past work you very likely performed algebraic additions without being conscious of the fact that you were making certain assumptions. We shall now list these assumptions.

1. The sum of two numbers is a uniquely determined number. That is, if a and b are two numbers, there is one and only one number x, such that $x = a + b$.
2. Addition is commutative; *i.e.*, the order of the numbers in addition may be changed without affecting the sum. Thus,

$$a + b = b + a$$

3. Addition is associative; *i.e.*, the numbers in addition may be grouped in any order without affecting the sum. Thus,

$$(a + b) + c = a + (b + c)$$

4. If equal numbers are added to equal numbers, the sums are equal numbers. Thus,

if $\quad a = b$

and $\quad c = d$

then $\quad a + c = b + d$

Since an unsigned number expresses only magnitude, such a number may be represented by an undirected line segment. The segment whose length represents the sum of two unsigned numbers is obtained by placing the segments representing the two numbers end to end so as to form a single segment.

Since a signed number represents direction as well as magnitude, geometrically it is represented by a *directed line segment.*

Let us consider two signed numbers a and b represented by two directed line segments of lengths $|a|$ and $|b|$ respectively, whose directions are the same or opposite, depending upon whether the numbers have the same or opposite signs.

The sum $a + b$ is represented by a directed line segment which expresses the net result of first moving the distance $|a|$

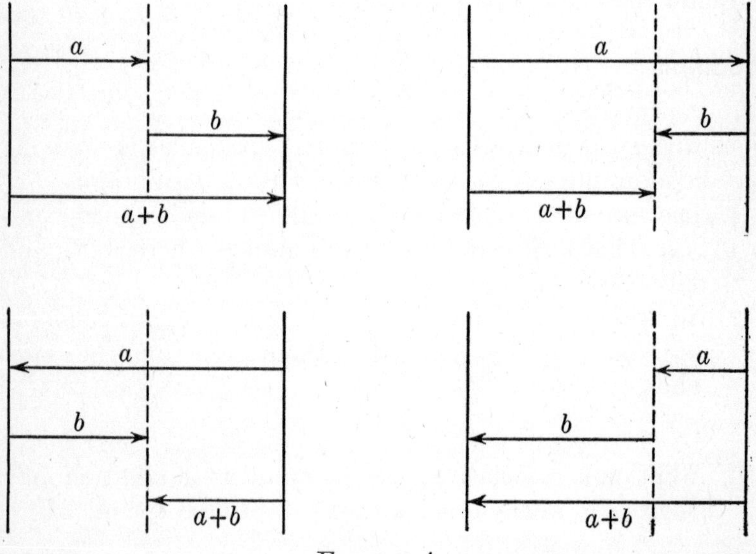

FIGURE 4

in the direction represented by a and then moving the distance $|b|$ in the direction represented by b. Four cases may be listed, as shown in Fig. 4. These four cases are readily illustrated by readings on a thermometer. Suppose the thermometer reads 5° above zero and rises 7°; what is the new temperature? Obviously it is $(+5°) + (+7°)$ or $+12°$. (The $+7°$ is enclosed in a parenthesis to separate it from the $+$ sign used for addition.)

If the temperature is 5° below zero and drops 7°, what is the new temperature? It is $(-5°) + (-7°)$ or $-12°$.

If the temperature is 5° above zero and drops 7°, what is the new temperature? It is $(+5°) + (-7°)$ or $-2°$.

If the temperature is 5° below zero and rises 7°, what is the new temperature? It is $(-5°) + (+7°)$ or $+2°$.

For example, we could write:

$$\begin{array}{r} +5 \\ +7 \\ \hline +12 \end{array} \qquad \begin{array}{r} -5 \\ -7 \\ \hline -12 \end{array} \qquad \begin{array}{r} +5 \\ -7 \\ \hline -2 \end{array} \qquad \begin{array}{r} -5 \\ +7 \\ \hline +2 \end{array}$$

From a study of the above examples can you state a rule for adding signed numbers? Would it read as follows? To add signed numbers with like signs, add the absolute values of the numbers and prefix the sign of the numbers, while in adding signed numbers with unlike signs, find the difference of their absolute values and prefix the sign of the numerically larger number. The following five examples illustrate addition of algebraic expressions:

EXAMPLE 1.
$$\begin{array}{r} +7x \\ +3x \\ \hline +10x \end{array}$$

EXAMPLE 3.
$$\begin{array}{r} +7b \\ -3b \\ \hline +4b \end{array}$$

EXAMPLE 2.
$$\begin{array}{r} -3y \\ -8y \\ \hline -11y \end{array}$$

EXAMPLE 4.
$$\begin{array}{r} +3y \\ -10y \\ \hline -7y \end{array}$$

EXAMPLE 5.
$$\begin{array}{r} 3x^3 - 7x^2 - 8x - 2 \\ -2x^3 + 5x^2 - 11x - 1 \\ \hline x^3 - 2x^2 - 19x - 3 \end{array}$$

We shall check this result by letting $x = 2$. Then,

$$\begin{array}{rcrcr} 3x^3 - 7x^2 - 8x - 2 & = & 24 - 28 - 16 - 2 & = & -22 \\ -2x^3 + 5x^2 - 11x - 1 & = & -16 + 20 - 22 - 1 & = & -19 \\ \hline x^3 - 2x^2 - 19x - 3 & = & 8 - 8 - 38 - 3 & = & -41 \end{array}$$

Does checking by numerical substitution prove that the algebraic work is correct? If the numbers check, the work is very likely correct; if the numbers fail to check, the work (or the checking) is certainly wrong.

EXERCISES

Perform each of the following additions and check by numerical substitution:

1. $$\begin{array}{r} 3a - 2b \\ \underline{4a - 3b} \end{array}$$

2. $$\begin{array}{r} 7x - 3y + 5z \\ \underline{-2x + 4y - z} \end{array}$$

3. $$\begin{array}{r} 6a - 3b - 2x \\ \underline{-9a + 5b + 3x} \end{array}$$

4. $$\begin{array}{r} a - 2b - 3c - d \\ \underline{-5a + 6b + 7c - 3d} \end{array}$$

5. $$\begin{array}{r} 6x - 3z - 3m + 8 \\ -2x + 5z - 2m - 3 \\ \underline{x - 6z + 3m + 8} \end{array}$$

6. $$\begin{array}{r} 3a - 2b - 5c + d \\ -2a + 3b + 7c - 2d \\ 3a - 2b - 9c + 3d \\ \underline{2a + 5b - 3c - 7d} \end{array}$$

Rearrange if necessary and add the expressions in each of the following examples:

7. $3a + 2b - 3c + d;\ 6a - 2b - 3c - 5d;\ 7a - 2b - 9c + 6d$
8. $3x - 2y - z - 7;\ 2x - 3;\ 7y - z - 1;\ 8x - z - 11$
9. $3a - 2b - c + d;\ 3b - 2d + a;\ 7c - b - 2d + 7a$
10. $3x^3 - 2x + 5x^2 - 7;\ 2 - x + x^3 - 3x^2;\ 7x^2 - 3x^3 - x + 11$
11. $7x^2 - 3x - 1;\ 2x^3 + 3x^2 + 4x + 5;\ -x^3 + x^2 - x + 1$
12. $3a^2b - 2ab^2 + ab - 1;\ 5ab^2 - 2a^2b - 1 + ab;\ 3 - 4ab + a^2b - 2ab^2$
13. $3x^2 - 7x^3 - 2x + 5;\ 1 - 7x + x^3 - x^2;\ 3x^3 - 2 - 7x + 5x^2$
14. $-xy - 2x^2 - 3b - c;\ -7b + 5c - 2xy - x^2;\ -7xy - 7b - 3c$
15. $1 - xy - y^2 - z^2;\ 3xy + 2y^2;\ -3z^2 - 5 + xy;\ 3xy - x^2 - z^2$
16. $27a^3b - 3a^2b - 7a^3b^2;\ 6a^2b + 8a^3b^2 - 7a^3b;\ -3a^3b + 10a^3b^2 - a^2b$
17. $-\frac{1}{3}x^2 - \frac{1}{4}x + \frac{1}{10};\ \frac{1}{6}x + \frac{1}{2}x^2 - \frac{1}{2};\ x^2 + x + 1$
18. $.4x^3 + .3x^2 - 1.7x + 2.8;\ 9.7x^2 - 3.4x^3 + 2x$

Subtraction

We shall assume that if a and b are given, then there is one and only one number x, such that $x + b = a$. Subtraction is then defined as the process of finding the number x in $x + b = a$. (See page 7.) We then write $x = a - b$ if $a > b$; $x = 0$ if $a = b$; $x = -(b - a)$ if $b > a$. Can the number x always be found in an algebraic scale? in an arithmetic scale?

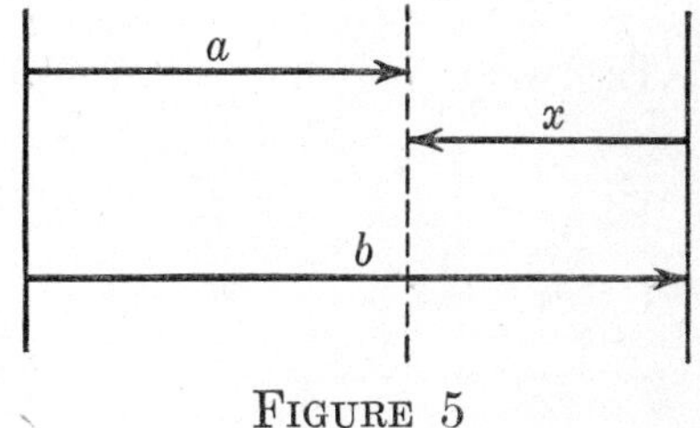

FIGURE 5

Representing a and b by directed segments having the same initial point, the meaning of addition tells us that the segment from the terminal point of b to the terminal point of a represents the desired number x. This shows, moreover, that to subtract a number b is equivalent to adding the number $-b$. (See Fig. 5.)

Suppose each of two boys wanted a pair of skis costing ten dollars. The father of one boy gave his son ten dollars to purchase the skis, while the other father bought the skis and had them charged. The financial standing of each father has been changed the same amount; that is, each is ten dollars poorer. If we consider money we have as + and money we owe as −, the first father has changed his account by $-(+10)$ and the second father has changed his account by $+(-10)$; but, as we have just seen, the change in both cases is the same. Hence we see that subtracting a positive ten dollars is equivalent to adding a negative ten dollars.

In general, *to subtract one signed number from another, change the sign of the subtrahend and add the result to the minuend.*

It is best to form the habit of making the change in the sign of the subtrahend *mentally* and not putting it down on paper.

The following five examples illustrate the rule:

EXAMPLE 1.
$$\begin{array}{r} +7\,a \\ +2\,a \\ \hline +5\,a \end{array}$$

EXAMPLE 2.
$$\begin{array}{r} +\ 7\,a \\ -\ 3\,a \\ \hline +10\,a \end{array}$$

EXAMPLE 3.
$$\begin{array}{r} -\ 7\,a \\ +\ 3\,a \\ \hline -10\,a \end{array}$$

EXAMPLE 4.
$$\begin{array}{r} -7\,a \\ -3\,a \\ \hline -4\,a \end{array}$$

EXAMPLE 5.
$$\begin{array}{r} 3\,a - 2\,b - 5\,c + 2\,d \\ 7\,a - 7\,b + 3\,c - 5\,d \\ \hline -4\,a + 5\,b - 8\,c + 7\,d \end{array}$$

Check. Let $a = 1$, $b = 2$, $c = 3$, $d = 4$; then

$$\begin{array}{rcr} 3\,a - 2\,b - 5\,c + 2\,d & = & -\ 8 \\ 7\,a - 7\,b + 3\,c - 5\,d & = & -18 \\ \hline -4\,a + 5\,b - 8\,c + 7\,d & = & 10 \end{array}$$

EXERCISES

Perform each of the following subtractions and check by numerical substitution:

1.
$$\begin{array}{r} 4\,a - 3\,b - 2\,c + \ \ d \\ 5\,a - 8\,b + 7\,c - 2\,d \\ \hline \end{array}$$

2.
$$\begin{array}{r} 6\,x - 3\,y + 7\,c + \ \ d - \ \ 7 \\ 3\,x + 8\,y - 5\,c + 7\,d - 11 \\ \hline \end{array}$$

3.
$$\begin{array}{r} 3\,x - \ \ y - \ \ z - \ \ w - \ \ 1 \\ 2\,x + 5\,y + 6\,z - 7\,w - 11 \\ \hline \end{array}$$

4.
$$\begin{array}{r} 3\,a - 2\,b - \ \ c - \ \ bc - 2\,de \\ 8\,a - 7\,b - 7\,c - 2\,bc + 3\,de \\ \hline \end{array}$$

In each of the following examples subtract the second expression from the first:

5. $6\,x - 3\,x^2 - 6\,x^3 - 1;\ 4\,x^2 + 6\,x^3 + 2\,x - 3$

6. $a + 2\,b - 3\,c - d - 3;\ 3\,b - 2\,a + 5\,d + 6$

7. $7\,a - 3\,b + d - 1;\ 2\,d - 3\,b - 11$

8. $7\,xy - 2\,x^2y - 3\,y^2 - 6\,x - 1;\ 11 - 3\,x^2y - xy - y^2$

9. $3\,a - 2\,b^2 - 4\,a^2 - 1;\ 2\,b^2 - 3\,a^2 - 2\,a + 5$

10. $4\,x^3 - 2\,x - 1;\ 2\,x^2 + 3\,x + 1$

11. $x^3 - x^2 + x - 1;\ 2\,x^2 - 3\,x^3 + 2\,x - 5$

12. $a^2b - 2\,ab^2 - 6;\ ab^2 - 2\,a^2b + 5$

13. $7\,x^3 - 2\,x^2 - 7 - 3\,x;\ 5\,x^2 - x^3 + x - 2$

14. $5\,ab - 3\,a^2b - 2\,a - 7;\ 10 + 5\,a^2b - 7\,ab - 3\,a$

15. $7\,y^3 - 3\,xy^2 + 5\,x^2y - 7\,y - 2\,x - 1;\ 7\,y^2 - 3\,y^3 + 5\,xy^2 + 6\,x^3 - 3$

Grouping of terms

Often in an algebraic expression we wish to group several terms together in order to indicate that they are to be treated as one term. The symbols of grouping are the parentheses ( ), the brackets [ ], the braces { }, and the vinculum $\overline{\quad}$. All such symbols are often called parentheses when there is no danger of confusion.

To remove parentheses, we have merely to obey the law of signs. For example, if a parenthesis is preceded by a minus sign, it means the quantity in the parentheses is the subtrahend, and we obey the rule of signs for subtraction when the parentheses are removed. Thus, $-(3\,x - y) = -3\,x + y$. Likewise, if we wish to place terms within parentheses preceded by a minus sign, the sign of each term must be changed from plus to minus or from minus to plus as the case may be. For example, $-3\,x + 2\,y = -(\ ?\ )$.

EXAMPLE 1. Simplify: $x - y - [3\,x - 2\,y]$

Solution.

$$\begin{aligned} x - y - [3\,x - 2\,y] &= x - y - 3\,x + 2\,y \\ &= y - 2\,x \end{aligned}$$

EXAMPLE 2. Simplify: $\{3 - (2 - x)\} - [x - \overline{4 - x}]$

Solution. When one pair of parentheses encloses another pair, we usually remove the inner parentheses first. Thus,

$$\begin{aligned} \{3 - (2 - x)\} - [x - \overline{4 - x}] &= \{3 - 2 + x\} - [x - 4 + x] \\ &= 3 - 2 + x - x + 4 - x \\ &= 5 - x \end{aligned}$$

EXAMPLE 3. Rewrite the expression, $a - 2\,x + 3\,by - c$, enclosing in parentheses preceded by a minus sign all terms containing x or y.

Solution.

$$\begin{aligned} a - 2\,x + 3\,by - c &= a - c - 2\,x + 3\,by \\ &= a - c - (2\,x - 3\,by) \end{aligned}$$

EXERCISES

Remove parentheses and simplify:

1. $(x - y) + (2x - 3y)$
2. $(x - 2y) - (3x - y)$
3. $p^2 - (p - p^2)$
4. $5 - \overline{6 - x}$
5. $x + [y - (x - y)]$
6. $a + x - [a - x - \overline{a - x}]$
7. $3(x - y - z) - 2(y - x - z)$
8. $x - [x - \{x - (-x)\}]$
9. $4a - \{a - (a - b) - [a - \overline{a - b}] - b\}$
10. $p - \{-(-[-x])\}$
11. $-(m - n) - \{-(2m - n)\}$
12. $p - 4 - [-\{-(-p - \overline{p - q})\}]$

Rewrite each of the following expressions, enclosing in parentheses preceded by a minus sign, all terms containing x or y.

13. $2p - x - y$
14. $3x - y - z - 2xy$
15. $x - y - 2x - y + 7$
16. $a - x + b - xy - 3x$
17. $a - 2ba + b - x + 2xy - y$
18. $4mx - x - y - p$

Multiplication

In multiplication we make the following assumptions:

1. The product of any two numbers is a uniquely determined number. That is, if a and b are two numbers, there is one and only one number x, such that $x = ab$. The numbers a and b are called *factors* of x.
2. Multiplication is commutative; *i.e.*, the order of the factors of a product may be changed without affecting the value of the product. Thus,

$$ab = ba$$

3. Multiplication is associative; *i.e.*, the factors of a product may be grouped in any way without affecting the value of the product. Thus,

$$(ab)c = a(bc) = abc$$

4. Multiplication is distributive with respect to addition; *i.e.*, the product of a factor by another which is the sum of two or more numbers is the same as the sum of the terms found by taking the product of the first factor into each of the numbers of the second factor. Thus,

$$a(b + c) = ab + ac$$

5. If equal numbers are multiplied by equal numbers, the products are equal numbers. Thus,

if $a = b$

and $c = d$

then $ac = bd$

Suppose two workmen moved into a town, each capable of earning $4 a day. Denoting the coming of these men by +2 and their earning power per day by +4, it is evident that the town is

$$(+2) \times (+4) = +8$$

dollars a day better off, assuming that the men spend their money in town.

Suppose these men leave town. Since their coming was denoted by +2, their departure is denoted by −2, and the town is −$8 richer, which is the same as $8 poorer per day.

Hence, $(-2) \times (+4) = -8$

Suppose two tramps come to town and it costs the town $4 a day to care for each man. Evidently the town is spending $8 a day. We can then write

$$(+2) \times (-4) = -8$$

If the same two tramps leave town, the town is \$8 a day better off; hence we can say

$$(-2) \times (-4) = 8.$$

Summarizing these results, we find they obey the familiar *law of signs.*

$$(+) \times (+) = + \qquad (+) \times (-) = -$$
$$(-) \times (+) = - \qquad (-) \times (-) = +$$

What is the sign of the product of two numbers with like signs? With unlike signs?

In algebra the multiplication sign $\times$ is usually omitted between numbers in parentheses. Simply placing numbers or groups of numbers in parentheses side by side means they are

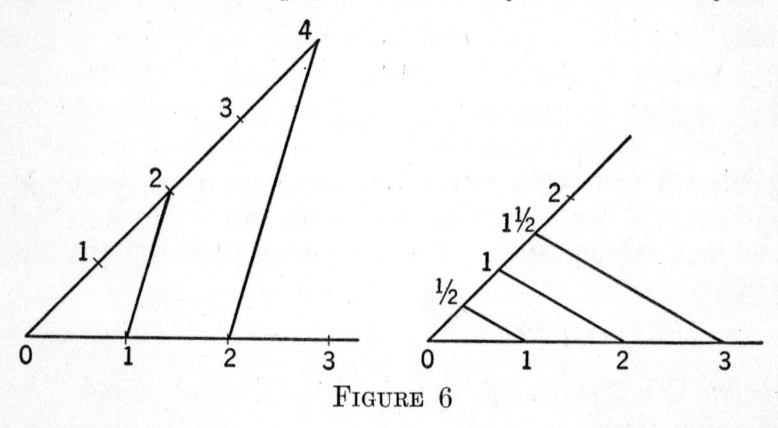

FIGURE 6

to be multiplied. For example, to indicate that $3a - b$ is multiplied by $2a + b$, we would write $(3a - b)(2a + b)$.

Geometrically, multiplication by a positive number, x, is equivalent to a uniform expansion or contraction of the scale away from or toward the origin in the ratio $|x| : 1$, according as x is greater than or less than 1. This statement will become clear on inspection of the accompanying diagrams (Fig. 6) which give the construction for the multiplication of every number on the scale by x. In the first figure, x has been taken equal to $+2$, while in the second it is equal to $+\frac{1}{2}$.

The geometric interpretation of multiplication by a negative number x consists of a similar expansion or contraction in the ratio $|x| : 1$ combined with a rotation of the whole scale about the origin through an angle of 180°. For such a rotation will change each positive number into the corresponding negative number, and vice versa, whichever the law of signs requires.

The following five examples illustrate the rule of algebraic multiplication.

EXAMPLE 1. $(+7x)(+3y) = +21xy$

EXAMPLE 2. $(+7x)(-3y) = -21xy$

EXAMPLE 3. Multiply $3a^2 - 2ab + b^2$ by ab.

Solution.

$$\begin{array}{l} 3a^2 - 2ab + b^2 \\ \underline{ab \qquad\qquad\qquad} \\ 3a^3b - 2a^2b^2 + ab^3 \end{array}$$

Each term is multiplied by ab.

EXAMPLE 4. Multiply $2x - 3y$ by $3x + 2y$.

Solution.

$$\begin{array}{rrr} 2x & -3y & \\ 3x & +2y & \\ \hline 6x^2 & -9xy & \\ & 4xy & -6y^2 \\ \hline 6x^2 & -5xy & -6y^2 \end{array}$$

First we multiply by $3x$ and then by $2y$. The partial products are now added.

EXAMPLE 5. Multiply $3x^2 - 2x - 1$ by $4x^2 + 3x + 5$ and check.

$$\begin{array}{rrrrr} & & 3x^2 & -2x & -1 \\ & & 4x^2 & +3x & +5 \\ \hline 12x^4 & -8x^3 & -4x^2 & & \\ & 9x^3 & -6x^2 & -3x & \\ & & 15x^2 & -10x & -5 \\ \hline 12x^4 & +x^3 & +5x^2 & -13x & -5 \end{array}$$

Check. Let

$$x = 2$$
$$3x^2 - 2x - 1 = 7$$
$$4x^2 + 3x + 5 = 27$$
$$12x^4 + x^3 + 5x^2 - 13x - 5 = 189 = 27 \times 7$$

In checking it is always better to take a value different from 1. For, if $x = 1$, such expressions as x^3, x^{23}, x^{107} have the same value.

EXERCISES

Perform each of the following multiplications:

1. $(7a^2 - 3a + 1)(2ab)$
2. $(3x^2 - 7x + 2)(3x^2y)$
3. $(-2x^2 + 7x - 1)(-4x^3)$
4. $(-8x^2 + 3x + 5)(-2xy)$
5. $(3x + 7y)(2x - 5y)$
6. $(a^2b - 3c + 1)(2a - c)$
7. $(a^2 - 2a)(2a + a^2)$
8. $(x^2 - 7)(-7 + x^2)$
9. $(x^2 + x + 1)(x - 1)$
10. $(7x^2 - 3x - 1)(2x - 4)$
11. $(3x^3 - 2x^2 - 4)(7x - 2)$
12. $(a^2 + 3a - 2)(a - 3)$
13. $(a^2 + 2a - 1)(a^2 - 2a + 1)$
14. $(a^2 + 3ab - b^2)(a - b)$
15. $(7x^3 - 2x + x^2 - 1)(3 + 2x^3 + x^2 - x)$
16. $(a^2 - 2a + a^3 - 7)(3 - a^2 + a)$
17. $(a^2 - x + ax - 1)(a - x - 1)$
18. $(a^2 - 2ab - b^2)(a - b)$
19. $(a + b + c)(a + b - c)$
20. $(12x^4 + x^3 + 5x^2 - 13x - 5)(3x^2 - 2x - 1)$
21. $(x^4 - y^4)(x - y)$
22. $(a + b + c - d)(a - b + c + d)$
23. $(a^2 + b^2 + c^2 - ab - ac - bc)(a + b + c)$
24. $(x^4 - x^3 + x^2 - x + 1)(x + 1)$
25. $(x^5 - 3x^3 + 3x^2 - 1)(x^2 - 2x + 1)$

Special products

What is the value of $(x + y)(x - y)$? of $(x + y)(x + y)$? of $(12x + 3y)(3x - 2y)$?

One should be able to find by inspection the following types of products.

I. $$(a + b)(a - b) = a^2 - b^2$$

That is, the product of the sum and difference of the *same* two numbers is equal to the difference between their squares. Thus,

$$(7x - 3y)(7x + 3y) = 49x^2 - 9y^2$$

II. $$(a + b)^2 = a^2 + 2ab + b^2$$
$$(a - b)^2 = a^2 - 2ab + b^2$$

That is, the square of a binomial whose terms have like (or unlike) signs equals the square of the first term plus (or minus) twice the product of the two terms, plus the square of the second term. Thus,

$$(2x + 3y)^2 = (2x)^2 + 2(2x)(3y) + (3y)^2$$
$$= 4x^2 + 12xy + 9y^2$$

and $$(5x - 3y)^2 = 25x^2 - 30xy + 9y^2$$

III. $(ax + b)(cx + d) = acx^2 + (ad + bc)x + bd$

That is, the product of any two binomials is equal to the product of their first terms, plus the algebraic sum of their cross products, plus the product of their second terms.

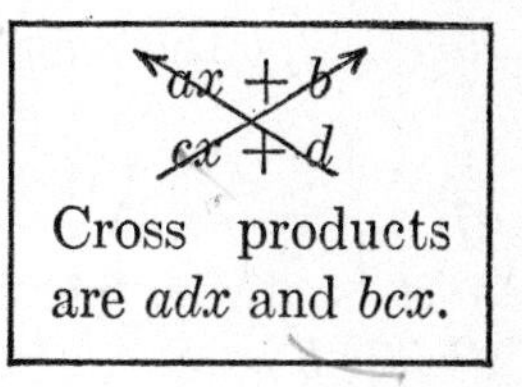

Cross products are adx and bcx.

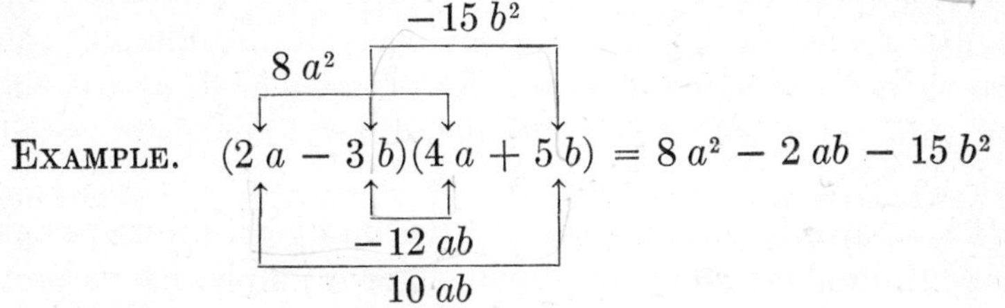

EXAMPLE. $(2a - 3b)(4a + 5b) = 8a^2 - 2ab - 15b^2$

EXERCISES

Find the following products by inspection:

1. $(x - 3)(x + 3)$
2. $(2x - 3)(2x + 3)$
3. $(3x - 4b)(4b + 3x)$
4. $(7x - 2y)(7x + 2y)$
5. $(2ab - 3)(3 + 2ab)$
6. $(xy - 1)(1 + xy)$
7. $(-1 + x)(x + 1)$
8. $(2x + 1)^2$
9. $(3x - y)^2$
10. $(4a - b)^2$
11. $(7x - 2y)^2$
12. $(5xy - 3)^2$
13. $\left(\frac{x}{2} + \frac{2}{y}\right)^2$
14. $\left(\frac{2a}{3} + \frac{3b}{2}\right)^2$
15. $(a^4 - y)(a^4 + y)$
16. $(a^5 - y)^2$
17. $(2x + 1)(3x - 1)$
18. $(2x - 5)(3x - 2)$
19. $(p^2 + 8)(p^2 - 4)$
20. $(a^4 + 2)(a^3 - 3)$
21. $(x^5 - 4)(x^5 - 5)$
22. $(y - \frac{1}{3})(y + \frac{1}{2})$
23. $(x - \frac{2}{3})^2$
24. $(6x + 11y)(5x - 3y)$
25. $(\frac{1}{2}x + y)(x - 2y)$

26. Show that $(a + b + c)^2 = a^2 + b^2 + c^2 + 2ab + 2ac + 2bc$.

27. Expand each of the following expressions:

a) $(x - 2y + z)^2$ c) $(2x - 5y + 3z)^2$

b) $(2x - y - 3z)^2$ d) $(x - y - 5z)^2$

Division

To divide a number a by a number b ($b \neq 0$) is to find a number x such that $bx = a$. Hence $x = \frac{a}{b}$. Here a is called the *dividend*, b the *divisor*, and $\frac{a}{b}$ the *quotient* of a and b. The quotient $\frac{1}{a}$ is called the *reciprocal* of a.

It is always possible to find the number x *except when the divisor b is zero.* If $b = 0$, we would then be required to find a number x such that $0 \cdot x = a$. Obviously, if a is different from zero there is no value of x such that $0 \cdot x = a$. If $a = 0$, then any value of x will satisfy the definition. For these reasons *division by zero is not permissible.*

It is interesting to note that if division by zero were permissible all numbers would be equal. For example, let us prove $5 = 73$.

Now $5 \times 0 = 0$

and $73 \times 0 = 0$

Since the right hand members are equal, the left hand members are equal. Hence,

$$5 \times 0 = 73 \times 0$$

Dividing by zero gives

$$5 = 73$$

EXAMPLE: Find the fallacy in the following argument.

Suppose $x = 2$.

Multiplying by x gives

$$x^2 = 2x$$

Subtracting 4 from both members gives

$$x^2 - 4 = 2x - 4$$

Which is the same as

$$(x - 2)(x + 2) = 2(x - 2)$$

Dividing by $x - 2$ gives

$$x + 2 = 2$$

But $x = 2$. Hence,

$$2 + 2 = 2$$
$$4 = 2$$
$$2 = 1$$

The question now arises, what is the sign of the quotient of two signed numbers?

Since $$(+2)(+3) = +6, \text{ then } \frac{+6}{+2} = ?$$

$$(-2)(-3) = +6, \text{ then } \frac{+6}{-2} = ?$$

$$(-2)(+3) = -6, \text{ then } \frac{-6}{-2} = ?$$

$$(+2)(-3) = -6, \text{ then } \frac{-6}{+2} = ?$$

What is the sign of the quotient of two numbers with like signs? with unlike signs?

For a geometric construction of division we need merely to reverse the construction for multiplication. To do this we

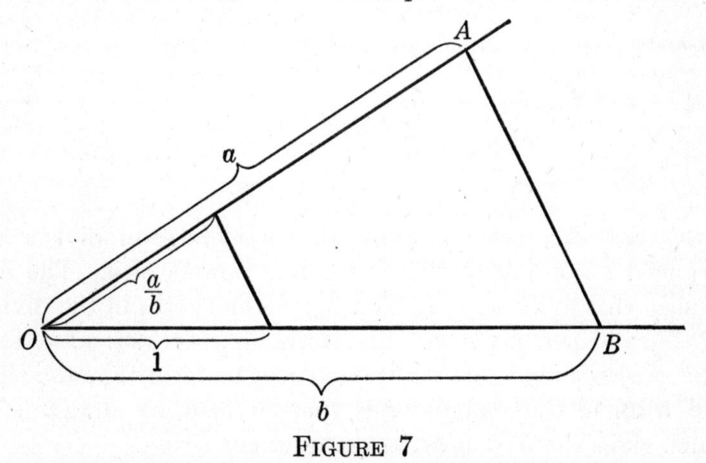

FIGURE 7

first join the end of b (point B) on the original scale to the end of a (point A) on the multiplied scale. Then from the end of the unit segment on the original scale draw a line parallel to line BA. This line will cut off on the multiplied scale the segment $x = \frac{a}{b}$.

The following examples illustrate division:

EXAMPLE 1. Divide $+21\,x^3$ by $-7\,x^2$.

Solution.

$$\frac{+21\,x^3}{-\;7\,x^2} = -3\,x$$

EXAMPLE 2. Divide $-35\,x^2$ by $-5\,x^5$.

$$\frac{-35\,x^2}{-\;5\,x^5} = \frac{7}{x^3}$$

EXAMPLE 3. Divide $a^3 - b^3$ by $a - b$ and check.

Solution.

$$\begin{array}{r|lll|l} a - b & a^3 & & - b^3 & a^2 + ab + b^2 \\ & a^3 - a^2b & & & \\ \hline & a^2b & & - b^3 & \\ & a^2b - ab^2 & & & \\ \hline & & ab^2 & - b^3 & \\ & & ab^2 & - b^3 & \\ \hline \end{array}$$

Check. Let $a = 2, b = 1.$

$a - b = 1$

$a^3 - b^3 = 7$

$a^2 + ab + b^2 = 7$

$\frac{7}{1} = 7$

Note that the terms in both the dividend and divisor are arranged according to the descending powers of a. The first term in the dividend is divided by the first term in the divisor $(a^3 \div a)$, which gives the first term in the quotient. Then $a^2(a - b)$ is found and subtracted just as in arithmetic. The first term in the remainder is then divided by a $(a^2b \div a)$, which gives the next term in the quotient.

EXERCISES

Perform each of the following divisions and check your answer:

1. $x^4 - 6x^2 - 16$ by $x^2 + 2$
2. $x^2 - 18 - 3x$ by $x - 6$
3. $5a^4 + a^3 - 3a^2 - a - 2$ by $a^2 - 1$
4. $y^3 - 8$ by $y - 2$
5. $8a^3 + 27b^3$ by $2a + 3b$
6. $x^8 + x^6 + x^4 + x^2 + 3x - 1$ by $x + 1$
7. $6a^3 + 10a - 7a^2 - 4$ by $2a - 1$
8. $x^5 - y^5$ by $x - y$
9. $2y^4 + 3y^3 - 7y^2 - 1 + 7y$ by $3y + y^2 - 1$
10. $x^4 - x^3 + 6x^2 - 1$ by $x^2 + 3x + 2$
11. $12x^4 + x^3 + 5x^2 - 13x - 5$ by $3x^2 - 2x - 1$
12. $x^4 - y^4$ by $x + y$
13. $x^4 - y^4$ by $x - y$
14. $a^3 + b^3 + c^3 - 3abc$ by $a + b + c$
15. $a^3 + b^3 - c^3 + 3abc$ by $a + b - c$

Factoring

If an algebraic expression is the product of two or more quantities, each of these quantities is called a *factor* of the original expression. The process of separating an expression into its factors is called factoring.

Removing monomial factors

Since multiplication is distributive,

$$a(x + y + z) = ax + ay + az$$

Hence it follows that the monomial factor a can be removed from $ax + ay + az$ by dividing each term by a.

EXAMPLE: Factor $3ax^2 - 6a^2x + 9a^3x$.

Solution. Inspection shows that $3ax$ is a factor of each term. Therefore,

$$3ax^2 - 6a^2x + 9a^3x^2 = 3ax(x - 2a + 3a^2x)$$

EXERCISES

Factor each of the following examples:

1. $x^2 - 3\,xy$
2. $a^3 + 9\,a^2$
3. $4\,x^2 - 6\,x + x^3$
4. $9\,x^3 - 81$
5. $x^{11} + px^{11}$
6. $b^{10}y - b^{10}$
7. $-4\,ax - 2\,xy + 6\,x^2$
8. $\dfrac{\pi\,hR^2}{3} + \dfrac{\pi\,hr^2}{3}$
9. $\dfrac{n^2d}{4} - \dfrac{nd^2}{8}$
10. $x(a + b) + y(a + b)$
11. $2\,x^3 + ax^2 + ax$
12. $y^{15} + y$
13. $2\,x^2 + 6\,x^3$
14. $3\,y^{11} - 12\,y^8 + 6\,y^5$
15. $\dfrac{\pi\,r^2h}{3} - \dfrac{\pi\,R^2h}{3}$

Common binomial factor

The following are illustrative examples.

EXAMPLE 1. Factor $x(a + b) - 3\,y(a + b)$.

Solution. The quantity $(a + b)$ can be treated as a monomial; hence,

$$x(a + b) - 3\,y(a + b) = (a + b)(x - 3\,y)$$

EXAMPLE 2. Factor $x(a - b) - 3\,y(b - a)$.

Solution. Since $b - a = -(a - b)$, we can write

$$\begin{aligned} x(a - b) - 3\,y(b - a) &= x(a - b) + 3\,y(a - b) \\ &= (a - b)(x + 3\,y) \end{aligned}$$

EXAMPLE 3. Factor $8\,ax + 3\,bd - 4\,ad - 6\,bx$.

Solution. By grouping the first and third terms, and the second and fourth terms, we have a common binomial factor in each group.

$$\begin{aligned} 8\,ax + 3\,bd - 4\,ad - 6\,bx &= 8\,ax - 4\,ad + 3\,bd - 6\,bx \\ &= 4\,a(2\,x - d) - 3\,b(2\,x - d) \\ &= (2\,x - d)(4\,a - 3\,b) \end{aligned}$$

EXERCISES

Factor each of the following expressions:

1. $x^2(p + q) - y(p + q)$
2. $x^2(a - b) - 7y^2(a - b)$
3. $2a(x + 7) - (x + 7)$
4. $m(a - b) - n(b - a)$
5. $2p(x - 2y) + 3q(2y - x)$
6. $4x(a - b)^2 + y(a - b)$
7. $a^3 + a^2 - 2a - 2$
8. $y^2 - ay + by - ab$
9. $a^4 + 3a^3 - a - 3$
10. $xy - 2y - 2x + y^2$
11. $x^3 + x^2 + x + 1$
12. $9ab + 12ac + 12db + 16dc$
13. $(x + 1)(x - 2) - 3(x - 2)$
14. $6a^2 - 2ab - 3ac - 2a + bc + c$
15. $ax + by + ay + bz + az + bx$
16. $xy + 1 + x + y$
17. $14x^3 - 6x^2 - 21x + 9$
18. $p^4 + p^2q^2 - t^2q^2 - p^2t^2$
19. $2a^3 + 3 + 6a + a^2$
20. $2x - ay - ax - az + 2y + 2z + bx + by + bz$

Trinomials that are perfect squares

Since $(a \pm b)^2 = a^2 \pm 2ab + b^2$, it is obvious that for a trinomial to be a perfect square, two terms must be perfect squares and the other term plus or minus twice the product of the positive square roots of the other two terms. Thus, $9x^2 - 12xy + 4y^2$ is a perfect square since $9x^2 = (3x)^2$, $4y^2 = (2y)^2$, and $-12xy = -2(3x)(2y)$. Hence, $9x^2 - 12xy + 4y^2 = (3x - 2y)(3x - 2y)$.

Is $x^2 + xy + y^2$ a perfect square? What can you say about $x^2 + 2x + 1$? $x^2 + 4y^2$? $x^2 + 6xy + 9y^2$?

EXERCISES

Factor each of the following expressions:

1. $x^2 - 4x + 4$
2. $x^2 - 6x + 9$
3. $a^2 + 10a + 25$
4. $4a^2 + 36ab + 81b^2$
5. $x^4 + 16x^2 + 64$
6. $\frac{x^2}{y^2} + \frac{y^2}{x^2} - 2$
7. $x^{12} + 2x^6 + 1$
8. $9(2x + y)^2 + 6(2x + y) + 1$
9. $9a^6 - 60a^3 + 100$
10. $-x^4 - 4x^2 - 4$
11. $\frac{x^2}{y^2} + \frac{4y^2}{x^2} - 4$
12. $16p^2q^4 - 88pq^2t + 121t^2$
13. $-49 - 14x - x^2$
14. $8x^2 - 24xy + 18y^2$
15. $75a^2 + 90ax + 27x^2$
16. $x^6 + 12x^3 + 36$
17. $y^{12} + 4y^6 + 4$
18. $64a^4 + 16a^2b^2 + b^4$
19. $\frac{9y^2}{x^2} + \frac{x^2}{9y^2} - 2$
20. $64a^2 + 32a + 4$

The difference of two squares

Since $(a - b)(a + b) = a^2 - b^2$, then the factors of $a^2 - b^2$ are $(a - b)(a + b)$. What are the factors of $a^2 - 1$?

EXAMPLE 1. Factor $9x^2 - \frac{25}{4}y^2$.

Solution. Since $9x^2$ is the square of $3x$ and $\frac{25}{4}y^2$ is the square of $\frac{5}{2}y$, the factors are the sum and difference of $3x$ and $\frac{5}{2}y$. That is,

$$9x^2 - \frac{25}{4}y^2 = (3x - \frac{5}{2}y)(3x + \frac{5}{2}y)$$

EXAMPLE 2. Factor $9x^2 - 36y^2$.

Solution. The monomial factor 9 should first be removed.

Hence,
$$\begin{aligned} 9x^2 - 36y^2 &= 9(x^2 - 4y^2) \\ &= 9(x - 2y)(x + 2y) \end{aligned}$$

EXAMPLE 3. Factor $a^2 - 4ab + 4b^2 - 4x^2 - 12xy - 9y^2$.

Solution. The six terms can be grouped into two trinomials, each of which is a perfect square. Thus,

$$\begin{aligned} &a^2 - 4ab + 4b^2 - 4x^2 - 12xy - 9y^2 \\ &\quad = (a^2 - 4ab + 4b^2) - (4x^2 + 12xy + 9y^2) \\ &\quad = (a - 2b)^2 - (2x + 3y)^2 \\ &\quad = (a - 2b - 2x - 3y)(a - 2b + 2x + 3y) \end{aligned}$$

EXERCISES

Factor each of the following expressions:

1. $a^2 - 36$
2. $x^2 - 4y^2$
3. $1 - 9x^2$
4. $49x^2 - 9y^2$
5. $x^2 - \frac{1}{9}$
6. $\frac{1}{16} - y^2$
7. $\frac{1}{16} - y^4$
8. $\frac{25}{16}x^2 - y^4$
9. $y^2 - .01$
10. $x^4 - y^4$
11. $x^6 - y^6$
12. $x^{12} - y^{12}$
13. $x^8 - 9y^8$
14. $81a^2 - 256b^4$
15. $1 - x^8$
16. $(a - b)^2 - 4$
17. $(2x - y)^2 - (4x - 2y)^2$
18. $9(3x - y)^2 - 16(2x + y)^2$
19. $x^2 + 2xy + y^2 - 9a^2$
20. $25 + 2a - 1 - a^2$
21. $100 - a^2 + 6ab - 9b^2$
22. $4a^2 + 8ab + 4b^2 - x^2 - 6xy - 9y^2$
23. $a^2 - x^2 + b^2 - y^2 - 2ab + 2xy$
24. $a^2 - 10a + 25 - 121y^8$
25. $x^4 - 2x^2y^2 + y^4 - 25a^4 - 40a^2b^2 - 16b^4$

Factoring the trinomial $x^2 + px + q$

Since $(x + a)(x + b) = x^2 + (a + b)x + ab$, it follows that if p equals the algebraic sum of the two numbers a and b, and q the product of the same two numbers, the factors of $x^2 + px + q$ are $x + a$ and $x + b$.

EXAMPLE 1. Factor $x^2 + 8x + 12$.

Solution. We must find two numbers whose sum is 8 and whose product is 12. These numbers are 6 and 2. Hence,

$$x^2 + 8x + 12 = (x + 6)(x + 2)$$

EXAMPLE 2. Factor $a^2 + a - 12$.

Solution. We must find two numbers whose sum is 1 and whose product is -12. These numbers are 4 and -3. Hence,

$$a^2 + a - 12 = (a + 4)(a - 3)$$

EXERCISES

Find the factors of each of the following expressions:

1. $x^2 + 2x - 3$
2. $p^2 + p - 42$
3. $a^2 + 2a - 48$
4. $x^2 + x - 12$
5. $c^2 - 3c - 40$
6. $a^2 - 7ab + 10b^2$
7. $x^2 - 17x + 30$
8. $2c^2 + c - 6$
9. $t^2 + 22ts + 72s^2$
10. $l^6 - 22l^3m^5 + 105m^{10}$
11. $x^8 - 10x^4y^3 - 96y^6$
12. $21 - 4b^2x^3 - b^4x^6$
13. $x^6 + 14x^3y^8 - 120y^{16}$
14. $84x^5 - 60x^3 + 2x^4$
15. $2p^4 + 17p^2 - 19$
16. $24a^2 - 28a - 20$
17. $5t^2 + 45tr - 180r^2$
18. $(a + b)^2 + 8(a + b) + 15$
19. $(x + y)^2 - 7(x + y) - 98$
20. $(p + 2q)^2 - 7(p + 2q) - 120$
21. $a^6 - 18a^3 + 81$
22. $x^4 - 15x^2 + 50$
23. $a^2 - 2a - 99$
24. $a^2b^4 - 3ab^2 - 40$
25. $m^4y^2 + 6m^2y - 40$

Factoring the general trinomial $px^2 + qx + r$

Now $(ax + b)(cx + d) = acx^2 + (bc + ad)x + bd$. Hence, if p is the product of a and c (*i.e.*, $p = ac$), if r is the product of b and d (*i.e.*, $r = bd$), and if q is the algebraic sum of the cross products of these two numbers (*i.e.*, $q = bc + ad$), then the factors of $px^2 + qx + r$ are $ax + b$ and $cx + d$.

EXAMPLE. Factor $6x^2 - 11x - 10$.

Solution. We know that the terms whose product is $6x^2$ are $3x$ and $2x$ or $6x$ and x. Likewise, the factors of 10 are 10 and 1 or 5 and 2. Moreover, since the sign of the last term is negative, these factors must be unlike in sign. The following combinations are possible.

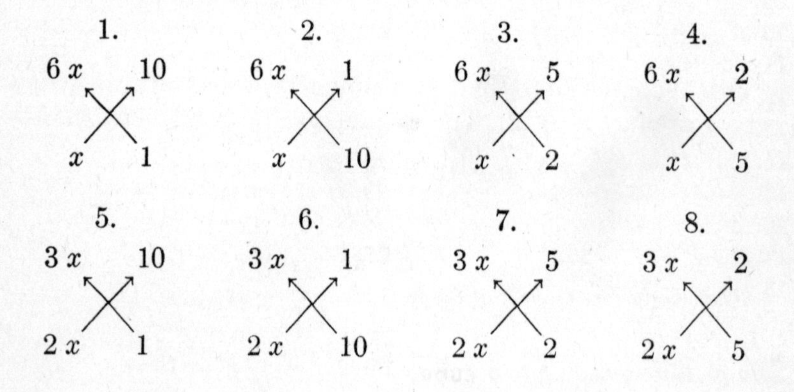

We must now select the pair in which a combination of the cross products gives $-11x$. For example, from 1 we have the cross products $6x$ and $10x$, and no combination of these terms will give $-11x$. Hence, 1 must be excluded. In similar manner 2 to 7 are excluded. From 8 we have the cross products $4x$ and $15x$. Since $4x - 15x = -11x$, we see that the required factors are $3x + 2$ and $2x - 5$. Hence, $6x^2 - 11x - 10 = (3x + 2)(2x - 5)$.

With a little practice it is possible to pick out very quickly by inspection the correct arrangement. However, it must be understood that *not every trinomial of the form $px^2 + qx + r$ can be factored if we require that the pairs of numbers sought shall be integers.* For example, $3x^2 + 7x - 11$ cannot be factored in this way.

EXERCISES

Factor each of the following expressions:

1. $3x^2 - x - 2$
2. $2a^2 + 5a + 2$
3. $3a^2 - 10a + 3$
4. $3x^2 - 5x - 2$
5. $3x^2 + 17x + 10$
6. $2y^2 - 7y + 6$
7. $3m^2 - 5m + 2$
8. $2a^2 + 13ab + 6b^2$
9. $6x^2 - 7xy - 3y^2$
10. $3 - x - 2x^2$
11. $12 - x - x^2$
12. $6y^2 - y - 7$
13. $2x^2 - 11xy + 12y^2$
14. $5x^2 + 34xy - 7y^2$
15. $24x^2 - 28x - 20$
16. $60x^2 - 42x - 36$
17. $30x^3 - x^2 - 20x$
18. $16x^2 + 32xy + 7y^2$
19. $(a - b)^2 + (a - b) - 2$
20. $12x^{10} - 7x^5 - 12$
21. $12 - 5x - 25x^2$
22. $3x^2 - 8xy - 3y^2$
23. $20x^2 - 8xy - 20y^2$
24. $4x^4 - x^2 - 5$
25. $4y^{12} + 7y^6 - 15$
26. $24a^2 + 18a + 3$
27. $15y^2 + 24y - 12$
28. $8p^2 + 2p - 1$
29. $4a^2 + 12ab + 9b^2$
30. $6x^2 - x - 77$
31. $6p^2 - 13p + 5$
32. $10 - y - 3y^2$
33. $6m^2 - 5m - 4$
34. $4a^4 + 7a^2 - 36$
35. $6y^2 + 7yz + 2z^2$

Sum or difference of two cubes

You can easily verify by multiplication that:

$$x^3 + y^3 = (x + y)(x^2 - xy + y^2)$$
$$x^3 - y^3 = (x - y)(x^2 + xy + y^2)$$

Notice: 1. That the sign in the binomial factor is the same as the sign in the original binomial.

2. That the sign of the second term of the trinomial is opposite to the sign in the binomial factor.

EXAMPLE 1. Factor $125x^3 - 8y^3$.

Solution. Since $125x^3 = (5x)^3$ and $8y^3 = (2y)^3$, we have

$$125x^3 - 8y^3 = [(5x) - (2y)][(5x)^2 + (5x)(2y) + (2y)^2]$$
$$= [5x - 2y][25x^2 + 10xy + 4y^2]$$

EXAMPLE 2. Factor $81x^4 + 3x$.

Solution. We must first remove the monomial factor $3x$.

Hence, $81x^4 + 3x = 3x(27x^3 + 1)$
$= 3x(3x + 1)(9x^2 - 3x + 1)$

EXERCISES

Factor each of the following expressions:

1. $p^3 - c^3$
2. $p^3 + c^3$
3. $8p^3 - c^3$
4. $8p^3 + c^3$
5. $27m^3 - 8p^3$
6. $27m^3 + 8p^3$
7. $27x^3 - 64y^6$
8. $27x^3 + 64y^6$
9. $\frac{x^3}{8} - \frac{y^3}{125}$
10. $\frac{x^3}{8} + \frac{y^3}{125}$
11. $1 - 27a^3$
12. $1 + 27a^3$
13. $x^6 + y^6$
14. $x^6 - y^6$
15. $x^9 + y^9$
16. $x^9 - y^9$
17. $125x^3 - 27y^3$
18. $\frac{x^3}{27} + \frac{8}{y^3}$
19. $\frac{x^3}{27} - \frac{8}{y^3}$
20. $\frac{(a - b)^3}{8} - \frac{125}{(2xy)^3}$
21. $(a + b)^3 - 8$
22. $27 + 8(x - y)^3$
23. $(a + 2)^3 - 8(a - 3)^3$
24. $125a^3 + 27b^6$
25. $32x^6 - 108y^3$

Factoring trinomials of the form $x^4 + ax^2y^2 + y^4$

Often trinomials of the above form can be written in the form $A^2 - B^2$ by the addition and subtraction of a term. Adding and subtracting the same term, of course, does not change the value of the expression.

EXAMPLE 1. Factor $4x^4 + 3x^2 + 1$.

Solution. What must the middle term be in order that the trinomial be a perfect square? Obviously it must be $4x^2$; hence we shall add and subtract x^2.

$$\begin{array}{r} 4x^4 + 3x^2 + 1 \\ x^2 - x^2 \\ \hline 4x^4 + 4x^2 + 1 - x^2 \end{array}$$

$$(2x^2 + 1)^2 - x^2 = (2x^2 + 1 - x)(2x^2 + 1 + x)$$

EXERCISES

Factor each of the following expressions:

1. $x^4 + x^2 + 1$
2. $x^8 + x^4 + 1$
3. $a^4 - 3a^2 + 9$
4. $25x^4 + x^2 + 1$
5. $1 - 15a^2 + 25a^4$
6. $64a^4 + 1$
7. $4a^8 + 1$
8. $4a^4 + b^4$
9. $4x^4 + 81y^4$
10. $64x^8 + 81y^4$
11. $x^4 + 4$
12. $25x^4 + 66x^2y^2 + 49y^4$
13. $36x^4 - 28x^2 + 4$
14. $9x^4 + 21x^2y^2 + 25y^4$
15. $49x^4 - 15x^2y^2 + 121y^4$

Factors of $x^n + y^n$ and $x^n - y^n$ where n is an integer

Is $x^3 + y^3$ exactly divisible by $x + y$? by $x - y$? If $x^5 - y^5$ is divided by $x - y$, what is the remainder?

By actual division the following statements will be found to be true for any positive integral value of n.

1. $x^n - y^n$
$= (x - y)(x^{n-1} + x^{n-2}y + x^{n-3}y^2 + x^{n-4}y^3 + \cdots + y^{n-1})$
whether n is even or odd.

2. $x^n + y^n$
$= (x + y)(x^{n-1} - x^{n-2}y + x^{n-3}y^2 - x^{n-4}y^3 + \cdots + y^{n-1})$
when n is odd.

3. $x^n - y^n$
$= (x + y)(x^{n-1} - x^{n-2}y + x^{n-3}y^2 - x^{n-4}y^3 + \cdots - y^{n-1})$
when n is even.

The above method is used *only* when the given expression cannot be factored either as (a) the difference of two squares or as (b) the sum or difference of two cubes. Thus we would not use this method in factoring $a^8 - b^8$ (the difference of two squares), $a^9 - b^9$ (the difference of two cubes), $a^9 + b^9$ (the sum of two cubes) but we would use it in factoring such expressions as $x^5 + y^5$ and $x^7 - y^7$. Incidentally $x^n + y^n$ is not divisible by $x + y$ when n is even.

EXAMPLE 1. Factor $x^7 - y^7$.

Solution. By formula 1,

$$x^7 - y^7 = (x - y)(x^6 + x^5y + x^4y^2 + x^3y^3 + x^2y^4 + xy^5 + y^6)$$

EXAMPLE 2. Factor $x^5 + y^5$.

Solution. By formula 2,

$$x^5 + y^5 = (x + y)(x^4 - x^3y + x^2y^2 - xy^3 + y^4)$$

EXAMPLE 3. Factor $a^8 - b^8$.

Solution. Since n is even, the expression is divisible by both $a + b$ and $a - b$. However, as stated before, the expression should be factored as the difference of two squares.

$$\begin{aligned} a^8 - b^8 &= (a^4 + b^4)(a^4 - b^4) \\ &= (a^4 + b^4)(a^2 + b^2)(a^2 - b^2) \\ &= (a^4 + b^4)(a^2 + b^2)(a + b)(a - b) \end{aligned}$$

EXERCISES

If possible, factor each of the following expressions:

1. $x^5 - y^5$
2. $x^7 + y^7$
3. $x^5 - 32\,y^5$
4. $a^6 - b^6$
5. $x^{10} + 1$
6. $a^{12} - b^{12}$
7. $128\,a^7 + b^7$
8. $a^5 - b^{10}$
9. $x^6 - y^{12}$
10. $x^{10} - y^{10}$
11. $x^9 + y^9$
12. $a^5 + 32$
13. $a^{12} + b^{12}$
14. $x^7 - y^{14}$
15. $128\,a^7 - 2187\,b^7$

Highest common factor and least common multiple

The highest common factor (H.C.F.) of two or more expressions is the expression which contains all the factors common to the given expressions and no others. What is the highest common factor of 6, 8, and 12?

The lowest common multiple (L.C.M.) of two or more expressions is the expression of lowest degree that is divisible by all the given expressions.

Examples of the highest common factor and the least common multiple are shown in the accompanying table.

Quantities	H.C.F.	L.C.M.
x^4 and x^3y	x^3	x^4y
x^3y and x^2y^4	x^2y	x^3y^4
$(a+b)^2$ and $(a+b)(a-b)$	$a+b$	$(a+b)^2(a-b)$

To find the H.C.F. and L.C.M. of polynomials, we must resolve each polynomial into its prime factors.

EXAMPLE 1. Find the H.C.F. and L.C.M. of $x^2 - 7x + 12$, $x^2 - 8x + 15$.

Solution.
$$x^2 - 7x + 12 = (x-3)(x-4)$$
$$x^2 - 8x + 15 = (x-3)(x-5)$$

H.C.F. is $x - 3$. L.C.M. is $(x-3)(x-4)(x-5)$.

EXAMPLE 2. Find the H.C.F. and L.C.M. of $3x^2 - 3x$, $5x^3 - 5x$, $15x$.

Solution.
$$3x^2 - 3x = 3x(x-1)$$
$$5x^3 - 5x = 5x(x-1)(x+1)$$
$$15x = 15x$$

H.C.F. is x. L.C.M. is $15x(x-1)(x+1)$.

EXERCISES

Find the H.C.F. and L.C.M. of the following expressions:

1. $x;\ 3xy;\ 7x^2y$
2. $9x;\ 3xy;\ 3x+3$
3. $a-1;\ a^2-1;\ a^3-1$
4. $a^2-b^2;\ a^2-2ab+b^2$
5. $a^2-3a-4;\ a^2-8a+16;\ a^3-16a$
6. $x^2+3x-18;\ x^3-27$
7. $a^2-4ab+4b^2;\ a^4-16b^4$
8. $a^3-a;\ a^3-a^2+a-1$
9. $4a^4-4a^2;\ 3a^2+6a+3;\ 6a^2-12a+6$
10. $1-a;\ a-1;\ a^2-1;\ 1-a^4$
11. $x^2+4x-21;\ x^2-3x-70;\ x^2-49$
12. $2x^2-x-1;\ 2x^2+7x+3;\ 2x^2+5x+2$
13. $10+x-2x^2;\ 15-x-2x^2;\ 4x^2-20x+25$

14. $x^3 - x$; $x^3 + 9x - 10x$; $x^6 - x$
15. $p^3 + p^2q - pq - q^2$; $p^5 - pq^2$

REVIEW EXERCISES

Find the factors of each of the following expressions:

1. $3x + 6$
2. $2x^2 + 3xy + 3x$
3. $a^3 - a + a^2$
4. $3(a - b) + 2(a - b)^2$
5. $5(x + 2y)^2 - 7(x + 2y)$
6. $3(x + 2y)^2 + 7(x + 2y)^3$
7. $3(a + b)^3 + 5(a + b)^2 + 2(a + b)$
8. $4x^2 + 4x + 1$
9. $16x^6 + 40x^3y + 25y^2$
10. $16x^2 - 8x + 1$
11. $9a^2 - 12a + 4$
12. $9x^2 - 6xy + y^2$
13. $144x^2 - 312xy + 169y^2$
14. $3ax - 2ay + 3bx - 2by$
15. $2ax + 3ay - 3by - 2bx$
16. $7am - 2bm + 7an - 2bn$
17. $3ap - 2bp - 6aq + 4bq$
18. $4x^4 + 4x^2y^2 + 25y^4$
19. $25x^4 - 9y^2$
20. $(a - 3b)^2 - (2x - b)^2$
21. $a^2 - 2ab + b^2 - c^2$
22. $x^2 - 4xy + 4y^2 - 9$
23. $x^2 - 9 + 6y - y^2$
24. $9x^2 - a^2 - 2ab - b^2$
25. $x^2 - 7x + 6$
26. $x^8 + 64y^4$
27. $x^2 + 8x + 12$
28. $7x^2 - 4x - 11$
29. $3x^2 - 5x - 2$
30. $3x^2 - 3xy - 60y^2$
31. $15a^2x - 16ax - 15x$
32. $3(x - y)^2 - 5(x - y)^2 + 2$
33. $6(a - b)^2 - 5(a - b) - 6$
34. $2y^2 + 17y - 19$
35. $3p^2 + p - 10$
36. $6a^2 - 21a + 18$
37. $4a^2 + 18ab - 10b^2$
38. $27x^3 - y^3$
39. $27x^3 + 125y^3$
40. $8x^3 - 125y^3$
41. $8x^3 + 125y^3$
42. $x^6 + 64$
43. $5a^4 + 135a$
44. $x^7 + 32x^2$
45. $32x^5 - 243$
46. $60a^2 - 5ab - 5b^2$
47. $8x^2 - 18x + 7$
48. $x^2 + x - 56$
49. $1 - 2x^4 - 63x^8$
50. $-12 + z^2 - z$
51. $x^4 + 2x^2y^2 + 9y^4$
52. $81x^2 - 16y^2$
53. $4x^4 + 19x^2y^4 + 49y^8$
54. $x^2 - x - 42$
55. $2500a^8 - 1$

Fractions

An algebraic fraction is the quotient of two algebraic expressions. If these expressions are denoted by a and b, the fraction is usually written in the form $\frac{a}{b}$.

The quantity a is called the numerator and the quantity b the denominator of the fraction. The numerator and denominator are called the *terms* of the fraction. The denominator of a fraction can never be zero. Why? The numerator may be zero. Under this condition what is the value of the fraction? No numbers which make the denominator zero can be substituted for the letters in a fraction. Thus, we cannot substitute $x = 1$ in $\frac{2x}{x-1}$. Why?

We shall assume the two fractions $\frac{a}{b}$ and $\frac{c}{d}$ to be equal if, and only if, $ad = bc$. It then follows that $\frac{ma}{mb} = \frac{a}{b}$; since $(ma)b = a(mb)$ by the associative and commutative axioms for multiplication.

Hence we have the fundamental principle that *the value of a fraction is unchanged if its numerator and denominator are both multiplied or both divided by the same quantity, provided this quantity is not zero.*

Fractions whose values are the same are called *equivalent.* Thus, $\frac{2}{3}$ and $\frac{10}{15}$ are equivalent. Are $\frac{x-1}{x+2}$ and $\frac{2x-2}{2x+4}$ equivalent? Are $\frac{a-b}{c-d}$ and $\frac{b-a}{d-c}$ equivalent? A fraction is said to be reduced to its lowest terms when the numerator and denominator are prime to each other; that is, when they have no common factor. Is $\frac{4x}{6x^2}$ in its lowest terms? If not, how would you write it?

EXAMPLE 1. Reduce $\frac{x^2-3x-4}{x^2+5x+4}$ to its lowest terms.

Solution. $$\frac{x^2-3x-4}{x^2+5x+4} = \frac{(x-4)(x+1)}{(x+4)(x+1)} = \frac{x-4}{x+4}$$

Notice that we have divided both numerator and denominator by their common factor, $x + 1$.

EXAMPLE 2. Reduce to lowest terms:

$$\frac{x + 3y}{(x^2 - 9y^2) + (x + 3y)}$$

Solution.

$$\frac{x + 3y}{(x^2 - 9y^2) + (x + 3y)} = \frac{x + 3y}{(x + 3y)(x - 3y + 1)}$$
$$= \frac{1}{x - 3y + 1}$$

Take particular notice that when $x + 3y$ is canceled (*i.e.*, divided out of both numerator and denominator) the numerator of the quotient is 1 and not 0.

Query. What is the value of $(3a + b) \div (3a + b)$? of $(3a - b) - (3a - b)$? Special notice should be taken to the fact that we can cancel only a factor of the *entire* numerator and *entire* denominator. Thus, we *cannot* cancel $(m - p)$ in $\frac{5x(m - p)}{5 + (m - p)}$. To do this would be to divide the numerator by $m - p$ and to subtract $m - p$ from the denominator.

EXERCISES

Simplify each of the following fractions:

1. $\frac{18}{27}$
2. $\frac{16}{120}$
3. $\frac{36a^2x}{18a^3y^2}$
4. $\frac{144m^2x^3y^2}{256m^3x^2n^2}$
5. $\frac{a^2 - ab}{a^2 - b^2}$
6. $\frac{x^2 - 1}{(x - 1)^2}$
7. $\frac{a^2 - 1}{a^2 + 3a + 2}$
8. $\frac{a^2 - 4}{a^3 - 8}$
9. $\frac{1 - y^2}{(1 + y)^2}$
10. $\frac{p + q - 2}{(p + q)^2 - 4}$
11. $\frac{a^2 + 7a - 18}{a^2 - 6a + 8}$
12. $\frac{x^2 + 6x + 9}{x^3 + 27}$
13. $\frac{x^6 + 4x^3 - 32}{x^6 - 64}$
14. $\frac{(p + q)^2 - 4(p + q)}{(p + q)^2}$
15. $\frac{r + s}{(r + s)^2 + s + r}$
16. $\frac{2 - a - 6a^2}{1 + a - 6a^2}$
17. $\frac{m^2 - (p + q)^2}{p - (m - q)}$
18. $\frac{a^2 + 2a + 1}{a^2 - 1}$
19. $\frac{x - xy + z - yz}{1 - 3y + 3y^2 - y^3}$
20. $\frac{x + y - z}{z^2 - (x + y)^2}$

Changing the sign before a fraction

In any fraction there are three signs to consider; namely, the sign of the numerator, the sign of the denominator, and the sign before the fraction. The rules governing the use of signs in division naturally apply to the signs of a fraction. The quotient of two expressions having like signs is positive; whereas the quotient of two expressions having unlike signs is negative. Thus,

$$\frac{-x}{-y} = \frac{x}{y}$$

while

$$\frac{-x}{y} = \frac{x}{-y} = -\frac{x}{y}$$

For example, we can write $\frac{1}{x-y}$ in the following forms:

$$\frac{1}{x-y} = \frac{-1}{-(x-y)} = -\frac{1}{-(x-y)} = -\frac{1}{-x+y}$$

$$= \frac{-1}{y-x} = -\frac{1}{y-x}$$

Often a fraction is written with both its numerator and denominator in factored form. When a fraction is so written, we can, by applying repeatedly the fundamental principle of fractions, together with the law of signs, change the signs of *an even number of these factors* (not terms) without changing the value of the fraction; whereas if we change the signs of an odd number of factors, the sign before the fraction is changed.

Thus, $$\frac{(x-y)(z-y)}{(x-2y)(3z-y)} = \frac{(x-y)(y-z)}{(x-2y)(y-3z)}$$

and $$\frac{(p-q)(r-q)}{(q-3p)(r-4q)} = -\frac{(p-q)(q-r)}{(3p-q)(4q-r)}$$

while $$\frac{(a+m)(m-a)}{(m+q)(m-q)} = \frac{(m+a)(m-a)}{(m+q)(m-q)}$$

One should carefully note that $a + m = m + a$, $x + y = y + x$, etc., and that $m - a = -(a - m)$, $y - x = -(x - y)$, etc.

EXERCISES

Are the following relations true or false?

1. $\dfrac{3}{(a-b)(b-c)(c-a)} = \dfrac{3}{(a-b)(c-b)(a-c)}$

2. $\dfrac{-3}{x-y} = \dfrac{3}{y-x}$

3. $\dfrac{(p-a)(q-b)}{(b-a)(c-a)} = \dfrac{(p-a)(b-q)}{(a-b)(c-a)}$

4. $\dfrac{2}{(a-b)(a-c)} + \dfrac{3}{(c-b)(c-a)} + \dfrac{2}{(a-c)(c-b)}$
$$= -\frac{2}{(a-b)(a-c)} - \frac{3}{(a-c)(b-c)} + \frac{2}{(c-a)(b-c)}$$

5. $\dfrac{(m-n)(m-r)(r-n)}{(n-r)(m-n)(r-m)} = 1$

Integral and mixed expressions

An algebraic expression which is in its simplest form and which does not contain a fraction is called *integral.* Thus x and $3x - 2y$ are integral expressions.

The algebraic sum of an integral expression and a fraction is called a *mixed expression.* Thus, $4x + \dfrac{a}{b}$ and $2m - \dfrac{3n + p}{m + p}$ are examples of mixed expressions.

Adding and subtracting fractions

The method of adding and subtracting fractions in algebra is the same as in arithmetic. If the fractions have the same denominator, we have merely to place the algebraic sum of the numerators over the common denominator. Symbolically we write,

$$\frac{x}{a} + \frac{y}{a} = \frac{x+y}{a} \quad \text{and} \quad \frac{x}{a} - \frac{y}{a} = \frac{x-y}{a}$$

Thus, $\frac{1}{8}+\frac{3}{8}-\frac{2}{8}=\frac{1+3-2}{8}=\frac{2}{8}=\frac{1}{4}$

$$\frac{a}{y}+\frac{b}{y}-\frac{c}{y}=\frac{a+b-c}{y}$$

$$\frac{a+2\,b}{m-n}-\frac{2\,a-b}{m-n}=\frac{(a+2\,b)-(2\,a-b)}{m-n}=\frac{3\,b-a}{m-n}$$

If the fractions do not have the same denominator, we must reduce them to equivalent fractions, all of whose denominators are equal. If the new denominator is the lowest common multiple of the given denominators, it is called the Lowest Common Denominator (L.C.D.) of the given fractions. The following examples illustrate the method of adding and subtracting fractions.

EXAMPLE 1. Simplify

$$\frac{a}{a^2-a-2}-\frac{2\,a+3}{a^2+4\,a+3}+\frac{a-1}{a^2+a-6}$$

Solution. In order to find the L.C.D. we shall write the given fractions with their denominators factored:

$$\frac{a}{(a-2)(a+1)}-\frac{2\,a+3}{(a+3)(a+1)}+\frac{a-1}{(a+3)(a-2)}$$

The L.C.D. is now seen to be $(a-2)(a+1)(a+3)$. In order to avoid errors it is advisable to draw the fraction line, write the L.C.D. as the denominator, then find the numerator and simplify the result. To find the new numerator we merely have to divide each denominator into the L.C.D. and multiply the corresponding numerator by the quotient just found. Thus the given fractions

$$=\frac{a(a+3)}{(a-2)(a+1)(a+3)}-\frac{(2\,a+3)(a-2)}{(a-2)(a+1)(a+3)}$$
$$+\frac{(a-1)(a+1)}{(a-2)(a+1)(a+3)}$$

$$=\frac{a(a+3)-(2\,a+3)(a-2)+(a-1)(a+1)}{(a-2)(a+1)(a+3)}$$

$$= \frac{a^2 + 3a - 2a^2 + a + 6 + a^2 - 1}{(a-2)(a+1)(a+3)}$$

$$= \frac{4a + 5}{(a-2)(a+1)(a+3)}$$

Check. Since the resulting fraction has no meaning when $a = 2$, $a = -1$, or $a = -3$, we cannot use one of these values of a to check our work.

Let us assume $a = 3$; then,

$$\frac{a}{a^2 - a - 2} - \frac{2a + 3}{a^2 + 4a + 3} + \frac{a - 1}{a^2 + a - 6} = \frac{3}{4} - \frac{3}{8} + \frac{1}{3} = \frac{17}{24}$$

Now $$\frac{4a + 5}{(a-2)(a+1)(a+3)} = \frac{17}{(1)(4)(6)} = \frac{17}{24}$$

These results agree as they should.

EXAMPLE 2. Simplify $a - b - \dfrac{3a - b^2}{a + b}$.

Solution. The integral expression $a - b$ may be thought of as a fraction with the denominator 1. That is $a - b = \dfrac{a - b}{1}$. The common denominator is $a + b$. Hence,

$$a - b - \frac{3a - b^2}{a + b} = \frac{(a - b)}{1} - \frac{(3a - b^2)}{a + b}$$

$$= \frac{(a - b)(a + b) - (3a - b^2)}{a + b}$$

$$= \frac{a^2 - 3a}{a + b}$$

Check. Let $a = 3$, $b = 2$. Then

$$a - b - \frac{3a - b^2}{a + b} = 3 - 2 - \frac{9 - 4}{3 + 2} = 3 - 2 - 1 = 0$$

$$\frac{a^2 - 3a}{a + b} = \frac{9 - 9}{3 + 2} = 0$$

These results agree as they should. Could we have used $a = 3$, $b = -3$?

EXERCISES

Simplify each of the following expressions and check:

1. $\dfrac{3}{x-1}-\dfrac{2}{x-1}$

2. $\dfrac{2}{a-3}+\dfrac{1}{a-2}$

3. $\dfrac{3}{x}+\dfrac{2}{-x}$

4. $-\dfrac{3}{a}+\dfrac{3}{-a}$

5. $\dfrac{2}{x-3}+\dfrac{5}{x+3}+\dfrac{1}{x^2-9}$

6. $\dfrac{1}{a-2}-\dfrac{3}{a^2-4}+\dfrac{2}{a+2}$

7. $3+\dfrac{2}{x-1}$

8. $\dfrac{x+2y}{x-2y}-\dfrac{x-2y}{x+2y}$

9. $\dfrac{3a}{a-1}-6+\dfrac{3a}{a+1}$

10. $\dfrac{2}{3}-\dfrac{x}{x-y}+\dfrac{y}{x+y}$

11. $\dfrac{x^2+3}{x^2-3}+1$

12. $\dfrac{x^2-1}{x^2-x-6}+\dfrac{3}{x-3}+1$

13. $\dfrac{a-b}{a^2-ab-6b^2}+\dfrac{a+2b}{a^2+4ab+4b^2}-\dfrac{a-2b}{a^2-ab-2b^2}$

14. $\dfrac{x}{(x-y)(x-z)}+\dfrac{y}{(y-x)(x-z)}$

15. $\dfrac{2}{a-b}+\dfrac{3}{b-a}+\dfrac{a}{a^2-b^2}$

16. $\dfrac{x+y}{(y-z)(y-x)}+\dfrac{y+z}{(z-x)(z-y)}+\dfrac{z+x}{(x-y)(x-z)}$

17. $\dfrac{3}{x-b}+\dfrac{4b}{(x-b)^2}-\dfrac{5b}{(x-b)^3}$

18. $\dfrac{x-2}{x-3}-\dfrac{2x^2+x-13}{x^2+2x-15}+\dfrac{x+1}{x+5}$

19. $\dfrac{x+1}{2(x+4)}-\dfrac{4x-1}{3x-3}+\dfrac{7}{6}$

20. $\dfrac{1}{x-2}+\dfrac{4}{x^2+4}-\dfrac{1}{x+2}-\dfrac{8x}{x^4-16}$

21. $3+x-\dfrac{x^2-1}{x}$

22. $\dfrac{x^2-2x+1}{x-1}-x+2$

23. $\dfrac{x-1}{x}-3+\dfrac{x+1}{x-1}$

24. $2x-1-\dfrac{3}{x}-\dfrac{x-2}{x+1}$

25. $5x - 2 - \frac{x+1}{2x^2 - x - 3}$

26. $\frac{x-2}{x^2 - 3x + 2} + \frac{1}{x^2 - 1} + \frac{x-3}{x^2 - 2x - 3}$

27. $\frac{x+y}{x-y} + \frac{x-y}{x+y} - \frac{x^2+y^2}{y^2-x^2}$

28. $\frac{p}{8p^2 - 2} + \frac{5}{3 + 6p} - \frac{5}{3 - 6p}$

29. $\frac{4}{x+3} - \left[\frac{2}{x-3} - \frac{1}{x^2-9}\right]$

30. $\frac{2}{1+x} - \left[\frac{6}{1-x} - \frac{3}{x^2-1}\right]$

Multiplication and division of fractions

As in arithmetic, the product of two fractions is the fraction whose numerator is the product of the two numerators and whose denominator is the product of the two denominators. Symbolically,

$$\frac{a}{b} \cdot \frac{c}{d} = \frac{ac}{bd}$$

If any mixed expressions are involved, they should be reduced to a single fraction. An integral expression is considered as a fraction having a denominator of 1. Since dividing x by y is equivalent to multiplying x by $\frac{1}{y}$, it follows that in the division of fractions one merely has to invert the divisor and proceed as in multiplication. Symbolically,

$$\frac{a}{b} \div \frac{c}{d} = \frac{a}{b} \cdot \frac{d}{c} = \frac{ad}{bc}$$

EXAMPLE 1. Simplify $\frac{4}{7} \times \frac{3}{8}$.

Solution. $\frac{\overset{1}{\cancel{4}}}{7} \times \frac{3}{\underset{2}{\cancel{8}}} = \frac{3}{14}$.

EXAMPLE 2. Simplify $\left(\frac{1}{2x+1}\right)\left(2+\frac{1}{x}\right)$.

Solution. $\left(\frac{1}{2x+1}\right)\left(2+\frac{1}{x}\right) = \left(\frac{1}{2x+1}\right)\left(\frac{2x+1}{x}\right)$

$$= \frac{1}{x}$$

EXAMPLE 3. Simplify

$$\left(m+\frac{mn}{m-n}\right)\left(\frac{mn}{m+n}-m\right) \div \frac{m^2+n^2}{m^2-n^2}$$

Solution.

$$\left(m+\frac{mn}{m-n}\right)\left(\frac{mn}{m+n}-m\right) \div \frac{m^2+n^2}{m^2-n^2}$$

$$= \left(\frac{m^2-mn+mn}{m-n}\right)\left(\frac{mn-m^2-mn}{m+n}\right)\left(\frac{m^2-n^2}{m^2+n^2}\right)$$

$$= \left(\frac{m^2}{m-n}\right)\left(\frac{-m^2}{m+n}\right)\left(\frac{m^2-n^2}{m^2+n^2}\right) = \frac{-m^4}{m^2+n^2}$$

It is left as an exercise for the student to check this result by letting $m = 3$, $n = 2$.

EXERCISES

Simplify each of the following expressions and check:

1. $\frac{2a^2b}{3ab^3} \div \frac{4ab}{7a^3b^2}$

2. $(x^2-6x+9)\left(\frac{x+3}{x-3}\right)^2$

3. $\left(1+\frac{6}{x}+\frac{5}{x^2}\right) \div \left(\frac{x^2+10x+25}{5x}\right)$

4. $\frac{x^2+6x+5}{x^2-1} \div \frac{x^2+3x+2}{x^3-1}$

5. $\left(1+\frac{2}{x}\right)\left(\frac{3x-6}{4x+8}\right) \div (x^2-4)$

6. $\frac{14y^2-7y}{12y^3+24y^2} \div \frac{2y-1}{y^2+2y}$

7. $\dfrac{y}{x(x-y)} \div \dfrac{x+y}{(y-x)^2}$

8. $\left(x - \dfrac{y^2}{x}\right)\left(\dfrac{x}{y} + \dfrac{y}{x}\right) \div \dfrac{x^4 - y^4}{xy}$

9. $\left(\dfrac{a}{a-b} - \dfrac{a}{a+b}\right) \div \left(\dfrac{b}{a-b} + \dfrac{a}{a+b}\right)$

10. $\dfrac{x^2 - 2x + 4}{x+5} \cdot \dfrac{x^3 + 4x^2 - 5x}{x^4 + 8x} \div \dfrac{x^2 - 2x + 1}{x^2 + x - 2}$

11. $\dfrac{p^2 - (q-r)^2}{r^2 - (q-p)^2} \div \dfrac{(q-r)^2 - p^2}{(p-q)^2 - r^2}$

12. $\dfrac{3x^2 + 8x + 4}{2x^2 + 7x + 3} \cdot \dfrac{x^2 + 2x - 3}{9x^2 + 12x + 4} \cdot \dfrac{2x^2 - x - 1}{3x^2 - x - 2}$

13. $\dfrac{2x^2 + 3x - 9}{4x^2 - 8x + 3} \cdot \dfrac{9x^2 - 6x}{6x^2 - 7x + 2} \div \dfrac{2x^2 + 6x}{2x^2 + 13x - 7}$

14. $\dfrac{x^4 - a^4}{x^3 + a^3} \cdot \dfrac{a^2 - x^2}{a^3 - x^3} \cdot \dfrac{x^6 - a^6}{a^2 + x^2}$

15. $\left(\dfrac{3x + 3y}{3x - 4y} - \dfrac{2x - 3y}{3x + 4y}\right) \div \dfrac{4x^2 - 9y^2}{9x^2 - 16y^2}$

16. $\dfrac{a^2 + 3a + 2}{a^2 - 3a - 10} \div \dfrac{a^2 + 8a + 7}{a^2 - 6a + 5}$

17. $\dfrac{3p + 2}{4q^3}\left(\dfrac{2}{3p} - 1\right) \div \left(\dfrac{9p^2 - 4}{4 - 9p^2}\right)$

18. $\dfrac{a^2 + ab}{a+b} \cdot \dfrac{a^2 + ab + b^2}{a^2 - ab} \div \dfrac{a^3 + a^2b + ab^2}{a - b}$

19. $\left(\dfrac{1-b}{a+a^2}\right)^2\left(\dfrac{1-a^2}{1+b}\right)\left(1 + \dfrac{a}{1-a}\right)$

20. Divide $\dfrac{1}{1-a} - \dfrac{1}{1+a}$ by $\dfrac{1}{1-a} + \dfrac{1}{1+a}$

21. $\dfrac{a^2 - b^2}{a^2 - 3ab + 2b^2} \cdot \dfrac{ab - 2b^2}{a^2 + ab} \div \dfrac{(a-b)^2}{a^2 - ab}$

22. $\left(2 - \dfrac{3}{a+1}\right) \div \left(4 - \dfrac{2a - 4}{a^2 - 1}\right)$

23. $\left(\dfrac{6x}{x^2 - 4} - \dfrac{3}{x-2}\right) \div \dfrac{3}{x^2 - x - 6}$

Complex fractions

A complex fraction is a fraction containing a fraction in its numerator, or its denominator, or in both. What is the value of $\frac{1 - \frac{2}{3}}{2 + \frac{4}{5}}$? To simplify a complex fraction we proceed as in arithmetic by reducing both the numerator and the denominator to single fractions, inverting the denominator, and multiplying.

EXAMPLE. Simplify $\dfrac{4 - \dfrac{1}{x^2}}{1 + \dfrac{1}{2x}}$.

Solution. Reducing the numerator and denominator to single fractions gives $\dfrac{\dfrac{4x^2 - 1}{x^2}}{\dfrac{2x + 1}{2x}}$.

Inverting the denominator and multiplying, we have

$$\frac{4x^2 - 1}{x^2} \cdot \frac{2x}{2x + 1} = \frac{(2x - 1)(2x + 1)}{x^2} \cdot \frac{2x}{2x + 1} = \frac{4x - 2}{x}$$

Check the answer by letting $x = 2$.

It is left as an exercise for the student to simplify the given fraction by multiplying both numerator and denominator by $2x^2$.

EXERCISES

Simplify each of the following fractions and check:

1. $\dfrac{1 - \frac{1}{2}}{3 + \frac{2}{3}}$

2. $\dfrac{\frac{3}{5} + \frac{1}{2}}{\frac{7}{8} - \frac{1}{3}}$

3. $\dfrac{x + y}{1 + \dfrac{y}{x}}$

4. $\dfrac{\dfrac{x}{y} - \dfrac{y}{x}}{1 - \dfrac{y}{x}}$

5. $\dfrac{2 + \dfrac{a - b}{a + b}}{3 - \dfrac{a + 2b}{a + b}}$

6. $\dfrac{\dfrac{2x+y}{x+y}-1}{1-\dfrac{y}{x+y}}$

7. $\dfrac{1-\dfrac{2}{a}+\dfrac{1}{a^2}}{1-\dfrac{1}{a^2}}$

8. $\dfrac{\dfrac{x}{y^2}+\dfrac{y}{x^2}}{\dfrac{1}{x^2}-\dfrac{1}{xy}+\dfrac{1}{y^2}}$

9. $\dfrac{\dfrac{1}{a}+\dfrac{1}{b}+\dfrac{1}{c}}{\dfrac{c}{a}+\dfrac{a}{b}+\dfrac{b}{c}}$

10. $\dfrac{\dfrac{a^2+b^2}{a^2-b^2}-\dfrac{a^2-b^2}{a^2+b^2}}{\dfrac{a+b}{a-b}-\dfrac{a-b}{a+b}}$

11. $\dfrac{3+\dfrac{3a}{a+2b}}{2-\dfrac{a^2-7b^2}{a^2-4b^2}}$

12. $\dfrac{\left\{x^2+\dfrac{y^4}{x^2-y^2}\right\}\left\{x^2+y^2\right\}}{\dfrac{x}{x+y}+\dfrac{y}{x-y}}$

13. $\dfrac{x-\dfrac{x-1}{x+1}}{x-1}-\dfrac{x-\dfrac{x+1}{x-1}}{x+1}$

14. $\left(p+\dfrac{p+1}{p-3}\right)\left(p-\dfrac{p+3}{p-1}\right)\div\dfrac{p}{\dfrac{1}{p}+\dfrac{1}{p^3-p}}$

15. If $x=\dfrac{p+1}{p-1}$ and $y=\dfrac{p^2+1}{p^2-1}$, find the value of $\dfrac{1+x^2}{1-x^2}\div\dfrac{1-y}{1+y}$.

16. $\left(\dfrac{x+y}{x-y}+\dfrac{x-y}{x+y}\right)\div\left(\dfrac{1}{x-y}-\dfrac{1}{x+y}\right)$

17. $\dfrac{\dfrac{a}{b}-\dfrac{b}{a}}{\dfrac{a}{b}+\dfrac{b}{a}+2}$

18. $\dfrac{\dfrac{a}{b}+\dfrac{b}{a}}{\dfrac{a}{b}-\dfrac{b}{a}}+\dfrac{\dfrac{a}{b}-\dfrac{b}{a}}{\dfrac{a}{b}+\dfrac{b}{a}}$

19. $\dfrac{\left\{1+\dfrac{c}{a+b}+\dfrac{c^2}{(a+b)^2}\right\}\left\{1-\dfrac{c^2}{(a+b)^2}\right\}}{\left\{1+\dfrac{c}{a+b}\right\}\left\{\dfrac{(a+b)^3-c^3}{(a+b)^3}\right\}}$

20. $\dfrac{\dfrac{x^2+y^2}{y}-x}{\dfrac{1}{y}-\dfrac{1}{x}}\div\dfrac{x^3-y^3}{x^2-y^2}$

CHAPTER III

Exponents

The laws of positive integral exponents

What is an integer? What is an exponent?

The expression x^n is read "x to the nth" or "x exponent n" or "x to the nth power". When n is a positive integer, x^n is a shorthand way of writing $x \cdot x \cdot x \cdot \cdot \cdot$ to n factors.

The following laws govern the use of positive integral exponents. The proof of all laws except the first is left as an exercise.

Law 1. $$x^m \cdot x^n = x^{m+n}$$

Proof. Since m and n are assumed to be positive integers,

$$\begin{aligned} x^m \cdot x^n &= (x \cdot x \cdot \cdot \cdot m \text{ times})(x \cdot x \cdot \cdot \cdot n \text{ times}) \\ &= x \cdot x \cdot x \cdot \cdot \cdot (m + n) \text{ times} \\ &= x^{m+n} \end{aligned}$$

For example, $$2^3 \cdot 2^4 = 2^7$$

while $$3^2 \cdot 3 \cdot 3^3 \cdot 3^5 = 3^{11}$$

Law 2. $$(x^m)^n = x^{mn}$$

For example, $$(2^3)^2 = 2^6$$

Law 3. $$\left(\frac{x}{y}\right)^m = \frac{x^m}{y^m}$$

For example, $$\left(\frac{2}{3}\right)^3 = \frac{2^3}{3^3} = \frac{8}{27}$$

Law 4. $\dfrac{x^m}{x^n} = x^{m-n}, \quad \text{if } m > n$

For example, $\dfrac{2^{10}}{2^3} = 2^7$

Law 5. $\dfrac{x^m}{x^n} = \dfrac{1}{x^{n-m}}, \quad \text{if } n > m$

For example, $\dfrac{3^2}{3^5} = \dfrac{1}{3^3} = \dfrac{1}{27}$

Law 6. $(abc)^m = a^m b^m c^m$

For example, $(2\,ax^2)^3 = 8\,a^3x^6$

EXERCISES

Simplify each of the following expressions:

1. $a^3 \cdot a^2$
2. $3^3 \cdot 3^2$
3. $5^5 \cdot 5^2$
4. $a^4 \cdot a^7$
5. $\dfrac{x^{10}}{x^3}$
6. $\dfrac{3^{10}}{3^4}$
7. $\dfrac{a^{27}}{a^{40}}$
8. $\dfrac{a^{11}}{a^{18}}$
9. $(a^3)^2$
10. $(2^2)^3$
11. $(3^2)^2$
12. $(a^3)^5$
13. $(ab)^3$
14. $(3\,x)^2$
15. $(3\,a^2b)^3$
16. $(2\,a^2x^3)^4$
17. $\left(\dfrac{a}{b}\right)^2$
18. $\left(\dfrac{2\,a}{3\,b}\right)^3$
19. $\left(\dfrac{3\,x}{2\,y}\right)^4$
20. $(2\,a)^2 + \dfrac{1}{(2\,a)^2}$

Writing large numbers

Scientists tell us that the earth weighs approximately 6,000,000,000,000,000,000,000 tons. Do you know how a scientist would write this number? He would write it as 6×10^{21}, which is read "six times ten to the twenty-first power".

EXERCISES

Write the following numbers as an integer times 10 to the proper power:

1. 73,000,000,000
2. 37,000,000,000,000
3. 2,000,000,000
4. 7,230,000,000,000,000,000
5. 277,700,000,000,000,000,000,000
6. 707,000,000,000,000

Write the following numbers without exponents:

7. 3×10^{12} **10.** 7007×10^{21}

8. 72×10^{15} **11.** 3.2×10^{8}

9. 7101×10^{10} **12.** 3.23×10^{11}

13. Write 173,000,000 as 1.73 times 10 with the proper exponent.

14. Write 273,000,000,000 as 27.3 times 10 with the proper exponent.

15. From the earth to the nearest fixed star is approximately 25×10^{12} miles. Write this number without exponents.

16. The mass of the sun is approximately 2.18×10^{25} tons. Write this number without exponents.

What is meant by $a^{\frac{1}{q}}$?

On page 51 we assumed that the exponents were positive integers. Let us see what meaning we may attach to such expressions as $a^{\frac{1}{4}}$, $a^{\frac{1}{10}}$, etc. It is customary to define them in such a way that the laws for positive integral exponents will hold for fractional exponents. This we shall do.

Assuming Law 1 to hold,

$$a^{\frac{1}{4}} \cdot a^{\frac{1}{4}} \cdot a^{\frac{1}{4}} \cdot a^{\frac{1}{4}} = a^{\frac{1}{4}+\frac{1}{4}+\frac{1}{4}+\frac{1}{4}} = a$$

Hence, if there exists a number whose fourth power is a, we shall define it to be $a^{\frac{1}{4}}$. The expression $a^{\frac{1}{4}}$ is often written $\sqrt[4]{a}$ and is read "fourth root of a".

In like manner, $a^{\frac{1}{q}}$, where q is a positive integer, is defined as a number whose qth power is a. Another way of writing $a^{\frac{1}{q}}$ is $\sqrt[q]{a}$, which is read "qth root of a". The symbol $\sqrt{\ }$ is called a *radical*, the quantity a the *radicand*, and q the *index*. If $q = 2$, we write $\sqrt{a}$, which is read "square root of a". How would you write the fifth root of a^3?

What is meant by $a^{\frac{p}{q}}$?

If p and q are positive integers, then by Law 1

$$\begin{aligned} a^{\frac{1}{q}} \cdot a^{\frac{1}{q}} \cdots \text{to } p \text{ factors} &= a^{\frac{1}{q}+\frac{1}{q}+\cdots \text{ to } p \text{ terms}} \\ &= a^{\frac{p}{q}} \end{aligned}$$

Therefore $a^{\frac{p}{q}}$ means the pth power of the qth root of a. That is

$$a^{\frac{p}{q}} = (\sqrt[q]{a})^p = \sqrt[q]{a^p}$$

On page 285 we shall see that any number except 0 has q distinct qth roots. For example, the number 9 has two square roots, namely, ± 3. However, for the present we shall assume that $a^{\frac{1}{p}} (a > 0)$ has one and only one value, namely, its real positive or principal value. Likewise, if $a < 0$ and p is an odd integer, we shall assume that $a^{\frac{1}{p}}$ has one and only one value, namely, its real negative or principal value. Hence,

$$\begin{aligned} 9^{\frac{1}{2}} &= 3 \\ (-125)^{\frac{1}{3}} &= -5 \\ 4^{\frac{3}{2}} &= 8 \\ (-8)^{\frac{5}{3}} &= -32 \end{aligned}$$

EXERCISES

Simplify each of the following expressions:

1. $8^{\frac{2}{3}}$ **5.** $125^{\frac{2}{3}}$ **9.** $16^{\frac{3}{4}}$ **13.** $(\frac{9}{16})^{\frac{1}{2}}$

2. $25^{\frac{3}{2}}$ **6.** $27^{\frac{4}{3}}$ **10.** $625^{\frac{3}{4}}$ **14.** $64^{\frac{7}{6}}$

3. $27^{\frac{2}{3}}$ **7.** $(-8)^{\frac{2}{3}}$ **11.** $-(625)^{\frac{3}{4}}$ **15.** $(\frac{16}{81})^{\frac{1}{4}}$

4. $81^{\frac{3}{4}}$ **8.** $(8)^{\frac{1}{3}}$ **12.** $(.49)^{\frac{1}{2}}$ **16.** $(\frac{243}{32})^{\frac{3}{5}}$

17. Multiply: a) $x^{\frac{2}{3}} + x^{\frac{1}{3}}$ by $x^{\frac{2}{3}} - x^{\frac{1}{3}}$

b) $x^{\frac{2}{3}} + x^{\frac{1}{3}}y^{\frac{1}{3}} + y^{\frac{2}{3}}$ by $x^{\frac{1}{3}} - y^{\frac{1}{3}}$

c) $a^{\frac{3}{2}} + 2 - a^{\frac{1}{2}}$ by $a^{\frac{1}{2}} - 3$

18. Divide: a) $3\,a + 10\,a^{\frac{2}{3}} - 5\,a^{\frac{1}{3}} + 12$ by $a^{\frac{1}{3}} + 4$

b) $25\,x^{\frac{5}{2}} - x^{\frac{3}{2}} - 8\,x^{\frac{1}{2}} - 2\,x$ by $5\,x - 4\,x^{\frac{1}{2}}$

c) $a^{\frac{4}{3}} + 9\,a^{\frac{2}{3}} + 81$ by $a^{\frac{2}{3}} - 3\,a^{\frac{1}{3}} + 9$

19. Find the value of $x^{\frac{2}{3}} + y^{\frac{2}{3}}$ when $x = 8$ and $y = 27$.

20. Evaluate $\dfrac{x^{\frac{2}{3}} - y^{\frac{2}{3}}}{x^{\frac{1}{6}} + y^{\frac{3}{2}}}$ when $x = 64$ and $y = 729$.

21. If $a^{\frac{2}{3}} = 4$, what does a equal? *Hint.* Raise both sides of the equality to the $\frac{3}{2}$ power.

22. Find x if $x^{\frac{3}{4}} = 27$.

23. Find m if $m^{\frac{3}{5}} = 8$.

24. Simplify $(y^{\frac{2}{3}} + 2\,a^{\frac{1}{4}}y^{\frac{1}{3}} + 4\,a^{\frac{1}{2}})(y^{\frac{2}{3}} - 2\,a^{\frac{1}{4}}y^{\frac{1}{3}} + 4\,a^{\frac{1}{2}})$.

25. Divide $a + b$ by $a^{\frac{1}{3}} + b^{\frac{1}{3}}$.

The meaning of a^0,

In order for Law 1 to hold, it is necessary that

$$a^0 \cdot a^m = a^{0+m} = a^m$$

or

$$a^0 = 1 \qquad \text{if} \qquad a \neq 0$$

Hence, any number a with the exponent 0 is defined to be 1 provided $a \neq 0$. We assign no meaning to the symbol 0^0. For example, $3^0 = 1$, $27^0 = 1$, $1^0 = 1$, $(a + b)^0 = 1$. What is the value of $(-3\,x + 7)^0$?

What is meant by a^{-m}?

If Law 1 holds,

$$a^{-m} \cdot a^m = a^{-m+m} = a^0 = 1$$

Hence,

$$a^{-m} = \frac{1}{a^m} \text{ if } a \neq 0$$

and

$$a^m = \frac{1}{a^{-m}} \text{ if } a \neq 0$$

For example,

$$3^{-2} = \frac{1}{3^2} = \frac{1}{9}$$

and

$$\frac{1}{2^{-3}} = 2^3 = 8$$

What is the value of 1^{-1}? 2^{-1}? $\frac{1}{3^{-2}}$?

We have defined fractional, zero, and negative exponents consistent with the first law of positive integral exponents. To be logically correct we should show that our definitions are consistent with the other laws, but we shall assume this to be the case.

Those interested in the complete proof are referred to Chrystal's *Algebra*, Part 1, page 182.

From the fact that $a^{-m} = \frac{1}{a^m}$, it follows that in a fraction we may transfer any factor of the whole numerator from the numerator to the denominator or vice versa, provided we change the sign of the exponent of the factor.

EXAMPLE 1. Write in simplest form with positive exponents:

$$\frac{(p + q)^0(a - x)^{-1}}{(m + n)^{-1}(t - x)^{-3}}$$

Solution. Each expression within parentheses is a factor of either the numerator or the denominator. Recalling the fact that $(p + q)^0 = 1$, we can write

$$\frac{(p + q)^0(a - x)^{-1}}{(m + n)^{-1}(t - x)^3} = \frac{(m + n)}{(a - x)(t - x)^3}$$

EXAMPLE 2. Write in simplest form with positive exponents:

$$\frac{a^{-1} - b^{-1}}{a^{-1} + b^{-1}}$$

Solution. Are a^{-1} and b^{-1} factors of the numerator? of the denominator? Since a^{-1} and b^{-1} are not factors of either the numerator or the denominator,

$$\frac{a^{-1} - b^{-1}}{a^{-1} + b^{-1}} = \frac{\frac{1}{a} - \frac{1}{b}}{\frac{1}{a} + \frac{1}{b}} = \frac{\frac{b - a}{ab}}{\frac{b + a}{ab}} = \frac{b - a}{b + a}$$

Query. What would be the result of multiplying the numerator and the denominator of the given fraction by ab?

EXERCISES

Simplify:

1. $a^{-3} \cdot a^{-4}$
2. $a^{-5} \cdot a^{-7}$
3. $3^{-3} \cdot 3^{-3}$
4. $\frac{3x^3}{x^{-1}}$
5. $\frac{5x^7}{2x^{-3}}$
6. $\frac{x^7}{5x^{10}}$
7. $\frac{25xy^{-3}}{x^{-2}}$

8. $\dfrac{4^{-2}\, a^3b^{-2}}{2^{-3}\, a^{-3}b^2}$

9. $(-2)^{-3}(-2)^{-3}$

10. $(-5)^{-2}(-5)^{-3}$

11. $(-2)^3(-a)^2(-a)^{-7}$

12. $\dfrac{a^{-x} + b^{-y}}{a^{3x} - b^{2y}}$

13. $\dfrac{7\, x^{-1} + y^{-4}}{a^{-1} + b^{-1}}$

14. $\dfrac{3^{-2}\, x^2y^{-5}}{x^{-3}y^{-1}}$

15. $\dfrac{2^{-1}\, a^{-3}b^2}{3\, a^2b^{-3}}$

16. $36^{-\frac{3}{2}}$

17. $625^{-\frac{1}{4}}$

18. $\dfrac{1}{32^{-\frac{2}{5}}}$

19. $\dfrac{1}{8^{-\frac{2}{3}}}$

20. $\dfrac{2^0}{4^{-\frac{3}{2}}}$

21. $8^{-\frac{2}{3}} \cdot 4^{-2}$

22. $25^{-\frac{1}{2}} \cdot 27^{\frac{2}{3}}$

23. $(\frac{1}{3})^0(\frac{1}{8})^{-\frac{1}{3}}(25)^{\frac{1}{2}}$

24. Multiply:
   a) $a^{-1} - b^{-2}$ by $a^{-1} + b^{-2}$
   b) $x + 2 - 3\, x^{-1}$ by $4\, x - 5$
   c) $x^{-1} + 1 + x$ by $x^{-1} - x$
   d) $a^{\frac{3}{4}} - 2\, a^{\frac{1}{4}} + 4\, a^{-\frac{1}{4}}$ by $a^{\frac{1}{4}} + 2\, a^{-\frac{1}{4}}$

25. Divide:
   a) $3\, a - 7 - a^{-1} + a^{-2}$ by $a - 2 - a^{-1}$
   b) $1 - 2\, a - 3\, a^2$ by $a^{-1} - 3$
   c) $6\, a^2 - 25 - 35\, a^{-1} + 10\, a + 14\, a^{-2}$ by $3\, a + 5 - 2\, a^{-1}$
   d) $2\, x - x^{\frac{1}{2}}y^{-\frac{1}{2}} - 3\, y^{-1}$ by $2\, x^{\frac{1}{2}} - 3\, y^{-\frac{1}{2}}$

26. $\dfrac{a^{-1} + b}{a^{-1} - b}$

27. $\dfrac{a^{-1} - 2\, b^{-1}}{a^{-1} + 2\, b^{-2}}$

28. $\left(\dfrac{1}{x^{-3}} + \dfrac{1}{y^{-3}}\right)^{-1}$

29. $1 + \dfrac{a^{-2} + b^{-2}}{a^{-1} - b^{-1}}$

30. $\dfrac{a^{-2} + b^{-2}}{a^{-1} - b^{-1}}$

31. $\left[\dfrac{a^{-1} - b^{-1}}{a^{-1} + b^{-1}} - \dfrac{a^{-1} + b^{-1}}{a^{-1} - b^{-1}}\right]^{-1}$

32. $\left\{\dfrac{5\, a^{-2} + b}{a^{-2}b} - \dfrac{a^2}{b^{-1}}\right\}^{-1}$

Writing small numbers

In some branches of mathematics and science many small numbers arise. They are usually written in exponential form similar to the manner in which very large numbers are written.

Now

$$0.1 = 10^{-1}$$
$$0.01 = 10^{-2}$$
$$0.001 = 10^{-3}$$
$$\cdots\cdots\cdots\cdots$$
$$0.0000001 = 10^{-7} \text{ etc.}$$

A scientist would write a small number like 0.000 000 9 as 9×10^{-7}. For, $0.000\,000\,9 = \frac{9}{10{,}000{,}000} = \frac{9}{10^7} = 9 \times 10^{-7}$.

EXERCISES

Write each of the following numbers as an integer times 10 to the proper power:

1. 0.000 000 1
2. 0.000 075
3. 0.000 000 000 7
4. $\frac{275}{1{,}000{,}000{,}000}$
5. $\frac{1.27}{1{,}000{,}000}$

Write as a decimal fraction without using exponents:

6. 3×10^{-5}
7. 2.57×10^{-7}
8. 1.01×10^{-10}

9. Two masses of one gram each with centers one centimeter apart attract each other with a force of 66.7×10^{-9} dynes. Express the number of dynes as a decimal.

10. One meter is equal to 1,000,000 microns. Express 38.72×10^{-11} meters in microns.

11. The distance from Venus to the sun is 67,200,000 miles, while that from Neptune to the sun is 2,800,000,000 miles. What is the ratio of the distances? Express the result, using 10 with an exponent.

Radical signs

We have just seen that the symbol $\sqrt{\ }$, called a radical sign, is used to indicate a root of a number. Thus the fourth root of a is written $\sqrt[4]{a}$; the cube root of 10 is written $\sqrt[3]{10}$; the square root of 10 is written $\sqrt{10}$; while the qth root of a is written $\sqrt[q]{a}$. In the expression $\sqrt[q]{a}$, a is called the *radicand* and q the *index*. (See page 53.)

Every positive number has two square roots since

$$(+a)(+a) = a^2$$

and

$$(-a)(-a) = a^2$$

Hence we say the square root of 100 is either plus or minus 10. When a square root is indicated by using a radical sign, $\sqrt{\ }$, mathematicians have agreed that the radical sign will indicate the *positive* or *principal* square root. (See page 54.) Thus:

a) The square roots of 100 are ± 10.
b) $\sqrt{100} = 10$ and not -10.
c) $-\sqrt{100} = -10$ and not $+10$.

We shall likewise assume for the present that $\sqrt[n]{a}$, $a > 0$, has one and only one value, namely, its real positive or principal value.

The root of a quantity indicated by a radical sign is called a *radical*. Thus $\sqrt{3}$ and $\sqrt{x+y}$ are radicals. If the root is a rational number, the radical is called *rational;* otherwise, it is called *irrational.* Thus $\sqrt{4}$ is rational while $\sqrt{7}$ is irrational. The expression $\sqrt[q]{a}$ is called a *surd* when a is rational and the root cannot be found exactly. The *order of a surd* is indicated by its index. For example, $\sqrt{x}$ is a surd of the second order, while $\sqrt[m]{x}$ is a surd of the mth order.

If surds are of the same order and contain the same quantity under the radical sign, they are called *similar.* Thus $3\sqrt{5}$ and $\frac{15}{2}\sqrt{5}$ are examples of similar surds. The product of a rational factor and a surd is called a *mixed surd.* Thus, $7\sqrt[3]{4}$ and $5\sqrt{3}$ are examples of mixed surds. The rational factor is called the *coefficient* of the surd. If the coefficient of a surd is unity, the surd is called an *entire surd.* Thus, $\sqrt{x}$ and $\sqrt{5}$ are examples of entire surds.

It follows at once from the laws of indices that:

$$\sqrt[n]{a}\sqrt[n]{b} = a^{\frac{1}{n}}b^{\frac{1}{n}} = (ab)^{\frac{1}{n}} = \sqrt[n]{ab} \text{ where } a > 0 \text{ and } b > 0 \qquad (1)$$

$$\frac{\sqrt[n]{a}}{\sqrt[n]{b}} = \sqrt[n]{\frac{a}{b}} \text{ when } a > 0 \text{ and } b > 0 \text{ or when } a < 0, b < 0 \qquad (2)$$

Note that $\sqrt{5}\sqrt{5} = \sqrt{25} = 5$. What is the value of $\sqrt{2}\sqrt{2}$? $\sqrt{x}\sqrt{x}$? Does our assumption allow us to say $\sqrt{-5}\sqrt{-5} = \sqrt{25} = 5$? It does not. What is the value of $\sqrt{\frac{4}{9}}$? $\sqrt{\dfrac{-4}{-9}}$?

If the radical sign cannot be removed, we reduce the radical to what is called its simplest form. By this we mean:

1. The index of the radical is to be as small a positive integer as possible.
2. The radicand is to contain no factor raised to a power equal to or greater than the index of the root.
3. There are to be no fractions under a radical sign.
4. There are to be no radicals in a denominator.

We shall now explain the first of these principles. Suppose we wish to reduce $\sqrt[pq]{x^{nq}}$. We know that $\sqrt[pq]{x^{nq}} = x^{\frac{nq}{pq}} = x^{\frac{n}{p}} = \sqrt[p]{x^n}$. Hence to simplify $\sqrt[6]{27}$ we write

$$\sqrt[6]{27} = \sqrt[6]{3^3} = 3^{\frac{3}{6}} = 3^{\frac{1}{2}} = \sqrt{3}$$

Likewise $$\sqrt[8]{16} = \sqrt[8]{2^4} = 2^{\frac{4}{8}} = 2^{\frac{1}{2}} = \sqrt{2}$$

EXERCISES

Simplify each of the following expressions:

1. $\sqrt[4]{4}$
2. $\sqrt[6]{8}$
3. $\sqrt[4]{9}$
4. $\sqrt[10]{32\,x^5}$
5. $\sqrt[6]{16\,x^2}$
6. $\sqrt[6]{25\,a^4}$
7. $\sqrt[4]{121\,x^2}$
8. $\sqrt[6]{9\,x^4}$
9. $\sqrt[4]{49\,y^2}$
10. $\sqrt[4]{100\,y^4}$
11. $\sqrt[6]{64\,y^{12}}$
12. $\sqrt[4]{169\,m^2n^2}$
13. $\sqrt[15]{32\,m^5}$
14. $\sqrt[8]{81\,m^4y^8}$
15. $\sqrt[6]{\dfrac{27\,y^3}{z^6}}$
16. $\sqrt[12]{64\,x^8}$

The second principle is illustrated by the following examples:

$$\sqrt{28} = \sqrt{4 \times 7} = 2\sqrt{7}$$

$$\sqrt{45\,x^3} = \sqrt{9\,x^2 \cdot 5\,x} = 3\,x\sqrt{5\,x}$$

$$\sqrt[3]{56} = \sqrt[3]{8 \cdot 7} = 2\sqrt[3]{7}$$

$$\sqrt[3]{128} = \sqrt[3]{64 \cdot 2} = 4\sqrt[3]{2}$$

EXERCISES

Simplify each of the following expressions:

1. $\sqrt{32}$
2. $\sqrt{72}$
3. $\sqrt{150}$
4. $\sqrt{24}$
5. $\sqrt{128}$
6. $\sqrt[3]{250}$
7. $\sqrt[3]{16}$
8. $\sqrt[3]{54}$
9. $\sqrt{20}$
10. $\sqrt{700\,x^3}$
11. $\sqrt{45\,x^4}$
12. $\sqrt{80\,x^3}$
13. $\frac{1}{b}\sqrt{b^2x}$
14. $-\frac{3\,a}{b}\sqrt{ab^3}$
15. $\sqrt[4]{16\,a^5}$
16. $\sqrt[3]{-8}$
17. $\sqrt[3]{-16}$
18. $\sqrt[4]{32\,a^5}$
19. $\sqrt{a^2+a^3}$
20. $\sqrt{a^3+2\,a^2x+ax^2}$
21. $\sqrt{288\,x^5}$
22. $\sqrt{a^2b^2+a^2c^2}$
23. $\sqrt{(a^2-4\,b^2)(a+2\,b)}$
24. $\sqrt{x^2+\frac{x^2}{4}}$
25. $\sqrt[7]{256\,a^7b^{10}}$

The third principle, which deals with a fractional radicand, is applied as follows:

EXAMPLE. Simplify: $\sqrt{\frac{3}{8}}$.

Solution. Multiplying the numerator and denominator of the fraction by 2 does not change its value, but it does make the denominator a perfect square. The fraction can now be factored in such a way that one factor which contains this denominator is a perfect square. Thus,

$$\sqrt{\tfrac{3}{8}}=\sqrt{\tfrac{6}{16}}=\sqrt{\tfrac{1}{16}\cdot 6}=\tfrac{1}{4}\sqrt{6}$$

Likewise $$\sqrt{2\tfrac{1}{3}}=\sqrt{\tfrac{7}{3}}=\sqrt{\tfrac{21}{9}}=\sqrt{\tfrac{1}{9}\cdot 21}=\tfrac{1}{3}\sqrt{21}$$

and $$\sqrt[3]{\tfrac{5}{4}}=\sqrt[3]{\tfrac{10}{8}}=\sqrt[3]{\tfrac{1}{8}\cdot 10}=\tfrac{1}{2}\sqrt[3]{10}$$

EXERCISES

Simplify each of the following expressions:

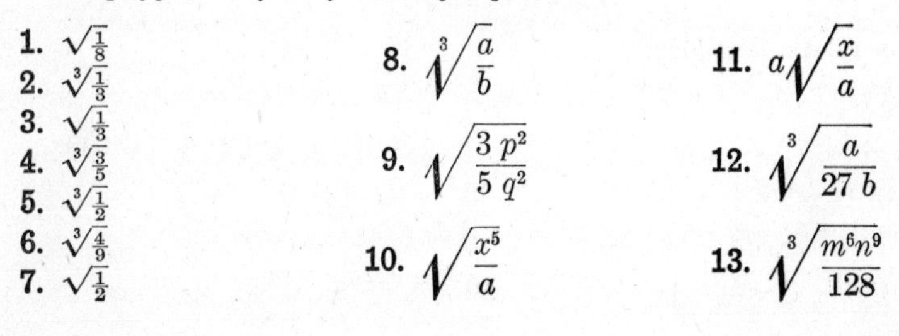

1. $\sqrt{\frac{1}{8}}$
2. $\sqrt[3]{\frac{1}{3}}$
3. $\sqrt{\frac{1}{3}}$
4. $\sqrt[3]{\frac{3}{5}}$
5. $\sqrt[3]{\frac{1}{2}}$
6. $\sqrt[3]{\frac{4}{9}}$
7. $\sqrt{\frac{1}{2}}$
8. $\sqrt[3]{\frac{a}{b}}$
9. $\sqrt{\frac{3\,p^2}{5\,q^2}}$
10. $\sqrt{\frac{x^5}{a}}$
11. $a\sqrt{\frac{x}{a}}$
12. $\sqrt[3]{\frac{a}{27\,b}}$
13. $\sqrt[3]{\frac{m^6n^9}{128}}$

14. $\sqrt[n]{\dfrac{x^{pn}}{y^{n-1}}}$

15. $\sqrt[m]{\dfrac{b^m}{a^{m-1}}}$

16. $\sqrt[5]{\dfrac{p^2}{81\,q^3}}$

17. $\sqrt{3\frac{2}{3}\,x}$

18. $\sqrt{1\frac{2}{3}\,a^3}$

19. $\sqrt{5-(\frac{1}{5})^2}$

20. $\sqrt{2\,x^2-\left(\dfrac{x}{2}\right)^2}$

Addition and subtraction of radicals

Before we can discuss the fourth principle which is connected with division, it is necessary that we learn how to perform the operations of addition and subtraction, as well as multiplication of radicals. The following examples will illustrate how we can add and subtract similar radicals.

EXAMPLE 1. Reduce to simplest form:

$$\sqrt{45}-\sqrt{20}+\sqrt{\tfrac{1}{5}}$$

Solution.

$$\begin{aligned}\sqrt{45}-\sqrt{20}+\sqrt{\tfrac{1}{5}} &= \sqrt{9\times 5}-\sqrt{4\times 5}+\sqrt{\tfrac{1}{25}\cdot 5}\\ &= 3\sqrt{5}-2\sqrt{5}+\tfrac{1}{5}\sqrt{5}\\ &= \tfrac{6}{5}\sqrt{5}\end{aligned}$$

EXAMPLE 2. Reduce to simplest form:

$$\sqrt{6}+\sqrt{\tfrac{1}{27}}+\sqrt{24}-\sqrt{\tfrac{4}{3}}$$

Solution.

$$\begin{aligned}\sqrt{6}+\sqrt{\tfrac{1}{27}}+\sqrt{24}-\sqrt{\tfrac{4}{3}} &= \sqrt{6}+\sqrt{\tfrac{1}{81}\cdot 3}+\sqrt{4\cdot 6}-\sqrt{\tfrac{4}{9}\cdot 3}\\ &= \sqrt{6}+\tfrac{1}{9}\sqrt{3}+2\sqrt{6}-\tfrac{2}{3}\sqrt{3}\\ &= 3\sqrt{6}-\tfrac{5}{9}\sqrt{3}\end{aligned}$$

EXERCISES

Reduce to simplest form:

1. $5\sqrt{18}-\sqrt{\frac{1}{2}}$
2. $\sqrt{8}+\sqrt{72}-\sqrt{50}$
3. $\sqrt{80}+\sqrt{20}+\sqrt{45}$
4. $3\sqrt{20}+7\sqrt{80}-3\sqrt{45}$
5. $\frac{1}{3}\sqrt{144}-\frac{2}{3}\sqrt{50}$
6. $\sqrt[3]{16}-3\sqrt[3]{54}$
7. $2\sqrt[3]{16}-3\sqrt[3]{250}+7\sqrt[3]{128}$
8. $\sqrt{32}+\sqrt{\frac{1}{2}}-\sqrt{\frac{1}{8}}$
9. $5\sqrt{5\frac{1}{3}}-3\sqrt{1\frac{1}{3}}$
10. $2\sqrt{\frac{16}{3}}-\sqrt{8\frac{1}{3}}$

11. $\sqrt{a^2} + \sqrt{a} - \sqrt{4a}$
12. $\sqrt{9 + 9a^2} + \sqrt{4 + 4a^2} - 3\sqrt{1 + a^2}$
13. $\sqrt{98x^3} + 3\sqrt{8x^3} - \sqrt{2x}$
14. $\sqrt[3]{\frac{x^3}{9}} + \sqrt[3]{\frac{y^3}{9}}$
15. $\sqrt{\frac{a}{b}} - \sqrt{\frac{b}{a}}$
16. $\sqrt{a + b} + 2\sqrt{(a + b)^3} - 3\sqrt{(a + b)^5}$
17. $\sqrt{(a - b)^3} - \sqrt{\frac{1}{a - b}}$
18. $\sqrt{3x^2 - 6x + 3} - \sqrt{3x^2 + 6x + 3}$
19. $\sqrt{\frac{x - y}{x + y}} - \sqrt{\frac{x + y}{x - y}}$
20. $\sqrt{a^3b^{-1}} - \sqrt{a^{-1}b}$
21. $\sqrt[3]{81} - 6\sqrt{24} - \sqrt[3]{24} + 4\sqrt{54}$
22. $3\sqrt{\frac{1}{2}} - 2\sqrt[3]{2} + \sqrt{\frac{1}{8}} + 3\sqrt[3]{16}$
23. $x\sqrt[3]{\frac{y}{x}} + y\sqrt[3]{\frac{x}{y}}$
24. $3\sqrt{\frac{2}{3}} + 2\sqrt{\frac{3}{2}}$
25. $\sqrt{98m^4} + \sqrt{75m^2} - 3\sqrt{32m^2}$

Multiplication of radicals

Suppose we wish to find the product of $\sqrt[n]{a}$ and $\sqrt[n]{b}$. Since $\sqrt[n]{a} = a^{\frac{1}{n}}$ and $\sqrt[n]{b} = b^{\frac{1}{n}}$, then $\sqrt[n]{a}\sqrt[n]{b} = a^{\frac{1}{n}}b^{\frac{1}{n}} = (ab)^{\frac{1}{n}} = \sqrt[n]{ab}$, $a > 0, b > 0$. After applying this principle, we should be sure that the result is reduced to its simplest form.

EXAMPLE 1. $\sqrt{3}\sqrt{6} = \sqrt{18} = \sqrt{9 \cdot 2} = 3\sqrt{2}$

EXAMPLE 2. $5\sqrt{2}\,3\sqrt{6} = 15\sqrt{12} = 15\sqrt{4 \cdot 3} = 30\sqrt{3}$

EXAMPLE 3. $\sqrt[3]{4}\sqrt[3]{16} = \sqrt[3]{64} = 4$

EXAMPLE 4. $\sqrt{\frac{3}{8}}\sqrt{\frac{1}{2}} = \sqrt{\frac{3}{16}} = \sqrt{\frac{1}{16} \cdot 3} = \frac{1}{4}\sqrt{3}$

EXERCISES

Perform the following multiplications and reduce each result to its simplest form:

1. $\sqrt{25}\,\sqrt{2}$
2. $\sqrt{50}\,\sqrt{2}$
3. $\sqrt{8}\,\sqrt{2}$
4. $5\sqrt{2}\,\sqrt{10}$
5. $4\sqrt{7}\,3\sqrt{7}$
6. $\sqrt[3]{16}\,\sqrt[3]{\tfrac{1}{2}}$
7. $\sqrt[3]{xy}\,\sqrt[3]{y^2}$
8. $4\sqrt[3]{3}\,\sqrt[3]{18}$
9. $5\sqrt[3]{4}\,3\sqrt[3]{2}$
10. $\sqrt{pq}\sqrt{pq}\sqrt{pq}$
11. $(4\sqrt{7})^2$
12. $(-3\sqrt{3})^3$
13. $\sqrt{x-1}\sqrt{x+1}$
14. $(2\sqrt{x}-1)^2$
15. $\sqrt{2\,xy}\,\sqrt{8\,xy}$
16. $\sqrt{\dfrac{1}{x}}\,\sqrt{x^5}$
17. $(3\sqrt[3]{x})^3$
18. $2\sqrt[5]{16\,x^2}\,\sqrt[5]{2\,x^3}$
19. $(2\sqrt{2}-1)^2$
20. $(\sqrt{3}-2)(\sqrt{3}+2)$
21. $(2\sqrt{3}+5)(2\sqrt{3}-5)$
22. $(\sqrt{x}+\sqrt{y})^2$
23. $(\sqrt{x}-\sqrt{y})(\sqrt{x}+\sqrt{y})$
24. $(2\sqrt{5}-3\sqrt{3})^2$
25. $(3\sqrt{2\,x}-2\sqrt{x})^2$
26. $(\sqrt{x-1}-\sqrt{x+1})^2$
27. $(2\sqrt{x-1}+3\sqrt{x+2})^2$
28. $(a\sqrt{b}-b\sqrt{a}+\sqrt{ab})(\sqrt{a}+\sqrt{b})$
29. $(\sqrt{a}-\sqrt{b}-\sqrt{c})(\sqrt{a}+\sqrt{b}-\sqrt{c})$
30. $(4\sqrt{3}+2\sqrt{2}-\sqrt{5})(3\sqrt{2}-\sqrt{3}+\sqrt{5})$
31. If $x=\sqrt{2}+1$, find the value of $x^2+3\,x-2$.
32. If $x=\dfrac{\sqrt{5}-2}{3}$, find the value of $\left(\dfrac{2\,x-1}{3}\right)^2$.

Changing radicals to the same order

Can you tell by inspection which is larger, $\sqrt{3}$ or $\sqrt[3]{5}$? If both radicals were reduced to the same order, could you answer the question by comparing their radicands?

Now,
$$\sqrt{3}=3^{\frac{1}{2}}=3^{\frac{3}{6}}=\sqrt[6]{3^3}=\sqrt[6]{27}$$
$$\sqrt[3]{5}=5^{\frac{1}{3}}=5^{\frac{2}{6}}=\sqrt[6]{5^2}=\sqrt[6]{25}$$

Since $27>25$, it follows that $\sqrt{3}>\sqrt[3]{5}$.

Likewise, suppose we wish to find the product of $\sqrt{2}$ and $\sqrt[3]{6}$. We learned on page 59 that we can multiply two surds if they are of the same order. Hence, we will first change both surds to the sixth order, for six is the least common multiple of the indices.

$$\sqrt{2} = 2^{\frac{1}{2}} = 2^{\frac{3}{6}} = \sqrt[6]{2^3} = \sqrt[6]{8}$$
$$\sqrt[3]{6} = 6^{\frac{1}{3}} = 6^{\frac{2}{6}} = \sqrt[6]{6^2} = \sqrt[6]{36}$$
$$\therefore \quad \sqrt{2}\sqrt[3]{6} = \sqrt[6]{8}\sqrt[6]{36} = \sqrt[6]{288}$$

EXERCISES

Arrange in order of magnitude:

1. $\sqrt{2}, \sqrt[3]{3}$
2. $\sqrt{5}, \sqrt[3]{11}$
3. $\sqrt[3]{4}, \sqrt[4]{5}$
4. $\sqrt{\frac{2}{3}}, \sqrt[6]{\frac{7}{27}}$
5. $\sqrt{50}, 2\sqrt[3]{32}$
6. $3\sqrt{15}, 2\sqrt[3]{3}$
7. $\sqrt[3]{\frac{3}{4}}, \frac{1}{3}\sqrt{6}$
8. $\sqrt[4]{10}, \sqrt[10]{900}$

Simplify:

9. $\sqrt[3]{2}\sqrt{3}$
10. $\sqrt[5]{5}\sqrt[4]{2}$
11. $\sqrt[3]{x}\sqrt{y}$
12. $\sqrt{10}\sqrt[3]{7}$
13. $\sqrt[n]{x}\sqrt[m]{y}$
14. $\sqrt{\frac{x}{y}}\sqrt[3]{\frac{y}{x}}$
15. $(\sqrt{2} + \sqrt[3]{3})^2$
16. $(\sqrt{3} - 2\sqrt[4]{3})^2$

Division of radicals

We will now consider the fourth principle of simplification. The main purpose in simplifying radicals is to shorten the work in numerical computation. For example, if we wished to find the value of $\sqrt{10} \div \sqrt{2}$, we could compute to as many decimal places as we desire the value of $\sqrt{10}$ and $\sqrt{2}$ and then divide the results. However, by using the fundamental principle $\frac{\sqrt[n]{a}}{\sqrt[n]{b}} = \sqrt[n]{\frac{a}{b}}$ (see page 59) we can simplify $\sqrt{10} \div \sqrt{2}$ by writing $\sqrt{5}$, and we then have to find but one square root. Likewise it is quite obvious that it is easier to add and to subtract fractions when there are no radicals in their denominators. The process of removing radicals from a denominator is called *ra-*

tionalizing the denominator. The following examples will illustrate the methods employed in division.

EXAMPLE 1. Simplify: $\dfrac{3\sqrt{12}}{\sqrt{3}}$

Solution. $\dfrac{3\sqrt{12}}{\sqrt{3}} = 3\sqrt{\dfrac{12}{3}} = 3\sqrt{4} = 6$

EXAMPLE 2. Simplify: $\dfrac{4\sqrt{8}}{3\sqrt{12}}$

Solution. $\dfrac{4\sqrt{8}}{3\sqrt{12}} = \dfrac{4}{3}\sqrt{\dfrac{8}{12}} = \dfrac{4}{3}\sqrt{\dfrac{2}{3}} = \dfrac{4}{3}\sqrt{\dfrac{1}{9}\cdot 6} = \dfrac{4}{9}\sqrt{6}$

EXAMPLE 3. Simplify: $\dfrac{3}{5\sqrt{7}}$

Solution. Multiplying both numerator and denominator by $\sqrt{7}$

gives,
$$\frac{3}{5\sqrt{7}} = \frac{3\sqrt{7}}{35}$$

EXAMPLE 4. Simplify: $\dfrac{5\sqrt{2} - \sqrt{3}}{2\sqrt{2} + \sqrt{3}}$

According to principle 4 laid down on page 60, we wish to write the fraction so that there will be no radicals in the denominator. We know that $(\sqrt{a} - \sqrt{b})(\sqrt{a} + \sqrt{b}) = a - b$; hence if we multiply both numerator and denominator by $2\sqrt{2} - \sqrt{3}$ (this is called the conjugate of $2\sqrt{2} + \sqrt{3}$) we shall remove the radicals in the denominator.

Hence
$$\frac{5\sqrt{2} - \sqrt{3}}{2\sqrt{2} + \sqrt{3}} = \frac{5\sqrt{2} - \sqrt{3}}{2\sqrt{2} + \sqrt{3}} \cdot \frac{2\sqrt{2} - \sqrt{3}}{2\sqrt{2} - \sqrt{3}}$$
$$= \frac{20 - 7\sqrt{6} + 3}{8 - 3} = \frac{23 - 7\sqrt{6}}{5}$$

Thus we have rationalized the denominator.

EXERCISES

Simplify each of the following expressions by rationalizing the denominator:

1. $\frac{\sqrt{6}}{\sqrt{2}}$
2. $\frac{3\sqrt{12}}{2\sqrt{3}}$
3. $\frac{6\sqrt{18}}{\sqrt{3}}$
4. $\frac{12\sqrt{18}}{3\sqrt{2}}$
5. $\frac{\sqrt{6}}{\sqrt{3}}$
6. $\frac{\sqrt[3]{16}}{\sqrt{2}}$
7. $\frac{\sqrt{3}}{\sqrt[3]{2}}$
8. $\sqrt{\frac{1}{2}} \div \sqrt{\frac{1}{8}}$
9. $\sqrt{abc} \div \sqrt{a^3bc}$
10. $\sqrt[3]{\frac{1}{4}} \div \sqrt[3]{\frac{3}{32}}$
11. $\frac{4}{3\sqrt{32}}$
12. $\frac{7}{2\sqrt{3}}$
13. $\frac{\sqrt[3]{a}}{\sqrt{a}}$
14. $\frac{a}{\sqrt[3]{a}}$
15. $\frac{x}{\sqrt[3]{y^2}}$
16. $\frac{\sqrt[3]{3}}{\sqrt{2}}$
17. $\frac{\sqrt{5}}{2\sqrt[3]{6}}$
18. $\frac{4}{\sqrt{3} - \sqrt{2}}$
19. $\frac{2}{\sqrt{5} - \sqrt{3}}$
20. $\frac{3\sqrt{3}}{\sqrt{3} - \sqrt{2}}$
21. $\frac{4 - \sqrt{3}}{2 - \sqrt{3}}$
22. $\frac{1 + \sqrt{x}}{1 - \sqrt{x}}$
23. $\frac{\sqrt{x} - \sqrt{y}}{\sqrt{x} + \sqrt{y}}$
24. $\frac{a + \sqrt{x}}{\sqrt{x} - a}$
25. $\frac{x + y}{\sqrt{x} - \sqrt{y}}$
26. $\frac{\sqrt{3} - 4}{3 + 2\sqrt{3}}$
27. $\frac{\sqrt{10} + \sqrt{3}}{\sqrt{10} - \sqrt{3}}$
28. $\frac{\sqrt{x-1} + \sqrt{x+1}}{\sqrt{x-1} - \sqrt{x+1}}$
29. $\frac{\sqrt{p-q} + m}{\sqrt{p-q} - m}$
30. $\frac{1 + \sqrt{2} + \sqrt{3}}{1 + \sqrt{2} - \sqrt{3}}$ *Hint.* Multiply numerator and denominator by $1 + \sqrt{2} + \sqrt{3}$.

Imaginary numbers

Since the square of a real number cannot be negative, it follows that the square root of a negative number can never be a real number. We shall see later (page 141) that in solving certain equations the square roots of negative numbers occur.

Such numbers are called *imaginary* and will be studied at length in Chapter XIV.

The symbol $\sqrt{-1}$ is usually denoted by the letter i. What is the value of i^2?

The square root of any negative number can be written in the form $a\sqrt{-1}$ or ai, where a stands for a real number. Thus,

$$\sqrt{-9} = \sqrt{9}\sqrt{-1} = 3\sqrt{-1} = 3\,i$$
$$\sqrt{-5} = \sqrt{5}\sqrt{-1} = \sqrt{5}\,i$$

On page 59 we assumed $\sqrt{a}\sqrt{b} = \sqrt{ab}$ when $a > 0$, $b > 0$. We shall now assume $\sqrt{-a}\sqrt{-b} = -\sqrt{ab}$ when $a > 0$, $b > 0$. The reason for this assumption is readily illustrated by a numerical example. Suppose we wished to multiply $\sqrt{-3}$ by $\sqrt{-2}$.

Now $\quad \sqrt{-3} = \sqrt{3(-1)} = \sqrt{3}\sqrt{-1} = \sqrt{3}\,i$

and $\quad \sqrt{-2} = \sqrt{2(-1)} = \sqrt{2}\sqrt{-1} = \sqrt{2}\,i$

Hence $\quad \sqrt{-3}\sqrt{-2} = (\sqrt{3}\,i)\cdot(\sqrt{2}\,i) = \sqrt{6}\,i^2 = -\sqrt{6}.$

EXERCISES

Write each of the following expressions in the form ai:

1. $\sqrt{-20}$
2. $\sqrt{-16}$
3. $\sqrt{-4}$
4. $\sqrt{-\frac{1}{4}}$
5. $\sqrt{-25\,x^2}$
6. $\sqrt{-\dfrac{36\,x^2}{49\,y^4}}$
7. $\sqrt{-192}$
8. $\sqrt{-40}$
9. $\sqrt{-108}$
10. $\sqrt{-32\,x^4}$

Square roots of binomial surds

Since $[\pm(\sqrt{a} \pm \sqrt{b})]^2 = (a + b) \pm 2\sqrt{ab}$, it follows that the square root of $(a + b) \pm 2\sqrt{ab}$ is $\pm(\sqrt{a} \pm \sqrt{b})$. We shall now apply this principle to numerical problems.

EXAMPLE 1. Find the square root of $5 + 2\sqrt{6}$.

Solution. Since $5 + 2\sqrt{6}$ is in the standard form $(a + b) + 2\sqrt{ab}$, we must find two numbers whose sum is 5 and whose product is 6. These numbers are 3 and 2. Hence, the square root of $5 + 2\sqrt{6}$ is $\pm(\sqrt{3} + \sqrt{2})$.

EXAMPLE 2. Find the square root of $9 - 3\sqrt{8}$.

Solution. The quantity $9 - 3\sqrt{8}$ is not in the standard form $(a + b) - 2\sqrt{ab}$, since the radical does not have a coefficient of 2. We must, therefore, reduce it to standard form.

$$9 - 3\sqrt{8} = 9 - \sqrt{72} = 9 - 2\sqrt{18}$$

We must now find two numbers whose sum is 9 and whose product is 18. These numbers are 6 and 3. Hence the square root of $9 - 2\sqrt{18}$ is $\pm(\sqrt{6} - \sqrt{3})$.

Query. Is there any difference between $\pm(\sqrt{6} - \sqrt{3})$ and $\pm(\sqrt{3} - \sqrt{6})$?

EXERCISES

Find by inspection the square roots of each of the following binomial surds:

1. $8 + 2\sqrt{15}$
2. $9 + 2\sqrt{14}$
3. $9 - 2\sqrt{18}$
4. $12 - \sqrt{140}$
5. $12 - \sqrt{108}$
6. $6 - 4\sqrt{2}$
7. $a + ax + 2\sqrt{xa^2}$
8. $9 + 6\sqrt{2}$
9. $2p + \sqrt{4p^2 - 64}$
10. $2x + 2\sqrt{x^2 - 1}$

TRUE-FALSE TEST

Tell if each of the following statements is true or false:

1. $p + q$ is the same as $q + p$.
2. If $x = 3$, then $5x^2 = 40$.
3. The result of subtracting -5 from 0 is -5.
4. The product of 27.8305 and 0 is 0.
5. 10 divided by 0 is 10.
6. $(a + b)^{-1} = \dfrac{1}{a + b}$
7. $a^{-1} + b^{-1} = \dfrac{1}{a + b}$
8. $2^3 \cdot 2^2 = 4^5$
9. $3^3 \cdot 3^{40} = 3^{43}$
10. $\dfrac{a}{x + y} = \dfrac{a}{x} + \dfrac{a}{y}$

11. $\dfrac{x+y}{a} = \dfrac{x}{a} + \dfrac{y}{a}$
12. $p(m+n) = pm + n$
13. $\dfrac{x^{10}}{x^2} = x^5$
14. $\sqrt{x^2+y^2} = x + y$
15. $x^2 + y^2 = (x+y)^2$
16. $\sqrt[3]{x^2} = x^{\frac{2}{3}}$
17. $5\,a^0 = 1$
18. $(2\,x^{\frac{2}{3}} + 3\,y^{-1})^0 = 1$
19. $8^{\frac{1}{3}} = \frac{8}{3}$
20. $(2\sqrt{x-1})^2 = 2(x-1)$
21. $\left(\dfrac{x}{y}\right)^{-2} = \left(\dfrac{y}{x}\right)^2$
22. $\dfrac{a^{-1}+b^{-1}}{c^{-1}} = \dfrac{c}{a+b}$
23. $(\frac{1}{8})^{-2} = 64$
24. $\dfrac{(x-y)(x+y)}{9-(x-y)^2} = \dfrac{x+y}{9-(x-y)}$
25. $\dfrac{3}{b-a} = -\dfrac{3}{a+b}$
26. $\dfrac{3}{\sqrt{3}} = \sqrt{3}$
27. $\dfrac{a}{b} + \dfrac{c}{b} = \dfrac{a+c}{b}$
28. $\dfrac{2\,x}{y} + \dfrac{3\,y}{x} = \dfrac{2\,x+3\,y}{x+y}$
29. $\dfrac{(x-a)(x-b)}{(x-a)(x-b)} = 0$
30. $(\sqrt{x+7} + \sqrt{x+3})^2 = 2\,x + 10$
31. $5 - \dfrac{x-y}{a} = \dfrac{5\,a-x-y}{a}$
32. $1^{4x+5} = 4\,x + 5$
33. $\dfrac{x}{y} = \dfrac{x+1}{y+1}$
34. $\dfrac{(a-b)(b-c)}{(c-d)(d-a)} = \dfrac{(b-a)(b-c)}{(c-d)(a-d)}$
35. $(x-y)(y+x) = y^2 - x^2$

36. The reciprocal of $x + y$ is $\dfrac{1}{x + y}$.

37. $\dfrac{-3}{(x - y)(z - y)} = \dfrac{3(y - x)}{(x - y)(z - y)}$

38. As x increases, $\dfrac{3}{x + 5}$ decreases.

39. $x + y + 2\sqrt{xy} = (\sqrt{x} + \sqrt{y})^2$

40. If $x = -2 + \sqrt{2}$ then $x^2 + 4x$ has the value -2.

41. $\sqrt{\frac{12}{3}}$ is irrational.

42. The H.C.F. of $x^2 - 1$ and $1 - x^3$ is $x - 1$.

43. The L.C.M. of $x - 1$ and $1 - x^2$ is $-(1 - x^2)$.

44. $\dfrac{-2^5}{2^3} = -1^2$

45. A bottle and a cork cost $1.10, and the bottle costs $1 more than the cork. Therefore, the cork costs 10 cents.

46. $2^2 \cdot 2^3 = (2 \cdot 2)^5 = 4^5$

47. $\dfrac{27^5}{81^3} = \dfrac{1^5}{3^3} = \dfrac{1}{3^3}$

48. $\dfrac{1}{5x - y} = -\dfrac{1}{5x + y}$

49. $\dfrac{1\not{6}}{\not{6}4} = \dfrac{1}{4}$

50. As x increases, $\dfrac{2}{5 + \dfrac{6}{x}}$ increases.

MASTERY TEST

1. Find the difference in time between the years 40 B.C. and 30 B.C.

2. Find the value of $\dfrac{x + y}{z} + \dfrac{z - y}{x}$ when $x = 3$, $y = 2$, $z = 4$.

3. Add: $2x + 3y - z$; $5x - 2y + 5z$; $-7x - y - 4z$

4. Add: $3.6x^2 + 7.2x + 3.5$; $-3.4x^2 - 2.8x - 7.6$

5. Subtract $3x^3 - 2x^2 - x - 1$ from $7x^5 + x^4 - 3x^3 + 6x + 1$

6. What is the coefficient of x^3y^5 in $-7x^3y^5$?

7. What must be subtracted from $3x^3 + 4x^2 - 11x + 7$ to leave $2x^3 + 5x^2 + x - 8$?

8. What must be added to x to produce y?

9. Multiply $2x^2 - x^3 + 3 - 4x$ by $x - 2 - 3x^2 + x^3$.

10. Divide $3a^2 + 12 + 3a^3 - 14a$ by $a + 3$.

11. The edge of a cube is $x + 2$.
a) Find the sum of all the edges.
b) Find the area of one face.
c) Find the area of the six faces.
d) Find the volume of the cube.
e) If the edge is doubled, what change takes place in the sum of the edges? in the area of the six faces? in the volume?

12. Factor: a) $5x^2 - 45$
b) $mx + 3nx - 4my - 12ny$
c) $a^2 - b^2 - c^2 + 2bc$
d) $14x^2 - 39x + 10$
e) $5x^3 - 20xy^4$
f) $x^{24} + x^{12} + 1$

13. Write down by inspection the following products:
a) $(x + 3)(x - 2)$
b) $(x + 7)(x + 8)$
c) $(x - 3a)(x + 3a)$
d) $(2x - 3)(7x + 5)$
e) $(8x + 11)(3x - 2)$

14. Simplify: $\dfrac{3a^2 + a - 2}{4a^2 - 4a - 3} \div \dfrac{2a^2 - a - 3}{6a^2 - a - 2}$

15. Simplify: $\dfrac{5}{a^2 - b^2} - \dfrac{3}{b - a} + \dfrac{6a}{b + a}$

16. Simplify: $\left(1 + \dfrac{1}{a - b}\right) \div \left(1 - \dfrac{1}{a + b}\right)$

17. Simplify: $\dfrac{\dfrac{x - y}{x} - \dfrac{x + y}{y}}{\dfrac{x - y}{y} + \dfrac{x + y}{x}}$

18. Multiply $5\sqrt{12}$ by $3\sqrt{6}$

19. Divide $-8\sqrt{15}$ by $2\sqrt{3}$

20. Simplify: $\dfrac{8^{\frac{1}{3}} \cdot 16^{\frac{1}{4}} \cdot 1^{3x}}{(-32)^{\frac{1}{5}}}$

21. Simplify: $\dfrac{2x}{y}\sqrt[n]{\dfrac{y^{2n}}{2^n x^{5n}}}$

22. Simplify: $5\sqrt[3]{250} - 3\sqrt[3]{686} + \sqrt[3]{1458}$

23. Rationalize the denominator of $\dfrac{5\sqrt{2} - 3\sqrt{3}}{2\sqrt{2} + 3\sqrt{3}}$.

24. Prove that $\dfrac{x - \sqrt{x^2 - 1}}{x + \sqrt{x^2 - 1}} = 2\,x^2 - 1 - 2\,x\sqrt{x^2 - 1}.$

25. Simplify: $\sqrt{\dfrac{ab}{2}} - \sqrt{\dfrac{ab}{32}} + \sqrt{\dfrac{ab}{128}}$

26. What is meant by the absolute value of a number?

27. What is a monomial? binomial? trinomial?

28. Give four interpretations of the symbol $+$.

29. Give three interpretations of the symbol $-$.

30. Does $\frac{7}{0}$ have a value?

31. Write $\dfrac{(6000000)(300000)}{.0001}$ as an integer times a power of 10.

32. Multiply $x^{2n} - 3\,x^n y^n + y^n$ by $x^n - 2\,y^n$

33. Simplify: $\sqrt[x]{\dfrac{(a+b)^{-2x}}{(a-b)^{-x}}}$

34. Find the value of $\dfrac{m^3 - n^3}{m^2 + n^2}$ when $m = x - \dfrac{1}{x}$ and $n = x + \dfrac{1}{x}$.

35. Simplify: $\dfrac{\dfrac{1}{a} + \dfrac{1}{b+c}}{\dfrac{1}{a} - \dfrac{1}{b+c}}\left(1 + \dfrac{b^2 + c^2 - a^2}{2\,bc}\right)$

36. Simplify: $mn^0 + (m+n)^0 - (mn)^0 - m$

37. Factor as the difference of two squares:

$$x - y; \quad \sqrt{x} - \sqrt{y}; \quad y^{\frac{2}{3}} - x^{\frac{4}{3}}$$

38. Find x when:

a) $2^x = 8$ c) $5^x = 125$

b) $3^x = 81$ d) $\dfrac{1}{2^x} = 64$

39. Simplify: $\left[\dfrac{a^{-\frac{1}{2}}b^{\frac{2}{3}}}{a^{-\frac{3}{5}}b^{-\frac{1}{2}}} \div (a^{-2}b^{-3})^{\frac{1}{5}}\right]^{\frac{3}{4}}$

40. Simplify: $[(a^{\frac{1}{2}})^3 \div (a^{-3}b^{-2})^{\frac{1}{4}}]^5$

41. Simplify: $\dfrac{a^{-2} - b^{-2}}{a^{-3} - b^{-3}}$

42. Simplify: $\dfrac{x^2 + y^2}{x^{-1} - y^{-1}} + \dfrac{x^{-2}y^{-2}}{x^{-2} + y^{-2}}$

43. Simplify: $8^{-\frac{2}{3}} + 9^{\frac{3}{2}} - 3^{-1} + 1^{7x} - (2\,x)^0$

44. Simplify: $\dfrac{2^n(2^{n-1})^n}{2^{n+1} \cdot 4^n}$

45. Simplify: $\dfrac{3^n \cdot 9^{n+1} \cdot 27^{n+2}}{81^{3n}}$

46. Simplify: $\left(\dfrac{e^x + e^{-x}}{2}\right)^2 - \left(\dfrac{e^x - e^{-x}}{2}\right)^2$

47. Simplify: $\sqrt{1 + \left(\dfrac{e^x - e^{-x}}{2}\right)^2}$

48. Simplify: $\sqrt[x]{\dfrac{3^{2x} \cdot 3^6}{27^{2x+1} 9^{3x+1}}}$

49. Simplify: $\sqrt{\dfrac{(e^x + e^{-x})^2}{(e^x + e^{-x})^2 - (e^x - e^{-x})^2}}$

50. Simplify: $\dfrac{x^{-1} - y^{-1}}{x^{-1} + y^{-1}} \div \left(\dfrac{x^{-2} + y^{-2}}{y^{-2} - x^{-2}}\right)^{-1} + (a^{-2} - \sqrt[n]{b^{-2}})^0$

51. Square the following binomials:

a) $2\sqrt{x} + 3\sqrt{x - 1}$

b) $a\sqrt{x - a} - b\sqrt{x - b}$

c) $3\sqrt{x + 2} - 2\sqrt{x - 1}$

52. Find by inspection the square root of $2p + 2\sqrt{p^2 - 4}$.

53. Simplify: $\dfrac{\sqrt[3]{4}}{\sqrt{8}}$

54. Which is greater $\sqrt[6]{3}$ or $\sqrt[4]{2}$?

55. Simplify: $\dfrac{x^2(x^2 - 4)^{-\frac{1}{2}} - \sqrt{x^2 - 4}}{x^2 - 4}$

56. Simplify: $\dfrac{(a^2 - x^3)^{\frac{1}{3}} - (a^2 - x^3)^{-\frac{2}{3}}}{(a^2 - x^3)^2}$

57. If $m = -\sqrt{\dfrac{y}{x}}$ and $\sqrt{x} + \sqrt{y} = \sqrt{a}$, show that

$$-\frac{x^{\frac{1}{2}}(\frac{1}{2}\, y^{-\frac{1}{2}} m) - y^{\frac{1}{2}}(\frac{1}{2}\, x^{-\frac{1}{2}})}{x} = \frac{1}{2}\sqrt{\frac{a}{x^3}}$$

58. If $m = -\dfrac{y^{\frac{1}{3}}}{x^{\frac{1}{3}}}$, $p = \dfrac{a^{\frac{2}{3}}}{3\, x^{\frac{4}{3}} y^{\frac{1}{3}}}$ and $x^{\frac{2}{3}} + y^{\frac{2}{3}} = a^{\frac{2}{3}}$ show that

$$\frac{(1 + m^2)^{\frac{3}{2}}}{p} = 3(axy)^{\frac{1}{3}}$$

CHAPTER IV

The Equation

One unknown

A statement that two expressions are equal is called *an equation*. Thus, $2(x - 1) = 5(x - 7)$ and $3y - 7 = 2y + 11$ are equations.

Equations are divided into two general classes: *identical equations* or *identities*, and *conditional equations*.

In an identical equation or identity, the two members remain equal for all values of the letters involved for which *both members have a meaning*. An identity is usually written with the sign $\equiv$ instead of $=$. The following are examples of identities:

$$x^2 - 4 \equiv (x - 2)(x + 2)$$
$$a^2 - 3a + 2 \equiv (a - 2)(a - 1)$$
$$\frac{y^2 - 4}{y + 2} \equiv y - 2$$

Is there any value of y for which one member of the last identity has no meaning?

A conditional equation is one whose members are equal only for certain values of the letters or unknowns. These values are said to *satisfy* the equation and are called *roots*. Thus the equation $3x - 9 = 0$ is satisfied only by $x = 3$, and 3 is a root. Moreover, the equation $x^2 - 3x + 2 = 0$ is satisfied only by $x = 1$ and $x = 2$; hence 1 and 2 are roots.

To solve an equation in one unknown is to find all values of the unknown which satisfy the equation; *i.e.*, to solve the equation means to find its roots. Unless otherwise stated, the word equation in this book shall henceforth always mean conditional equation.

EXAMPLE 1. Is 2 a root of $x^2 - 5x + 3 = 0$?

Solution. Substituting $x = 2$

gives $$4 - 10 + 3 \stackrel{?}{=} 0$$

Since $$-3 \neq 0$$

It follows that *2 is not a root.*

EXERCISES

1. Is 4 a root of $4x - 3 = 0$?
2. Is 3 a root of $x^2 - 6x + 9 = 0$?
3. Is 1 a root of $x^3 - x^2 - x + 1 = 0$?

Equivalent equations

Two equations are equivalent when each equation is satisfied by *all* the solutions of the other. Thus $x - 1 = 0$ and $2x - 2 = 0$ are equivalent equations. Are $(x - 2)(x + 3) = 0$ and $(x - 2)^2(x + 3) = 0$ equivalent equations?

The following three operations lead to equivalent equations.

1. Adding the same number to or subtracting it from both members of an equation.[1]
2. Multiplying or dividing both members by the same constant k, provided $k \neq 0$.
3. Changing the signs of all terms, which is the same as multiplying both members by -1.

[1] Let us consider the equation $2x - 5 = x + 3$. If we add to both members $5 - x$, we have $x = 8$. It should be noted that when $5 - x$ is added to both members the derived equation is the same as if the quantities 5 and x had been transferred or transposed from one member to the other and their signs changed.

Thus $$2x - 5 = x + 3$$ $$2x - x = 5 + 3$$ $$x = 8$$

This operation is called transposition. *Any term of an equation may be transposed from one member to the other provided its sign is changed.*

For example, given

$$x - 3 = 4 \tag{1}$$

Adding 1 to both members gives

$$x - 2 = 5 \tag{2}$$

Subtracting 7 from both members of (1) gives

$$x - 10 = -3 \tag{3}$$

Multiplying both members of (1) by -3 gives

$$-3\,x + 9 = -12 \tag{4}$$

Dividing both members of (1) by 2 gives

$$\frac{x}{2} - \frac{3}{2} = 2 \tag{5}$$

Changing the signs of all terms of (1) gives

$$-x + 3 = -4 \tag{6}$$

Equations 1, 2, 3, 4, 5, 6 are all equivalent.

It is very important to note, however, that we can perform certain other operations on the two members of an equation and the resulting or derived equation will not necessarily be equivalent to the original. The following examples will make this point clear.

EXAMPLE 1. Consider the equation $3\,x - 1 = x + 1$ which is satisfied by $x = 1$. If we multiply both members by $x - 2$, we have

$$(x - 2)(3\,x - 1) = (x + 1)(x - 2)$$

an equation which is satisfied by $x = 1$ and $x = 2$. But $x = 2$ is not a root of the given equation. Hence, the derived equation is not equivalent to the original.

EXAMPLE 2. Consider the equation $x^2 = 5\,x$ which is satisfied by $x = 0$ and $x = 5$. Dividing both members by x gives $x = 5$, an equation whose only root is 5. Hence, the given equation and the derived equation are not equivalent.

EXAMPLE 3. Consider the equation $\sqrt{x} = -2$. Squaring both members gives the equation $x = 4$. The derived equation is satisfied by $x = 4$, but the original equation is not. Hence, the given equation and the derived equation are not equivalent.

The above examples illustrate the following facts:

1. If both members of an equation are multiplied by an integral expression in the unknown, the derived equation may have more roots than the original equation.
2. If both members of an equation are divided by an expression in the unknown, the derived equation may have fewer roots than the original equation.
3. If both members of an equation are squared, the derived equation may have more roots than the original equation. The student should note carefully that the above statements all say "may have" and not "do have." For example, if both members of an equation are squared, the derived equation does not necessarily have more roots than the given equation; but it *may have* more roots, as illustrated by example 3.

In conclusion, we see that unless we know that the operations performed on an equation lead to equivalent equations, we *should always check the result by substitution.*

Solving a linear equation in one unknown

An equation of the form $ax + b = 0$, $a \neq 0$, is known as a linear equation in the unknown x. By employing the three operations mentioned on page 76, we can solve any such equation for x. The following examples will illustrate the method.

EXAMPLE 1. Solve $x - 3 = 7$.

Solution. By the first principle (page 76), we can add 3 to both members which is equivalent to transposing the -3 to the right, where it becomes $+3$.

Hence
$$x = 7 + 3$$
$$x = 10$$

Check.
$$10 - 3 = 7$$
$$7 = 7$$

EXAMPLE 2. Solve $\frac{1}{2}x = 3$.

Solution. By the second principle, we can multiply both members by 2.

Hence $$x = 6$$

Check. $$\tfrac{1}{2}(6) = 3$$
$$3 = 3$$

EXAMPLE 3. Solve $7x = 12$.

Solution. Again using the second principle, we can divide both members by 7. Hence,

$$x = \tfrac{12}{7}$$

Check. $$7(\tfrac{12}{7}) = 12$$

EXAMPLE 4. Solve $4x - 3 + x = 5 - 5x + 2$.

Solution. We shall first place in the left hand member all terms containing x and in the right hand member all the constant terms. Hence

$$4x + x + 5x = 5 + 2 + 3$$
$$10x = 10$$
$$x = 1$$

Check. $$4 - 3 + 1 = 5 - 5 + 2$$
$$2 = 2$$

EXAMPLE 5. Solve for x:

$$1 + (2x - 1)(x - 1) = (x + 3)(2x + 7) + 3x.$$

Solution. Simplifying, we have,

$$1 + 2x^2 - 3x + 1 = 2x^2 + 13x + 21 + 3x$$

Hence $$-3x - 3x - 13x = 21 - 1 - 1$$
$$-19x = 19$$
$$x = -1$$

Check. $$1 + (-3)(-2) = (2)(5) - 3$$
$$7 = 7$$

EXERCISES

Solve each of the following equations for x and check:

1. $2x - 1 = x + 5$
2. $3x - 7 = 2$
3. $6x - 1 = 2x + 5$
4. $5x - 2x - 17 = -1 + 6x - x$
5. $3x - 1 = 2(x - 1)$
6. $x - (x + 1)(x - 3) = 4x - 8 - x^2$
7. $(x - 3)(x + 3) - (x + 2)(x - 2) - 3x = 8$
8. $4(x + 3)^2 - 3(x - 4)^2 = (x - 2)^2$
9. $2 - (x - 1)(x + 3) + (x + 7)(x - 3) = 10$
10. $11x - 2(x - 1)(x + 3) = 4 - (2x - 1)(x + 2)$
11. $(x + 3)(x - 5) = (x + 2)(x + 1)$
12. $4x - [2x - (3x - 1)] = 4 - 2x$
13. $(5x - 2)(6x - 1) + 1 = (30x - 1)(x + 2)$
14. $2 - 3(x - 7) - 7x = 4(x - 2) + 8$
15. $(x - 2)(x - 3) - 2(x - 4)(x - 3) = 1 - (x + 7)(x - 5)$
16. $3ax - a^3 = 0$
17. $ax + b^2 = bx + a^2$
18. $3ax - 2b = 3b - 2ax$
19. $x^2 + 2ax = (x - a)(x + a)$
20. $(x + 1)(p - q) = (x - 1)(p + q)$

Fractional equations in one unknown

A fractional equation may be reduced to an equation containing no fractions if both members of the equation are multiplied by the lowest common denominator (L.C.D.) of the fractions. If the L.C.D. is an expression containing the unknown, the derived equation may have roots which are not roots of the original equation (see page 78). These roots are called *extraneous;* hence *all final results should be checked.* The process of reducing an equation containing fractions to one without fractions is called *clearing of fractions.*

EXAMPLE 1. Solve for x:

$$\frac{x - 1}{2} + \frac{x + 1}{3} = 4$$

Solution. The least common denominator is 6. Multiplying each term by 6 gives the *equivalent* equation,

$$\begin{aligned} 3(x-1)+2(x+1) &= 24 \\ 3x-3+2x+2 &= 24 \\ 5x &= 25 \\ x &= 5 \end{aligned}$$

Check. $\frac{5-1}{2}+\frac{5+1}{3}=2+2=4$

Hence, $x = 5$ is a root.

It should be noted that the check is for error only as we multiplied the terms only by a constant.

EXAMPLE 2. Solve for x:

$$\frac{3}{x^2-1}=-\frac{4}{1-x}-\frac{5}{1+x}$$

Solution. This equation can be written

$$\frac{3}{x^2-1}=\frac{4}{x-1}-\frac{5}{x+1}$$

If we multiply both members by x^2-1, we clear all fractions. Can we conclude that the resulting equation is equivalent to the original?

$$\begin{aligned} 3 &= 4(x+1)-5(x-1) \\ 3 &= 4x+4-5x+5 \\ x &= 6 \end{aligned}$$

Check. $\frac{3}{36-1}=\frac{4}{6-1}-\frac{5}{6+1}$

$$\frac{3}{35}=\frac{4}{5}-\frac{5}{7}=\frac{28-25}{35}=\frac{3}{35}$$

Hence, $x = 6$ is a root.

It should be noted that the check is both for error and for extraneous roots.

EXAMPLE 3. Solve for x:

$$\frac{4}{x-1} = \frac{x}{x-1} - \frac{3}{1-x}$$

Solution. The equation can be written as

$$\frac{4}{x-1} = \frac{x}{x-1} + \frac{3}{x-1}$$

If we multiply both members by $x - 1$, we clear all fractions; but can we conclude that the resulting equation is equivalent to the original?

$$4 = x + 3$$
$$x = 1$$

But $x = 1$ does not satisfy the given equation, since division by 0 is not permissible. Hence, the given equation has no roots.

EXERCISES

Solve and check the following equations:

1. $\frac{6-x}{4} - \frac{3x+10}{3} = 2$

2. $\frac{x}{x-1} - \frac{3}{x+1} = 1$

3. $\frac{3}{x} + 5 = \frac{2}{x}$

4. $\frac{3x+10}{x^2+5x+6} = \frac{x}{x+3} - \frac{x}{x+2}$

5. $\frac{4x}{x+7} = \frac{2x}{x+3} + 2$

6. $\frac{x+3}{3} - \frac{x}{x+4} = \frac{x-3}{3}$

7. $\frac{7x-10}{7x-6} = \frac{5x-4}{5x}$

8. $\frac{3}{x+1} = \frac{3}{1-x} - \frac{24}{1-x^2}$

9. $\frac{x^2}{x^2-9} - \frac{x-3}{x+3} = \frac{3}{x-3}$

10. $\frac{4x}{2x-3} - \frac{1}{2} = \frac{3x}{2x+3}$

11. $\frac{2-x}{x-3} + \frac{3}{x-3} + \frac{7}{5} = 0$

12. $\frac{3x}{x-2} - \frac{3x}{x+3} + \frac{2}{2-x} = 0$

13. $\frac{2x+7}{4} - \frac{4x+3}{8} = \frac{3x+8}{5x+3}$

14. $\frac{2x-1}{5} + \frac{2x-4}{7x-13} = \frac{6x+1}{15}$

15. $\frac{x}{a} - \frac{x+2a}{b} = \frac{b}{a} - 3$

16. $\frac{1}{x} - \frac{1}{a} = \frac{1}{a} - \frac{1}{x}$

17. $\frac{x+a}{6a} - \frac{x+2a}{x-a} = \frac{2x-a}{12a}$

18. $\frac{x-b}{x-a} + \frac{x-a}{b-x} = \frac{2a-2b}{x-a-b}$

19. $\frac{22}{2x-3} + \frac{23x+26}{4x^2-9} = \frac{51}{2x+3}$

20. $\frac{26x-25}{x^2-x-20} - \frac{3}{5-x} = \frac{7}{x+4}$

Formulas

A formula is an equation showing the relation between two or more quantities. For example, the formula for the perimeter p of a rectangle of length l and width w is $p = 2l + 2w$. What formula expresses the area A of the rectangle in terms of l and w? in terms of p and w?

To evaluate a formula is to find the numerical value of one of its letters when the numerical value of the other letters is known.

EXAMPLE 1. The formula for finding simple interest is $I = PRT$, where I = interest, P = principal, R = rate, T = time in years. Find I when P = \$1000, R = .06 and T = 3 years.

Solution. Listing the letters for which values are given and noting that the value of I is to be found (denoted by ?) we have,

$$I = ?$$
$$P = \$1000$$
$$R = .06$$
$$T = 3$$

Substituting, $I = \$1000(.06)(3) = \$180.$

EXAMPLE 2. Given the formula $s = \frac{n}{2}(a + l)$, evaluate l when

$$s = 1800,\ n = 50,\ a = 2$$

Solution. Listing the letters and their values,

$$s = 1800$$
$$n = 50$$
$$a = 2$$
$$l = ?$$

Substituting

$$1800 = \tfrac{50}{2}(2 + l)$$
$$1800 = 50 + 25\,l$$
$$1750 = 25\,l$$
$$70 = l$$

EXERCISES

1. If $p = 2\,l + 2\,w$, evaluate p, if $l = 10$, $w = 30$.
2. If $p = 2\,l + 2\,w$, evaluate l, if $p = 70$, $w = 20$.
3. If $p = 2\,l + 2\,w$, evaluate w, if $p = 120$, $l = 30$.
4. If $V = 2\,\pi R(R + H)$, evaluate V, if $R = 3$, $H = 10$, $\pi = 3.14$.
5. If $V = 2\,\pi R(R + H)$, evaluate H, if $V = 352$, $R = 4$, $\pi = 3\frac{1}{7}$.
6. If $F = \dfrac{MV}{t}$, find F, if $M = 20$, $V = 10$, $t = 2$.
7. If $F = \dfrac{MV}{t}$, find V, if $F = 100$, $M = 10$, $t = 3$.
8. If $h = K\left(1 + \dfrac{t}{273}\right)$, find h, if $K = 90$, $t = 70$.
9. If $h = K\left(1 + \dfrac{t}{273}\right)$, find t if $h = 1.5$, $K = 90$.
10. If $s = \dfrac{rl - a}{r - 1}$, find r, if $s = 242$, $a = 2$, $l = 162$.

Deriving a formula from a formula

The formula $d = \sqrt{\frac{KL}{R}}$ is used in electricity. Derive a formula for K.

Solution. $$d = \sqrt{\frac{KL}{R}}$$

Squaring both sides gives

$$d^2 = \frac{KL}{R}$$

Hence $$d^2R = KL$$

and $$K = \frac{d^2R}{L}$$

EXERCISES

1. Given the formula $p = 2\,l + 2\,w$; derive a formula for w.

2. Given the formula $I = \frac{E}{R + n}$; derive a formula for R.

3. Given the formula $\frac{1}{f} = \frac{1}{a} - \frac{1}{b}$:

a) Solve the formula for a.
b) Solve the formula for b.
c) Derive a formula for f.
d) Find f if $a = 10$ when $b = 15$.

4. Solve the formula $F = \frac{Mv}{t}$ for v.

5. From the formula $V = 2\,\pi R(R + H)$ derive a formula for H.

6. Solve the formula $h = K(1 + \frac{1}{273}\,t)$ for t.

7. Solve the formula $s = at - \frac{1}{2}\,gt^2$ for a.

8. Given the formula $s = p(1 + r)^n$; derive a formula for p.

9. Solve the formula $s = \frac{rl - a}{r - 1}$ for r.

10. Solve the formula $T = 2\,lh + 2\,wh + 2\,lw$ for l and for h.

11. The formula $H = \frac{PLAN}{33000}$ is used to determine the horse power of a steam engine. Find A in terms of the other letters.

12. A gas engine formula is $P = \frac{D^2N}{2.5}\cdot$ Find N in terms of the other letters.

13. A formula used in pulley problems is $Pr = \frac{W(R - r)}{2}$.

a) Find R in terms of the other letters.
b) Find r in terms of the other letters.

14. Given the formula $C = \frac{E}{R + \frac{r}{n}}$; derive a formula for n in terms of the other letters.

15. If it costs $40 to set the type and 4 cents to print each copy of a pamphlet, write a formula for the total cost C in dollars of x copies.

16. Water is run into a rectangular cistern whose base is 10 ft. by 5 ft. Find the formula giving the volume V of water which is x ft. deep.

17. The speed of a boat in still water is 12 miles per hour. Write a formula giving the distance d the boat can run upstream in h hours against a current flowing c miles per hr.

18. A rectangular box is to be made from a sheet of tin 24 inches square by cutting equal squares from each corner and bending up the sides. If the side of each square cut out is x, write a formula for the volume V of the box.

The general idea of a function

Our daily activities continually furnish us with examples of things that are related to one another, of quantities which depend on certain other quantities, which change when certain other quantities change. Thus, a man's health is related to the food he eats, the exercise he takes, and to many other things. The price of any manufactured article depends on the cost of production, while the latter cost in turn depends on the cost of the raw material, the cost of labor, etc. The weather depends on a variety of conditions. These are complicated examples of dependence. But there are also simple examples. Thus the price paid for a certain quantity of sugar depends on the number of pounds bought and the price per pound; the area of a square depends on the length of one of its sides; and so forth.

In all such cases, where some quantity depends on some other quantity or quantities, we say that the former is a *function* of the latter. Thus the price of an article is a function of the cost of production; the area of a square is a function of the length of one of its sides, etc.

Constants and variables

In algebra a *constant* is a symbol which represents the same value throughout a discussion, while a *variable* is a symbol which may represent various numbers throughout a discussion. For example, in the formula $s = \frac{1}{2} gt^2$, which gives the distance s (in feet) a body falls in t seconds, s and t are variables and g is a constant for which we may take 32 as an approximation.

If two variables are so related that when a value of one is given a corresponding value of the second is determined, the second is called a *function* of the first. For example, if $y = 3x - 1$, then y is a function of x; because when a value is assigned to x, a corresponding value of y is determined. Likewise, x is a function of y. The variable to which we assign values is called the *independent variable;* the variable whose value is then computed is called the *dependent variable*, or simply the function. If in $y = x^2 - 7x + 5$, we assign the values to x, then x is the independent variable, and y is the function.

Often a variable is a function of two or more other variables. For example, the volume V of a cylinder is a function of the area of its base B and its altitude H, since $V = BH$. Assuming $B > 0$, $H > 0$, is H a function of V and B? Is B a function of V and H?

EXERCISES

Complete the following statements:

1. The quantity $3y^2 - 7y - 7$ is a function of ———.
2. The circumference of a circle is a function of its ———.
3. The area of a parallelogram with base 6″ is a function of its ———.
4. The simple interest on $1000 for n years, is a function of ———.

5. The height of mercury in a thermometer is a function of ——.

6. The height of mercury in a barometer is a function of ——.

7. The distance a train traveling 40 miles an hour goes in x hours is a function of ——.

8. The amount A which \$100 will amount to at simple interest of i per cent for n years is a function of —— and ——.

9. The area of a rectangle is a function of its —— and ——.

10. The area of a triangle is a function of its —— and ——.

11. In the formula $F = \frac{9}{5} C + 32$, F is a function of ——.

12. In the formula $V = \frac{4}{3} \pi R^3$, V is a function of ——.

13. In the formula $T = mg - mf$, where $m = 250$, T is a function of —— and ——.

14. In the formula $A = \dfrac{\pi r^2 E}{180°}$, where $E = 140°$, A is a function of ——.

15. In the formula $C = \dfrac{nE}{R + nr}$, where n and E are constants, C is a function of —— and ——.

Functional notation

Rather than write out each time in full detail a given function of x, we often represent it by the symbols $f(x)$, $\phi(x)$, etc., and then speak of the "f function," "ϕ function," etc. Moreover, this notation can be used to represent the value of the function in question for a given value of the independent variable. For example, if $f(x) = x^2 + 3x + 4$, the symbol $f(2)$ denotes the value of this function when $x = 2$. Thus $f(2) = 2^2 + 3(2) + 4 = 14$. What is the value of $f(0)$?

A function of x and y can be represented by the symbols $f(x, y)$, $\phi(x, y)$, etc. Thus, if $f(x, y) = x^2 + y^2$, then $f(2, 1) = 2^2 + 1^2 = 5$.

It should be noted that it is meaningless to talk about $f(2)$, $f(3)$, etc., unless one knows $f(x)$.

EXAMPLE 1. Given $f(x) = x^2 - 3x + 1$. Find $f(2)$; $f(0)$; $f\left(\frac{1}{y}\right)$.

Solution.

$$\begin{aligned} f(2) &= (2)^2 - 3(2) + 1 \\ &= 4 - 6 + 1 = -1 \\ f(0) &= 0 - 0 + 1 = 1 \\ f\left(\frac{1}{y}\right) &= \frac{1}{y^2} - 3\left(\frac{1}{y}\right) + 1 \\ &= \frac{1}{y^2} - \frac{3}{y} + 1 \end{aligned}$$

EXAMPLE 2. Given $\phi(x) = e^x + e^{-x}$

Prove $\phi(x + y)\phi(x - y) = \phi(2\,x) + \phi(2\,y)$

Solution.

$$\begin{aligned} \phi(x + y) &= e^{x+y} + e^{-x-y} \\ \phi(x - y) &= e^{x-y} + e^{-x+y} \\ \therefore\ \phi(x + y)\phi(x - y) &= (e^{x+y} + e^{-x-y})(e^{x-y} + e^{-x+y}) \\ &= e^{2x} + e^{-2y} + e^{-2x} + e^{2y} \qquad (1) \\ \phi(2\,x) &= e^{2x} + e^{-2x} \\ \phi(2\,y) &= e^{2y} + e^{-2y} \\ \therefore\ \phi(2\,x) + \phi(2\,y) &= e^{2x} + e^{-2x} + e^{2y} + e^{-2y} \qquad (2) \end{aligned}$$

Since (1) equals (2)

$$\phi(x + y)\phi(x - y) = \phi(2\,x) + \phi(2\,y)$$

EXERCISES

1. Given $f(x) = 2\,x^2 - 3\,x + 1$. Find $f(1)$; $f(0)$; $f\left(\frac{1}{y}\right)$.

2. Given $f(x) = \frac{x}{x + 3}$. Find $f(2)$; $f(-2)$; $f\left(\frac{1}{1 + x}\right)$.

3. Given $f(x) = a^x + a^{-x}$. Find $f(0)$; $f(1)$.

4. Given $f(x) = \dfrac{x - \frac{1}{x}}{x + \frac{1}{x}}$. Find $f(a + b)$.

5. Given $f(x) = \dfrac{\left(x - \frac{1}{x}\right)\left(x^2 - \frac{1}{x^2}\right)}{x^3 - \frac{1}{x^3}}$. Prove that $f(y) = -f\left(\frac{1}{y}\right)$.

6. Given $f(x) = x^2 + 3$. Find $f(f(x))$.

7. Given $f(x) = x^2 + x + 1$. Find $f\left(\frac{1}{y}\right)$.

8. Given $f(x) = \frac{x-1}{x+1}$. Prove that $\frac{f(x) - f(y)}{1 + f(x)f(y)} = \frac{x-y}{1+xy}$.

9. Given $f(x) = ax + 1$. Find a if $f(1) = 1$.

10. Given $f(x) = 3x + b$. Find b if $f(-4) = 7$.

11. Given $f(x, y) = 2x^2 + 3y^2 - xy - 2$. Find $f(3, 1)$; $f(2, 2)$; $f(0, 0)$.

12. Given $f(x, y) = \frac{x+y}{x-y}$. Prove that $f(a, b) + f(b, a) = 0$.

13. If $f(x) = x^2 - 2x + 1$, find the value of $\frac{f(x+h) - f(x)}{h}$.

14. If $f(x) = \frac{1-x}{1+x}$, find the value of $\frac{f(x+h) - f(x)}{h}$.

15. If $f(x) = ax^2 + bx + c$ and $f(-x) = f(x)$, prove that $b = 0$.

Implicit and explicit functions

An equation which defines a function of x and y can usually be written in several forms. For example, let us consider the equation $y = mx + b$. This equation can also be written as $y - mx = b$, $y - b = mx$, and $\frac{y-b}{m} = x$, $m \neq 0$. It should be noted that *in all cases y is the same function of x*. If the equation defining a function of x and y is solved for y, we say y is an *explicit* function of x, while if the equation is not solved for y, we say y is an *implicit* function of x. Thus the equations $y = 3x - 7$ and $y - 3x + 7 = 0$ define y as the same function of x, but in the first case y is written as an explicit function of x, while in the second case it is an implicit function of x. In both cases x is an implicit function of y. Why?

Not all functions can be expressed explicitly. For example, $x^7 + tx^5 - (t^3 + 1)x^2 + 15x - 11 = 0$, expresses x implicitly in terms of t, but since we cannot solve the seventh degree equation for x in terms of t (see page 305), we cannot express x as an explicit function of t.

EXAMPLE 1. Write y as an explicit function of x when

$$3xy + y - x + 7 = 0$$

Solution.

$$3xy + y = x - 7$$
$$y(3x + 1) = x - 7$$
$$y = \frac{x - 7}{3x + 1}$$

EXAMPLE 2. Write x as an implicit function of y when

$$x = \frac{3y - 7}{5}$$

Solution.

$$x = \frac{3y - 7}{5}$$
$$5x = 3y - 7$$

Is this the only solution? If not, give two other solutions.

EXERCISES

Write y as an explicit function of x:

1. $3x + 2y = 8$
2. $y + x^2 - 7 = 0$
3. $y + 3xy - 7x = 10$
4. $y + 2xy - x^2 = 3$
5. $y^2 - x = 0$
6. $x^2 + y^2 = 5$

Write x as an explicit function of y:

7. $x + 3y - 1 = 0$
8. $x + 5y^2 = 0$
9. $x - xy + 1 = 0$
10. $x + 3xy - y^2 = 4$
11. $x + 3y = 1$
12. $x^2 + y^2 = 7$
13. $y = x^2 + 3$
14. $y = \frac{2}{x - 1}$
15. $y = \sqrt{x - 5}$

Expressing functional relationships

EXAMPLE. If it costs $100 to set the type and 10 cents to print each booklet, express the cost C (in dollars) of printing x copies, as a function of x.

Solution. To print each copy costs 10 cents or $\frac{1}{10}$ of a dollar. To print x copies costs $\frac{x}{10}$ dollars. Hence

$$C = 100 + \frac{x}{10}$$

EXERCISES

1. Express the area of an equilateral triangle as a function of its side x.

2. The legs of an isosceles triangle are each 10 inches, and the length of the base is $2x$ inches. Express the area of the triangle as a function of x.

3. A rectangle of sides x and y is inscribed in a circle of constant radius r. Express the area A of the rectangle as a function of x.

4. A right circular cylinder is inscribed in a sphere of constant radius r. If the altitude of the cylinder is y and the radius of its base is x, express its volume V as a function of y.

5. From the four corners of a piece of tin 12″ by 16″, squares of side x are cut out. If the remaining piece of tin is then bent to form a box, express the volume V of the box as a function of x.

6. A farmer estimates that if he digs his potatoes today he will have 400 bushels worth \$2 a bushel, but if he waits the crop will increase 40 bushels per week while the price will drop 10 cents a bushel. If these conditions continue for x weeks, express the value V of the crop as a function of x.

7. A monument consists of two cubical blocks of marble, the smaller resting on the larger. If the edge of the larger block is x and of the smaller y, and if $x + y = a$, express the exposed surface as a function of x.

8. A right circular cone of altitude y is inscribed in a sphere of constant radius r. Express the volume V of the cone as a function of y.

Reading a temperature chart

The following chart made by a recording thermometer shows the temperature on a certain day in New York City, from 5 A.M. until noon.

1. What was the temperature at 5 A.M.? 11 A.M.?
2. When was the temperature the lowest?
3. How much higher was the temperature at noon than at 7 A.M.? than at 5 A.M.?
4. At what times was the temperature 54°? 56°? 57°? 53°? 51°?

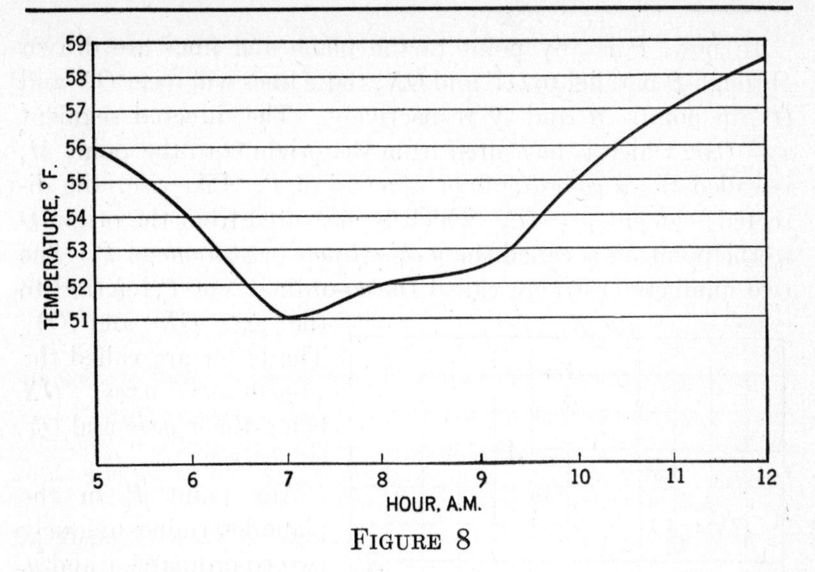

FIGURE 8

To locate points in a plane

To locate a point in a plane we make use of two mutually perpendicular lines, OX and OY, on each of which an algebraic scale has been established such that the origin on each scale is at the point of intersection O of the two lines and such that the positive direction on OY is obtained from the positive direction of OX, by rotating OX through a right angle in a counterclockwise direction. The units of length on the two scales need not be equal but are usually taken so.

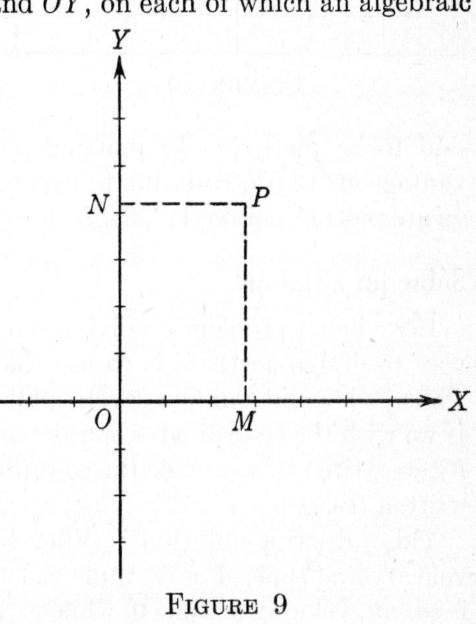

FIGURE 9

If, now, P is any point in the plane and lines are drawn through P parallel to OY and OX, these lines will meet OX and OY in points M and N respectively. The directed segment $x = OM$, which is measured from the origin O to the point M, is called the x *co-ordinate* or *abscissa* of P. Likewise, the directed segment $y = ON$, which is measured from the origin O to the point N, is called the y *co-ordinate* or *ordinate* of P. The two numbers (x, y) are called the co-ordinates of P referred to the axes OX and OY. The latter are called the *co-ordinate axes*, OX being the x *axis* and OY the y *axis*.

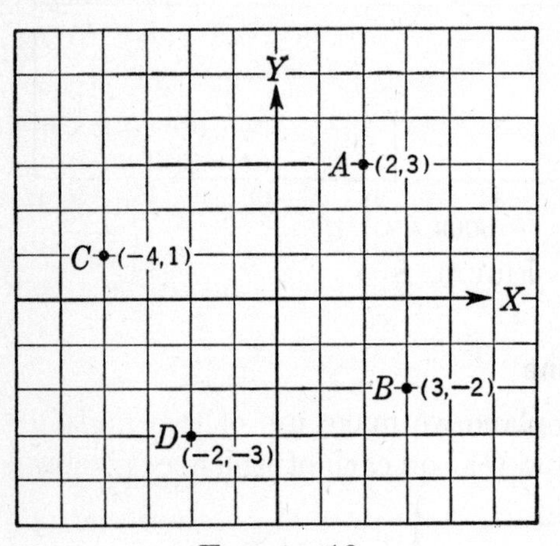

FIGURE 10

Any point P in the plane determines uniquely two co-ordinates x and y. Conversely, to every pair of numbers, x and y, there corresponds a point P whose co-ordinates are (x, y).

When a point is located as described above, it is said to be plotted. In plotting points it will be found advantageous to use co-ordinate paper such as in Fig. 10, whereon are plotted points $A(2, 3)$, $B(3, -2)$, $C(-4, 1)$, $D(-2, -3)$.

Subscript notation

If we had a problem involving ten points, a very convenient way to designate them is to use the notation P_1, P_2, P_3, etc. Thus P_7 is point number seven, while P_{10} is point number ten. If we wish the co-ordinates of any particular point, for example P_5, we write (x_5, y_5), while the co-ordinates of point P_2 would be written (x_2, y_2).

This subscript notation is often used in exercises involving velocity and time. For example v_0 denotes initial velocity; that is to say, velocity at time 0, while v_3 denotes the velocity at the end of 3 seconds. Moreover, when a subscript is attached to a variable to denote a particular value of that variable, the resulting quantity is a constant. For example, if $v = 3t + 1$, then $v_2 = 6 + 1 = 7$. What is the value of v_0? v_1?

The locus of an equation

We have seen that if a system of co-ordinate axes is set up, then to every pair of real numbers (x, y) there corresponds a point in the plane. If x and y are variables connected by an equation, then this equation will in general be satisfied by an infinite number of pairs of values of x and y, each pair of values being the co-ordinates of a point. These points are not, however, scattered indiscriminately over the plane, but usually lie on a curve whose form will vary according to the equation under consideration. This curve is called the *locus* of the given equation.

Plotting the locus of an equation

If we assign a series of values to one co-ordinate, say x, we can then determine the corresponding values of the other co-ordinate y. By this process we can determine the co-ordinates of a series of points which are situated on the required graph or curve. If we plot a sufficiently large number of these points and draw a smooth curve through them, we have an approximation to the required curve. By choosing a sufficiently large number of points close to each other, this approximation will vary but slightly from the required curve. The following examples will illustrate the method.

EXAMPLE 1. Plot the locus of $y = x + 1$.

Solution. Assigning values to x and computing the corresponding values of y, we construct the table.

x	-3	-2	-1	0	1	2	3	4
y	-2	-1	0	1	2	3	4	5

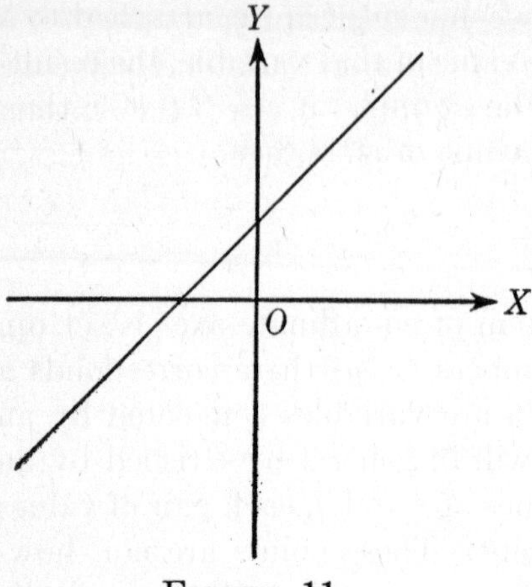

FIGURE 11

Plotting these points (Fig. 11), we see they appear to lie on a straight line; but *we cannot conclude that this is the case.* In the next chapter we shall prove that they are actually on a straight line.

EXERCISES

1. Plot the points (1, 2), (3, 5), (2, 4), (1, 3).

2. What is the ordinate of every point on the x axis?

3. What is the abscissa of every point on the y axis?

Plot the loci of the following equations:

4. $x = 4$
5. $x = 0$
6. $5x = 0$
7. $y = 3$
8. $y = -3$
9. $y = 0$
10. $x - y = 0$
11. $x + y = 0$
12. $2x - y = 5$
13. $2x - y = 0$
14. $2x + 3y = 12$
15. $y = 2x^2$
16. $y = -3x^2$
17. $y = 3x^2 - 4$
18. $x = y^2$
19. $x = 3y^2 - 4$
20. $y = x^2 - 2x$
21. $y = x^2 - 4x + 3$
22. $y = -x^2 + 3x - 2$
23. $y = -x^2 - 2x + 3$
24. $y = x^3 - 2$
25. $xy = -4$
26. $xy = 4$
27. $y = -x^2$
28. $y^2 = x$
29. $x^2 + y^2 = 25$
30. $y^2 - x^2 = 25$

Polynomials

The most general form of a polynomial of degree n in x may be written

$$f_n(x) = a_0x^n + a_1x^{n-1} + a_2x^{n-2} + \cdots + a_{n-1}x + a_n \quad (1)$$

where the coefficients $a_0, a_1, \cdots a_n$ are constants either real or imaginary and $a_0 \neq 0$.

In calculus it is proved that the graph of every function of the form (1), where n is a positive integer and the coefficients are all real numbers, is a *continuous* curve. In higher mathematics the word continuous has a highly technical meaning, but for our purpose it is sufficient to say a function $f(x)$ is continuous when the graph of $y = f(x)$ has no breaks.

DEFINITION. The two polynomials $a_0x^n + a_1x^{n-1} + \cdots + a_n$, $a_0 \neq 0$, and $b_0x^n + b_1x^{n-1} + \cdots + b_n$, $b_0 \neq 0$, are said to be equal if, and only if the coefficients of like powers of x are equal, that is

$$\begin{aligned} a_0 &= b_0 \\ a_1 &= b_1 \\ &\vdots \\ a_n &= b_n \end{aligned}$$

A zero of a function

By a zero of the function $f(x)$ we mean a value of x, which, when substituted in $f(x)$, reduces the function $f(x)$ to zero. Thus 2 is a zero of the function $f(x) = 3x^2 - 4x - 4$ because $f(2) = 3(2)^2 - 4(2) - 4 = 0$. Is 1 a zero of this function?

Evidently the zeros of $f(x)$ are the roots of the equation $f(x) = 0$, and if they are real numbers they are also the abscissas of the points which the curve $y = f(x)$ has *in common* with the x axis. For example, the zeros of $x^2 - 4x + 3$ are 1 and 3, and the roots of the equation $x^2 - 4x + 3 = 0$ are $x = 1$ and $x = 3$. The abscissas of the points where $y = x^2 - 4x + 3$ cuts the x axis are $x = 1$ and $x = 3$.

EXERCISES

Find the zeros of the following functions:

1. $x^2 - 1$
2. $x^2 - 3x + 2$
3. $x^2 - 2x$
4. $4x^2 + 4x + 1$
5. $64x^2 - 25$
6. $x^2 - \frac{2x}{3} + \frac{1}{9}$
7. $x^2 - 4x - 12$
8. $3x^2 - x - 2$
9. $15x^2 - 14x - 8$

10. $x^2 - x - 6$
11. $x^2 - 19x + 18$
12. $x^2 + 3x - 154$
13. $2 + 3x - 5x^2$
14. $42 + x - x^2$
15. $x^2 + 11x - 210$
16. $x^2 + 8x + 12$
17. $15 + 2x - x^2$
18. $6 - 13x + 2x^2$
19. $6 + x - x^2$
20. $15 - 13x + 2x^2$

Representation of a function

Many functions may be represented three different ways.

1. By means of an algebraic expression. This is known as an analytic representation.
2. By means of a table. This is known as a tabular representation.
3. By means of a graph. This is known as a graphic representation.

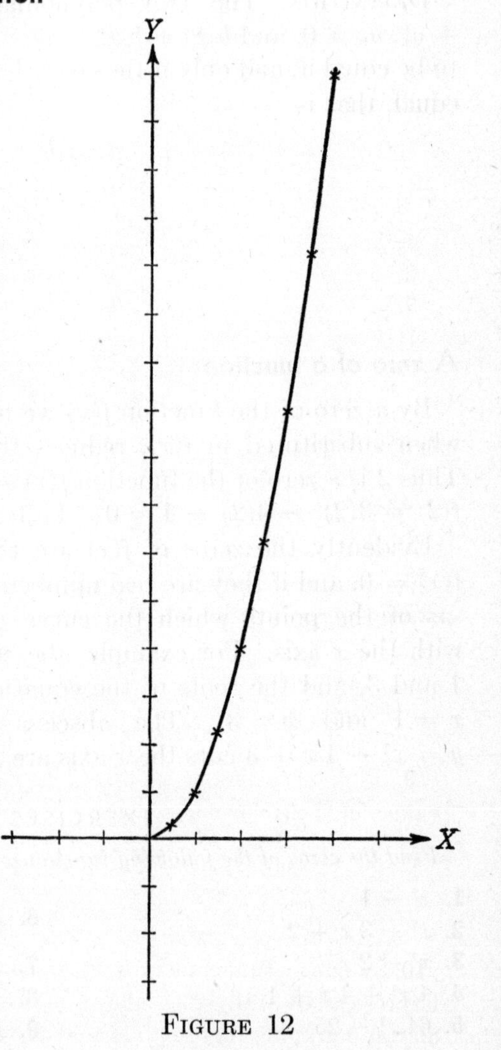

FIGURE 12

Let us consider how the area of a square varies as its side changes in length. If the area of the square in square inches is y and its side in inches is x, then $y = x^2$.

Thus we have found an analytic representation of the function. From this equation we can form the following table which is a tabular representation of the function.

x (inches)	0	0.5	1.0	1.5	2.0	2.5	3.0	3.5	4.00
y (square inches)	0	0.25	1.00	2.25	4.00	6.25	9.00	12.25	16.00

From the values in the above table we can readily construct the graph in Fig. 12. This is a graphic representation of the function.

EXERCISES

Make a tabular and graphic representation of the following functions:

1. $y = 3x + 1$

2. $y = x^2$

3. $y = x^2 - 4x$

4. $y = x^3$

5. $y = x^3 + 1$

6. $y = x^3 - x^2$

7. Copy and complete the following table for the volume of a cube.

Edge x	1	2	3		5	6	
Volume V	1	8	27	64			

Write an analytic representation of this function.

Draw a graphic representation of the function from $x = 0$ to $x = 6$.

8. Copy and complete the following table. Write a formula which expresses the functional relation between W and D.

Diameter of sphere D	2	3	4	5	6
Weight W	8	27			

9. Find an algebraic equation $y = f(x)$ which is satisfied by the values in the following table.

x	0	1	2	3	4
y	-1	2	5	8	11

10. A piece of machinery costs $5000 and depreciates $500 a year. Express analytically the value V at the end of x years. Make a tabular and graphic representation of the function.

Verbal problems

Verbal problems vary so in character that only certain general principles can be stated concerning their solution. In solving a verbal problem—

1. Read the problem carefully and make certain you understand all the conditions whether stated or implied.
2. Represent the unknown quantity by a letter. If there is more than one unknown, represent one unknown by a letter and then express the other unknowns in terms of this letter.
3. Translate the statements of the problem into the form of an equation.
4. Solve the equation and check the results.

EXAMPLE 1. A gives B a start of 30 yards in a half-mile race. A runs 18 ft. a second and B 16 ft. a second. In how many seconds will A overtake B?

Solution. Let x = the number of seconds both A and B run before A overtakes B.

Then $18x$ = the number of feet A runs to overtake B

and $16x$ = the number of feet B runs until overtaken by A

By the problem A runs 30 yd. or 90 ft. more than B. Hence

$$18x - 16x = 90$$

or

$$x = 45 \text{ seconds}$$

The check is left as an exercise.

EXAMPLE 2. If 19 pounds of gold loses 1 pound, and 10 pounds of silver loses 1 pound when weighed in water, find the amount of each in a bar of gold and silver weighing 106 pounds in air and 99 pounds in water.

Solution. Let x = the number of pounds of gold in the bar. Then, $106 - x$ = the number of pounds of silver in the bar.

Since gold loses $\frac{1}{19}$ of its weight and silver $\frac{1}{10}$ of its weight when weighed in water, then

$$\begin{aligned}
\tfrac{1}{19}x + \tfrac{1}{10}(106 - x) &= 106 - 99 = 7 \\
10x + 19(106 - x) &= 1330 \\
9x &= 684 \\
x &= 76
\end{aligned}$$

Hence, in the bar there is 76 lb. of gold and 30 lb. of silver. It is left as an exercise for the student to check this answer.

EXAMPLE 3. Mary, who is now 24 years old, is twice as old as Ann was when Mary was as old as Ann now is. How old is Ann?

Solution. We shall first construct and fill in a table like the following:

	Past	Present
Mary's age		
Ann's age		

By the conditions of the problem, Mary's present age is 24 and Ann's past age is half of 24 or 12. Moreover, Mary's past age and Ann's present age are the same; call it x. Hence the table filled out is,

	Past	Present
Mary's age	x	24
Ann's age	12	x

Now $24 - x = x - 12$. Why?

$$\begin{aligned}
2x &= 36 \\
x &= 18
\end{aligned}$$

Hence Ann's age is 18 years. The check is left as an exercise.

EXERCISES

1. Find three consecutive positive integers whose sum is 36.

2. Find three consecutive even positive integers whose sum is 78.

3. Is the difference between the squares of two odd integers even or odd?

4. The sum of two numbers is 50. If the smaller number is decreased by 2, the result is equal to one third of the larger number. What are the numbers?

5. Together three men have $100,000. How much has each man if the first has three times as much as the second and the third has twice as much as the first?

6. If A can do a piece of work alone in 3 days, B in 5 days, and C in 6 days, find how many days will be required to do the work if all three work together.

7. A man 72 years old is 24 years older than his son. How many years ago was the son half as old as his father?

8. How much water must be added to 20 quarts of a 15 per cent salt solution to reduce it to a 10 per cent solution?

9. A chemist has a 50 per cent solution and a 10 per cent solution. How many ounces of each solution should he take in order to obtain 8 ounces of a 25 per cent solution?

10. A man has $1800, part of which he invests at 5 per cent and the balance at 6 per cent. If his total income from both investments is $100 a year, how much has he invested at 6 per cent?

11. How much pure alcohol must I add to 30 quarts of a 20 per cent solution in order to produce a 35 per cent solution?

12. When a fisherman was asked the length of a fish he caught, he replied: "The tail was 4 inches long. The head was as long as the tail and $\frac{1}{7}$ of the body, while the body was as long as the head and $\frac{1}{7}$ of the tail." How long was the fish?

13. A man's age is such that $\frac{2}{5}$ of it, less $\frac{1}{9}$ of what it will be a year from now, is equal to $\frac{1}{3}$ of what it was 5 years ago. How old will the man be in 5 years?

14. In a certain orchard there are twice as many trees in a row as there are rows. If the number of rows is increased by 3 and the number of trees in each row is increased by 2, the orchard will contain 126 more trees. How many trees are there in the orchard?

15. At what time between 3 and 4 o'clock are the hands of a watch together?

16. Divide 30 into two parts such that the square of the greater exceeds the square of the lesser by 600.

17. What percentage of evaporation takes place in order to change an 8 per cent solution of salt and water to a 12 per cent solution?

18. What number must be subtracted from each of the four numbers 16, 27, 20, and 24, so that the product of the first two remainders shall equal the product of the second two?

19. A man can row 4 miles per hour in still water. If it took him 9 hr. to row downstream and back when the current was flowing 1 mi. per hour, how far downstream did he row?

Honor problems

20. The planet Venus makes a circuit about the sun in $7\frac{1}{2}$ months and the earth in 12 months. Find the number of months between two successive times when Venus is between the earth and the sun.

21. If a father takes 3 steps while his son takes 5, and if 2 of the father's steps are equal in length to 3 of the son's, how many steps will the son have to take before he overtakes his father, who is 36 of his own steps ahead?

22. A freight train overtakes a man who is walking beside the track at the rate of 4 miles an hour. If the train is 1 mile long and is traveling 25 miles an hour, how far will the man walk while the train is passing him?

23. A clock gains 4 minutes a day. What time should it indicate at 6 o'clock in the morning in order that it may be right at 7:15 P.M. on the same day?

24. It is between two and three o'clock; a person looking at his watch mistakes the hour hand for the minute hand and thinks that the time of day is 55 minutes earlier than it really is. What is the true time?

25. As an army 5 miles long began to march, a courier left the rear for the front. Upon reaching the front he immediately started for the rear and reached there after the army had traveled 5 miles. How far did the courier travel?

MASTERY TEST

1. Simplify:

a) $(x + 2)(x - 4) - (1 - 4x)(x - 4)$
b) $(a + b)(a - b) - (b + a)(b - a)$
c) $(x^a + y^a)(x^a - y^a) - (x^a + y^a)^2$
d) $(x^3 + 3x^2 + x - 5)(x^2 - 2x - 1)$

2. Divide:

a) $x^3 - 6x^2 + 12x - 8$ by $x^2 - 4x + 4$
b) $x^4 + x^2y^2 + y^4$ by $x^2 + xy + y^2$
c) $1 - 16x^4$ by $2x - 1$
d) $a^{4x} - b^{4y}$ by $a^x + b^y$

3. Factor:

a) $m^2 - 20 + m^4$
b) $16(x - y)^3 - x + y$
c) $432 + 2q^3$
d) $p^3 + 3p^2 - p - 3$
e) $a^3 + a + b^3 + b$
f) $ax^2 + (b - a)x - b$

4. Simplify:

a) $\left(\dfrac{2}{a+1} - \dfrac{a-1}{a}\right) \div \left(\dfrac{a}{a+1} + \dfrac{a-1}{a}\right)$

b) $\left(\dfrac{1}{x-y} + \dfrac{1}{x+y}\right) \div \left(\dfrac{x+y}{x-y} + \dfrac{x-y}{x+y}\right)$

c) $\left(1 + \dfrac{1}{x}\right) \div \left(1 - \dfrac{1}{x}\right)\left(x - \dfrac{1}{x}\right)$

d) $\dfrac{1 - \dfrac{2ab}{(a+b)^2}}{1 + \dfrac{2ab}{(a-b)^2}} \div \left[\dfrac{1 - \dfrac{b}{a}}{1 + \dfrac{b}{a}}\right]^2$

5. If $s = at - \frac{1}{2}gt^2$, find s when $a = 400$, $t = 4$, $g = 32.2$.

6. If $A = \dfrac{\pi r^2 E}{180°}$, find A when $r = 12$, $E = 140°$, $\pi = 3.14$.

7. Express as formulas the following functional relations:

a) The volume V of a pyramid is equal to one third the product of the area of its base B and its height h.
b) The volume V of a sphere is $\frac{4}{3}$ the product of π and the cube of the radius r.
c) The force F is equal to the mass m times the acceleration a.

8. Write the following numbers as an integer times 10 to some power:

a) 79,000,000,000
b) 0.000 000 79
c) 231,000,000,000,000
d) 0.000 000 000 000 23

9. Simplify:

a) $(a^{-2} + a^{-1} + 1)(a^2 + a + 1)$
b) $(p^{-3} + 27) \div (p^{-1} + 3)$
c) $(a^2 - b^2) \div (a^{\frac{2}{3}} - b^{\frac{2}{3}})$
d) $\dfrac{a^{-2} - b^{-2}}{a^{-1} + b^{-1}}$
e) $\dfrac{a^{-1}}{a^{-1} + b^{-1}}$

10. Find the value of:

a) $\dfrac{1}{3^{-1} + 2^{-1}}$
b) $(81)^{-\frac{3}{4}}$
c) $(5^{\frac{2}{3}})^0 + 64^{\frac{2}{3}} + 25^{-\frac{1}{2}}$
d) $10^4 \times 10^0 \times 10^{-3.5} \div 10^{-0.5}$

11. Solve for x:

a) $(3x - 1)(2x + 1) - (6x - 5)(x + 11) = 0$
b) $\dfrac{3}{3x + 2} - \dfrac{4}{1 - 2x} = \dfrac{3}{x - 2}$
c) $\dfrac{1}{b} + \dfrac{1}{a} = \dfrac{1}{x}$
d) $\dfrac{2x - 1}{x + 3} = \dfrac{4x - 5}{2x + 3}$

12. Express x as an explicit function of y:

a) $3x + y = 7$
b) $\dfrac{x - y}{2} = \dfrac{3y + 7}{5}$
c) $\dfrac{x - y}{5} = \dfrac{2x + \frac{1}{5}x^2}{x + y}$

13. Draw the graphs of the following functions:

a) $y = x + 5$
b) $y = x^2 - 4$
c) $y = x^3$
d) $y = \sqrt{x}$
e) $y = -\sqrt{x}$

14. If $f(x) = \dfrac{x^2 - 2x + 1}{x^2 - 4}$, find:

a) $f(0)$

b) $f(1)$

c) $f(a)$

d) $f(2a)$

e) $f\left(\dfrac{1}{x}\right)$

f) $f(-y)$

15. Write an algebraic equation $y = f(x)$ which is satisfied by the values in the following table:

x	0	1	2	3	4	5
y	0	3	6	9	12	15

16. What is meant by equivalent fractions?

17. State three operations one may perform on both members of an equation and expect the resulting equation to be equivalent to the original equation.

18. State three operations one may perform on both members of an equation and not be certain the resulting equation is equivalent to the original.

19. If in the fraction $\dfrac{3}{x}$, x is doubled, then the value of the fraction is ———.

20. Solve for x:

$$x - \left(\frac{x+1}{3} - \frac{x+3}{2}\right) = -\frac{1-x}{4}$$

21. Solve for x:

$$\frac{x}{x-b} - \frac{x}{x+b} = \frac{3ab}{b^2 - x^2}$$

22. Evaluate S in the formula $S = \dfrac{a}{1-r}$ when $a = 3$, $r = .01$

23. Solve for x:

$$\frac{\dfrac{x-1}{b}}{\dfrac{x}{b-1}} = \frac{\dfrac{x+b}{b}}{\dfrac{x}{b+1}}$$

24. Solve for x:

$$\frac{b}{x+b} = \frac{b^2+4b}{x^2+x-b^2+b} - \frac{1}{x-b+1}$$

25. Solve for y:

$$y = \frac{(y-a)(2y-a)}{2y+a} - a$$

26. Evaluate $M = \dfrac{25L}{Ff}$ for f when

$$M = 1200,\ L = 20,\ F = 1.5$$

27. Solve for a:

$$\frac{p+1}{p} = \frac{a}{a+4}$$

CHAPTER V

Linear Functions

General linear function

Any function of the first degree in terms of its variables is called a *linear function* of the variables. Thus $Ax + C$ where A and C are constants and $A \neq 0$ is the general linear function in x; likewise, $Ax + By + C$ where A, B, and C are constants and $A \neq 0$, $B \neq 0$, is the general linear function in x and y.

How would you write the general linear function in the variables x, y, and z?

Let us consider the following problem. Suppose a railroad train starts 5 miles west of Chicago and travels west at the rate of 20 miles per hour. How far west of Chicago is the train at the end of x hours?

In x hours the train has traveled $20\,x$ miles. If we denote the distance of the train from Chicago by y, then

$$y = 20\,x + 5$$

Hence, the distance y is a linear function of the time x.

Let us now see how a change in the variable x is related to the corresponding change in the function y. For example, we note that as x changes from $x = 0$ to $x = 1$, the function y changes from $y = 5$ to $y = 25$. Therefore, a change of 1 unit in x produces a change of $25 - 5$ or 20 units in y. The relative change is 20/1 or 20. As x increases from $x = 0$ to $x = 2$, the function y changes from $y = 5$ to $y = 45$ or 40 units. The relative change is 40/2 or again 20, which is the rate of the train.

Let us see what the situation is in general. Suppose any two particular values of x are x_1 and x_2 and the corresponding values of y are y_1 and y_2. The change in the variable x is evidently $x_2 - x_1$ and the corresponding change in the function y is $y_2 - y_1$. We are trying to find the value of the ratio (called *change ratio*)

$$\frac{y_2 - y_1}{x_2 - x_1}$$

From our data $\qquad y_2 = 20\,x_2 + 5$

and $\qquad y_1 = 20\,x_1 + 5$

Subtracting $\qquad y_2 - y_1 = 20(x_2 - x_1)$

Therefore $\qquad \dfrac{y_2 - y_1}{x_2 - x_1} = 20$

Hence, we see in this example that the change ratio is always 20, which is the rate of the train.

Theorem 1. *If a function is of the form $mx + b$, then the change ratio is the constant m.*

Proof. Let (x_1, y_1) and (x_2, y_2) be any two pairs of corresponding values. Then

$$y_2 = mx_2 + b$$

$$y_1 = mx_1 + b$$

Subtracting $\qquad y_2 - y_1 = m(x_2 - x_1)$

and $\qquad \dfrac{y_2 - y_1}{x_2 - x_1} = m$

But m is a constant; therefore the change ratio is constant. What is the change ratio of the function $3\,x + 9$? $2\,x - 7$? $-4\,x + 11$?

Theorem 2. *If the change ratio of a function y of x is constant and equal to m, the function is $y = mx + b$ where b is a constant.*

Proof. Let (x_1, y_1) be a particular pair of corresponding values, and (x, y) *any* other pair of corresponding values. Since the change ratio is m, we have

$$\frac{y - y_1}{x - x_1} = m$$

or

$$y = mx - mx_1 + y_1$$

Since m, x_1, and y_1 are constants, then $-mx_1 + y_1$ is a constant. Call it b.

Hence

$$y = mx + b$$

It is left as an exercise for the student to prove that b will have the same value even if another pair of values (x_2, y_2) is used. Thus, if the change ratio of a function is 6, the function is $y = 6x + b$ where b is a constant. What is the function whose change ratio is -3?

The graph of $y = mx + b$ $(m \neq 0)$

From any point $P_1(x_1, y_1)$ on the graph of $y = mx + b$ draw to the right a horizontal segment. On this segment take two points Q_2 and Q_3 and through these points draw vertical lines meeting the graph in points P_2 and P_3 respectively. Let the co-ordinates of P_2 and P_3 be (x_2, y_2) and (x_3, y_3) respectively. The segments Q_2P_2, Q_3P_3 are positive if P_2 and P_3 are above P_1 and negative if below P_1.

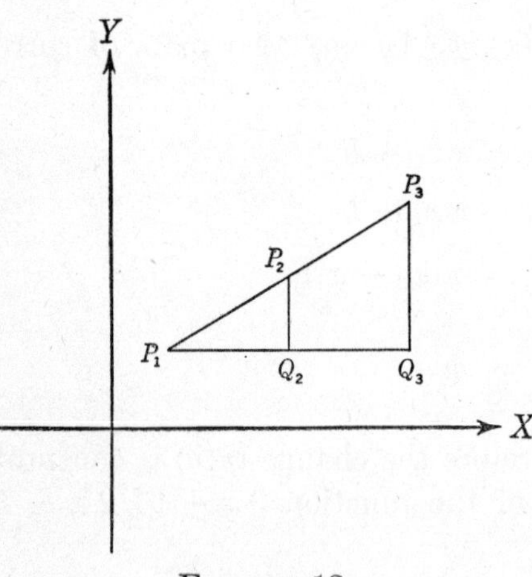

FIGURE 13

If the change ratio is constant, then

1. Points P_2 and P_3 are either both above P_1 or both below P_1 according to whether the constant is positive or negative. Why?

2. The triangles $P_1Q_2P_2$ and $P_1Q_3P_3$ are similar. Why?

Therefore the points P_1, P_2, and P_3 are collinear if and only if the change ratio is constant. Hence:

Theorem. *The graph of the function $y = mx + b$, $m \neq 0$, is a straight line.*

To draw the graph of such a function, it is only necessary to plot two points of the graph and draw a straight line through them. Why? As a check it is desirable to find a third point. Moreover, it is advisable to take these points as far apart as convenient. Why?

EXAMPLE 1. Draw the graph of the function $y = 2x + 1$.

Solution.
If $x = 0$ then $y = 1$
If $x = 3$ then $y = 7$

If we plot the points (0, 1) and (3, 7) and draw the straight line through them, we have the graph (Fig. 14) of $y = 2x + 1$. Check by plotting a third point.

EXAMPLE 2. Draw the graph of $2x - 5y = 9$.

Solution. Solving for y, we have

$$y = \frac{2x - 9}{5}$$

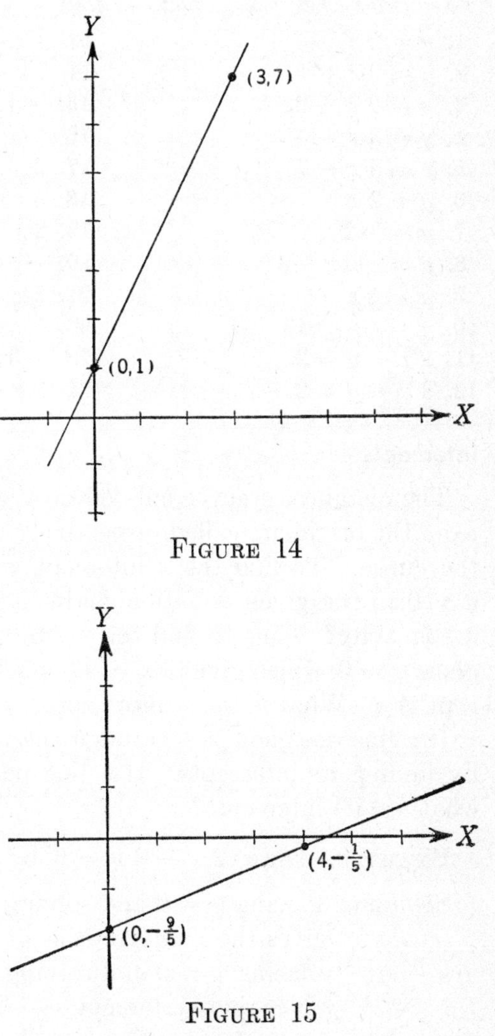

FIGURE 14

FIGURE 15

$$\text{If } x = 0, \text{ then } y = -\tfrac{9}{5}$$
$$\text{If } x = 4, \text{ then } y = -\tfrac{1}{5}$$

Plotting the points $(0, -\frac{9}{5})$, $(4, -\frac{1}{5})$ and drawing the line (Fig. 15) through them gives the graph of $2x - 5y = 9$. Check by plotting a third point.

EXERCISES

Draw the lines whose equations are:

1. $y = 2x$
2. $y = 2x + 1$
3. $y = 2x - 2$
4. $y = 3x + 4$
5. $y = 3x - 7$
6. $y = 2x$
7. $y = -2x$
8. $y = -2x - 3$
9. $y = \frac{1}{2}x$
10. $y = \frac{1}{2}x + 10$
11. $2x + y = 3$
12. $3x - y = 2$
13. $4x + 2y = 5$
14. $2x - 3y = 3$
15. $-4x + 2y = 7$
16. $-x + 3y = -2$
17. $2x + 5y = 8$
18. $5x + 7y = -4$
19. $2x - 3y = 7$
20. $-3x + 5y = 11$
21. $5x - 3y = 12$
22. $7x + 2y = -5$
23. $-3x + 8y = 11$
24. $8x - 7y = 7$

Intercepts

The distances a curve cuts off on the x and y axes measured from the origin are called respectively the x and y intercepts of the curve. To find the x intercept we merely have to place $y = 0$ in the given equation and solve the resulting equation for x. Why? Thus to find the x intercept of $3x + 4y = 12$, place $y = 0$, which gives $3x = 12$ or $x = 4$. Hence, the x intercept is 4. What is the y intercept?

If a line does not pass through the origin, it is easily drawn by finding its intercepts. If a line passes through the origin what are its intercepts?

EXAMPLE. Draw $2x - 3y = 6$ by finding the intercepts.

Solution. Placing $y = 0$ and solving for x gives the x intercept as 3.
Placing $x = 0$ and solving for y gives the y intercept as -2.

By marking off these intercepts the line is readily drawn (Fig. 16).

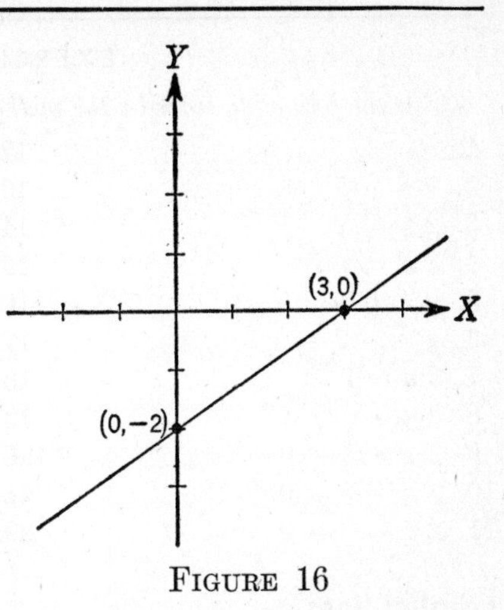

FIGURE 16

A line parallel to the y axis has an x intercept and no y intercept (Fig. 17). Suppose the x intercept is a. Note that the abscissa of every point in the line is a and conversely that any point that has its abscissa equal to a lies on the given line. Hence we say the equation of the line is $x = a$.

A line parallel to the x axis has a y intercept and no x intercept (Fig. 18). Suppose the y intercept is b. Note that the ordinate of every point in the line is b and conversely that any

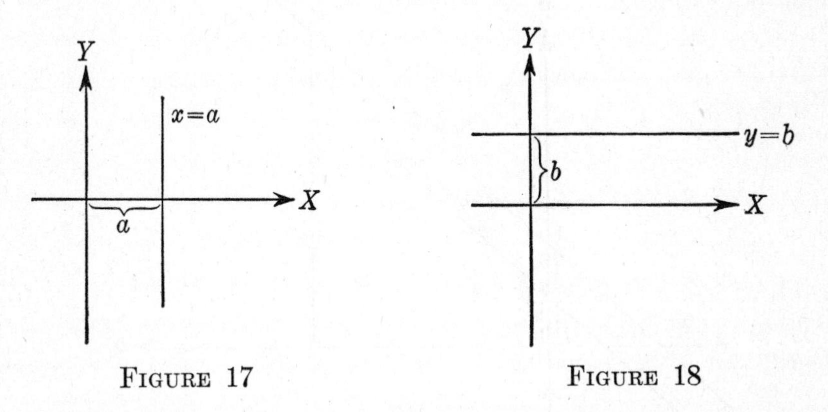

FIGURE 17 FIGURE 18

point that has its ordinate equal to b lies on the given line. Hence, we say the equation of the line is $y = b$.

Note that if $m = 0$, the equation $y = mx + b$ reduces to $y = b$. Hence, we can conclude that the graph of $y = mx + b$ is a straight line for all values of m.

Query. What can you say about the relative positions of the lines whose equations are $x = a$ and $y = b$?

EXERCISES

Draw the following lines by the method of intercepts:

1. $x = 3$
2. $x = -5$
3. $2x = 5$
4. $3x = -7$
5. $y = 6$
6. $y = -2$
7. $3y = 7$
8. $3y = -8$
9. $2x - 3 = 0$
10. $3x + 7 = 0$
11. $2y - 9 = 0$
12. $2y + 11 = 0$
13. $2x - 3y = 6$
14. $4x + y = 8$
15. $-2x + y = 4$
16. $6x - y = 12$
17. $3x + 4y = 5$
18. $7x + 8y = 11$
19. $8x - 5y = 20$
20. $-7x - 2y = 15$
21. $3x + 7y = 20$
22. $14x + 2y = 33$

Parallel lines

Theorem. *The graphs of* $y = mx + b$ *and* $y = mx + k$ $(b \neq k)$ *are parallel lines.*

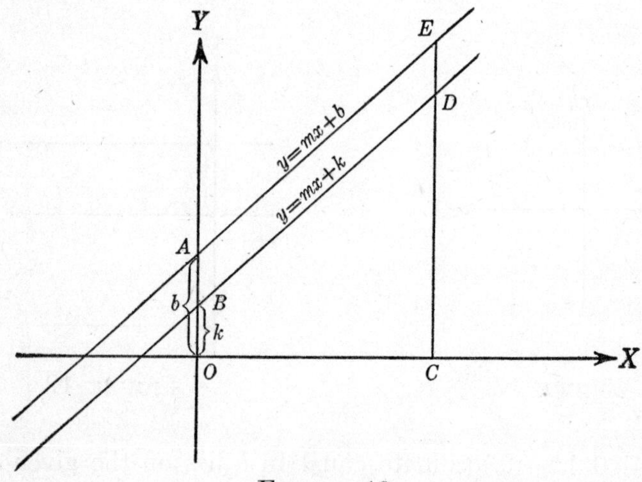

FIGURE 19

The y intercept of $y = mx + b$ is b and the y intercept of $y = mx + k$ is k. That is $OA = b$, $OB = k$; hence $BA = b - k$. If $x = 1 = OC$, then $CE = m + b$ and $CD = m + k$; hence $DE = (m + b) - (m + k) = b - k$. Moreover, $OA \parallel CE$ (why?); hence $ABDE$ is a parallelogram since it has $BA = DE$

and $BA \parallel DE$. Therefore $AE \parallel BD$; *i.e.*, the line whose equation is $y = mx + b$ is parallel to the line whose equation is $y = mx + k$. If $m = 0$, what particular position do the two lines assume? What happens if $b = k$?

EXERCISES

Which of the following lines are parallel?

1. $y = 3x + 2$
   $y = -3x + 2$
   $y = 3x - 2$
2. $2x + 3y = 5$
   $2x - 3y = 5$
   $2x + 3y = 7$
3. $4x - 3y = 1$
   $8x - 6y = 5$
   $2x + 3y = 1$
4. $x - 2y = 3$
   $2x + 4y = 1$
   $3x - 6y = -2$
5. $x - 7 = 0$
   $2x - 3 = 0$
   $4y + 1 = 0$
6. $3x - 7 = 0$
   $2y - 1 = 0$
   $5y + 2 = 0$

Simultaneous linear equations in two unknowns

To determine a pair of values which satisfy $a_1x + b_1y = c_1$, one merely has to assign a value to x and then solve the equation for the corresponding value of y. Since any value can be assigned to x, there is an unlimited number of pairs of values x and y which satisfy $a_1x + b_1y = c_1$. If we have a second equation, $a_2x + b_2y = c_2$, it also is satisfied by an unlimited number of pairs of values of x and y, which in general will be different from those satisfying the first equation. The question now arises whether there are any pairs of values which satisfy both equations and if so how can we find them. If such pairs of values exist, they are called *solutions of the equations*. If there is but one pair of values which satisfy the two equations, the equations are called *consistent*. We shall discuss in this chapter both graphic and algebraic methods for finding solutions of pairs of such equations.

The method of graphs

Suppose we wished to solve graphically the equations $2x - y = 3$ and $x + y = 3$. There are an infinite number of points lying on the graph of $2x - y = 3$, and corresponding to each of these points there is a pair of values of x and y which satisfy

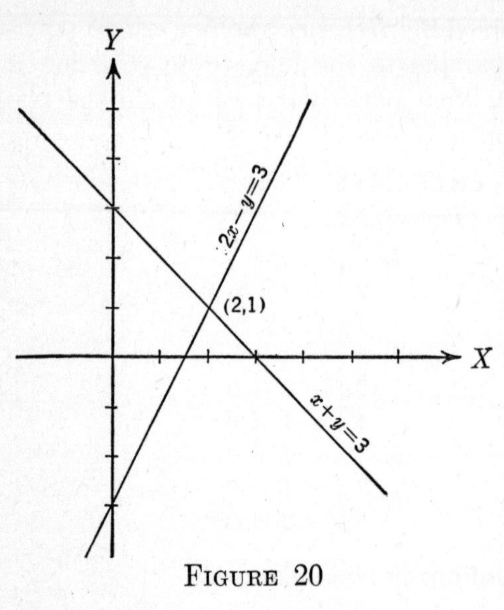

FIGURE 20

$2x - y = 3$. Likewise there are an infinite number of points lying on the graph of $x + y = 3$, and corresponding to each of these points there is a pair of values of x and y which satisfy $x + y = 3$. However, there is just one point that lies on both lines and its co-ordinates are the only set of values which satisfy both equations. Hence, to solve the equations we must find the co-ordinates of their point of intersection. From the graph it appears that $x = 2$ and $y = 1$. Do these values check?

Do you think a graphic solution is always accurate? Suppose the algebraic solution of two equations were $x = \frac{101}{100}$, $y = \frac{103}{100}$. What values do you think one would read from the graph?

EXERCISES

Solve graphically the following sets of equations:

1. $x + y = 1$
$2x - y = 1$

2. $3x + y = 7$
$x - y = 1$

3. $x + y = 3$
$2x - y = 3$

4. $x + y = -4$
$2x - 3y = -3$

5. $2x + y = 5$
$x - y = 7$

6. $2x - y = -8$
$x + 2y = 6$

7. $x + 2y = 5$
$2x - y = 4$

8. $3x + 4y = 12$
$4x - 3y = 12$

9. $x - y = 4$
$x + y = 10$

10. $2x + y = 4$
$6x - 3y = 1$

11. $3x - 2y = 6$
$2x + 5y = 10$

12. $x - 2y = 0$
$3x + 4y = -12$

13. $x + y = 2$
$x - 1 = 0$

14. $x - 2y = 3$
$y = 1$

15. $x - 3 = 0$
$2y + 1 = 0$

16. $2x + y = 3$
$x + y = 3$

17. $3x - 5 = 0$
$x + y = 4$

18. $2x - 7 = 0$
$4y + 3 = 0$

Solving algebraically

The following examples will illustrate the methods most generally used.

EXAMPLE 1. Solve the simultaneous equations:

$$3x - 5y = 7 \qquad (1)$$
$$2x + 3y = -8 \qquad (2)$$

Solution. From the given equations in two unknowns we shall derive a new equation in one unknown. The process of getting rid of one of the unknowns is called *elimination.* We know that if we multiply an equation by a constant different from zero the resulting equation is equivalent to the original equation. We shall, therefore, multiply equations (1) and (2) by numbers that will make the coefficients of one of the unknowns in both equations numerically equal. Thus, multiplying (1) by 3 and (2) by 5 gives:

$$9x - 15y = 21$$
$$10x + 15y = -40$$

Adding
$$19x = -19$$
$$x = -1$$

Substituting $x = -1$ in equation (1) gives $y = -2$.

Check. Substituting $x = -1$, $y = -2$ in equations (1) and (2) gives:

$$3(-1) - 5(-2) = -3 + 10 = 7$$
$$2(-1) + 3(-2) = -2 - 6 = -8$$

Query. Why is it necessary in the check to substitute in both equations? Suppose in solving we had found $x = 4$, $y = 1$. Do these values check in the first equation? the second?

EXAMPLE 2. Solve the simultaneous equations:

$$\frac{3x}{5} - \frac{y}{2} = 2$$

$$\frac{2x}{3} - \frac{3y}{5} = \frac{32}{15}$$

Solution. Clearing both equations of fractions gives:

$$6x - 5y = 20 \qquad (1)$$
$$10x - 9y = 32 \qquad (2)$$

Multiplying (1) by 10 and (2) by 6 gives:

$$60x - 50y = 200$$
$$60x - 54y = 192$$

Subtracting $\qquad 4y = 8$

$$y = 2$$

Substituting $y = 2$ in (1), gives $x = 5$.

Check. Substituting $x = 5$, $y = 2$ in the *original* equations gives

$$3 - 1 = 2$$

$$\frac{10}{3} - \frac{6}{5} = \frac{50 - 18}{15} = \frac{32}{15}$$

Query. Would substituting in equations (1) and (2) constitute a valid check?

EXAMPLE 3. Solve the simultaneous equations

$$3x - 2y = 7$$
$$4x + 5y = 1$$

We shall solve these equations by the method of substitution. This means we shall solve one of the equations for one of the variables in terms of the other and then substitute this value in the second equation.

Solution. Solving the first equation for x gives

$$x = \frac{7 + 2y}{3}$$

Substituting this value in the second equation gives

$$4\left(\frac{7 + 2y}{3}\right) + 5y = 1$$

or $$28 + 8y + 15y = 3$$
$$23y = -25$$
or $$y = -\tfrac{25}{23}$$

Substituting this value in the first equation gives
$$x = -\tfrac{37}{23}$$

The check is left as an exercise for the student.

EXERCISES

Solve and check the following sets of equations:

1. $2x + 3y = 5$
   $4x - y = 3$
2. $x + 3y = 5$
   $3x - y = 5$
3. $x + 2y = 0$
   $3x - y = 5$
4. $4x + 3y = 5$
   $2x - y = 7$
5. $5x - 2y = 7$
   $3x - y = 8$
6. $2x + 3y = 7$
   $5x - y = -3$
7. $x - y = 5$
   $2x + \frac{y}{3} = 4$
8. $\frac{x}{2} + \frac{y}{5} = 1$
   $\frac{x}{3} + \frac{y}{7} = 1$
9. $\frac{2x}{3} - \frac{y}{5} = 4$
   $\frac{3x}{2} + \frac{4y}{3} = 9$
10. $\frac{7x}{3} - \frac{2y}{5} = \frac{13}{15}$
    $x = \frac{2y}{3} - 1$
11. $12x - y = 11$
    $\frac{3x}{4} - \frac{y}{2} = 25$
12. $\frac{x}{2} + \frac{y}{5} = 2$
    $\frac{x}{3} - \frac{y}{3} + 1 = 0$
13. $12x - 7y = 3$
    $2x + y = 4$
14. $\frac{4x}{3} + \frac{y}{5} = 7$
    $\frac{2x}{3} + \frac{5y}{4} = -\frac{9}{4}$
15. $\frac{2x - 7y}{3} = \frac{x + 3y}{21}$
    $\frac{x + y}{3} = \frac{x - y + 4}{5}$
16. $6.5 + 2y = \frac{x + 3}{4}$
    $4x - \frac{y + 3}{4} + 4 = 0$
17. $.3x - .5y = 1$
    $.2x + 1.2y = 11.4$
18. $.3x - .4y = 1.6$
    $.4x - .3y = 2.6$
19. $3x + 5 = 0$
    $4x - 2y = 3$
20. $5y - 7 = 0$
    $3x + 2y + 4 = 0$

Inconsistent and dependent equations

When two straight lines are drawn in a plane, they may assume one of the following three positions: (1) They may intersect; (2) they may be parallel; (3) they may coincide.

How many points do the lines have in common if they intersect? if they are parallel? if they coincide?

Examples illustrating the first case have already been discussed. The following examples will illustrate the last two cases.

EXAMPLE 1. Solve: $2x - 3y = 4$ (1)

$$4x - 6y = -7 \quad (2)$$

Solution. Multiplying (1) by 2 and repeating (2) gives:

$$4x - 6y = 8 \quad (3)$$
$$4x - 6y = -7 \quad (4)$$

Since the left hand members of (3) and (4) are the same while the right hand members are different, the equations are called

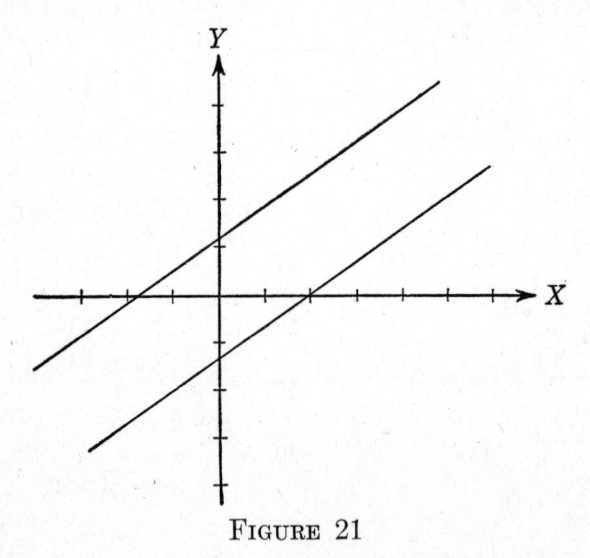

FIGURE 21

inconsistent or *incompatible*. Since the equations differ only in the constant terms the lines are parallel. (See page 114.)

EXAMPLE 2. Solve:

$$3x - 2y = 5 \qquad (1)$$
$$6x - 4y = 10 \qquad (2)$$

Solution. Multiplying (1) by 2 and repeating (2) gives:

$$6x - 4y = 10 \qquad (3)$$
$$6x - 4y = 10 \qquad (4)$$

These two equations are identical. Hence, any pair of values which satisfies (1) satisfies (2); *i.e.*, the equations have an *infinite*

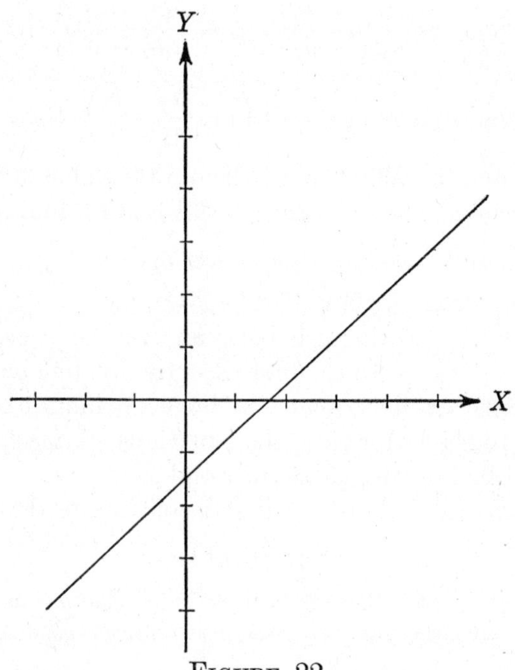

FIGURE 22

number of solutions, and the lines coincide. Such equations are called *dependent*, and the lines are *identical.*

Let us now consider the general equations:

$$a_1x + b_1y = c_1 \qquad (5)$$
$$a_2x + b_2y = c_2 \qquad (6)$$

We shall assume that none of the constants is zero. We learned on page 76 that if an equation is multiplied by a constant not zero the resulting equation is equivalent to the original equation. Hence, if we multiply (5) by b_2 and (6) by b_1 and subtract, we eliminate y and obtain

$$(a_1b_2 - a_2b_1)x = c_1b_2 - c_2b_1$$

In like manner, by eliminating x we obtain

$$(a_1b_2 - a_2b_1)y = a_1c_2 - a_2c_1$$

Now, if $a_1b_2 - a_2b_1 \neq 0$ we have

$$x = \frac{c_1b_2 - c_2b_1}{a_1b_2 - a_2b_1}, \quad y = \frac{a_1c_2 - a_2c_1}{a_1b_2 - a_2b_1}$$

If, however, $a_1b_2 - a_2b_1 = 0$ $\left(i.e., \frac{a_2}{a_1} = \frac{b_2}{b_1}\right)$, then we cannot solve for x and y. Why? If we denote the value of these fractions by k, we have $a_2 = a_1k$; $b_2 = b_1k$ and (5) and (6) become

$$a_1x + b_1y = c_1$$
$$ka_1x + kb_1y = c_2$$

We must now distinguish between two cases according as $c_2 = kc_1$ or $c_2 \neq kc_1$. In the first case, by dividing out k, we see the equations are *dependent* and have an infinite number of solutions. In the latter case, the equations are *inconsistent* and are not satisfied by any values of x and y.

Discuss the cases that arise if some of the constants are zero.

EXERCISES

Tell whether the following sets or systems of equations are consistent, inconsistent, or dependent. In each case illustrate your solution by a graph.

1. $2x + y = 3$
$x - y = 0$

2. $2x + y = 3$
$4x + 2y = -5$

3. $2x - y = 5$
$4x - 2y = 10$

4. $3x - y = 7$
$2x + y = 3$

5. $4x - y = 0$
$y - 4x = 3$

6. $3x - 2y = 7$
$4y - 6x = -14$

7. If none of the constants of $a_1x + b_1y = c_1$, $a_2x + b_2y = c_2$ is zero, prove the equations are (a) dependent when $a_1/a_2 = b_1/b_2 = c_1/c_2$ and (b) inconsistent when $a_1/a_2 = b_1/b_2 \neq c_1/c_2$.

8. A man has 20 bills, part in \$5 bills and the rest \$1 bills. If their value is \$80, find the number of each.

9. A fraction is such that if 3 be added to each of its terms the resulting fraction is $\frac{10}{11}$; if 3 be subtracted from each of its terms, the resulting fraction is $\frac{4}{5}$. Find the fraction.

10. Two boys are 96 yards apart. If they start running toward each other at the same time, they meet in 8 seconds; while if they run in the same direction, the faster boy, running the greater distance, will overtake the slower boy in 48 seconds. Find the rate of each.

11. If one number is divided by 5 and added to a second number, the result is 23. If the second number is divided by 4 and added to the first number, the result is 58. Find the numbers.

12. The altitude of a rectangle is 20 per cent less than the base. Find the dimensions of the rectangle if the perimeter is 36 inches.

13. A steamer going up a river against the current makes 16 miles an hour. Going down the river with the current it makes 24 miles an hour. Find the rate of the current.

14. Two passengers traveling from town A to town B have 500 pounds of baggage. The first pays \$1.75 for excess above weight allowed, the second \$1.25. If all the baggage belonged to the second passenger, he would have to pay \$4 excess. How much baggage is allowed a single passenger?

15. Two men are running at uniform rates on a circular track 150 feet in circumference. When they run in opposite directions, they meet every 5 seconds. When they run in the same direction, they are abreast every 25 seconds. What are their rates?

16. A man invested two sums of money, one at 5 per cent and one at 3 per cent, and his total income was \$135.00. If the sums had been reversed, his income would have been \$145.00. Find the two amounts.

17. At what time between 4 and 5 o'clock are the hands of a watch together?

18. A chemist has 4 quarts of an 8 per cent solution of acid. How much water should he add to reduce it to a 4 per cent solution?

19. A chemist has two bottles, one containing a 40 per cent solution of acid and the other a 15 per cent solution of the same acid. How many cc. of each solution should he use in order to make 100 cc. of a 25 per cent solution?

20. Milk testing 4 per cent butter fat is to be mixed with cream testing 28 per cent butter fat. How many quarts of each must be used in order to give a mixture of 8 gallons testing 15 per cent butter fat?

21. The rear wheel of a carriage is 3 feet greater in circumference than the front wheel. If the front wheel makes as many revolutions in going a mile as the rear one does in going 2200 yards, find the perimeter of each wheel.

22. How many pints of 80 per cent antifreeze and 40 per cent antifreeze should be mixed to produce 10 quarts of 70 per cent antifreeze?

23. A train dispatcher needs a formula for determining the time trains pass. Derive such a formula from the following data: A train traveling m miles an hour starts t hours after another train traveling r miles an hour. In how many hours will the later train overtake the former, assuming $m > r$?

Linear equations containing more than two unknowns

It is easy to see that the algebraic methods used in solving a system of two simultaneous equations in two unknowns may also be employed in solving a system of three or more equations involving as many unknown quantities as there are independent equations. Solve:

$$x + 2y + z = 8 \quad (1)$$
$$3x - 2y + 5z = 14 \quad (2)$$
$$5x + 3y - 3z = 2 \quad (3)$$

Adding (1) and (2) and dividing by 2 gives

$$2x + 3z = 11 \quad (4)$$

Adding 3 times (2) to 2 times (3) gives

$$19x + 9z = 46 \quad (5)$$

Solving (4) and (5) by the method of page 117, gives $x = 1$, $z = 3$. Substituting these values in (1), we obtain $y = 2$. It is readily seen that $x = 1$, $y = 2$, $z = 3$ satisfy (1), (2), and (3).

EXERCISES

Solve the following sets of simultaneous equations:

1. $2x + 4y + z = 12$
$3x + y - z = 3$
$x + y + z = 7$

2. $x + y + z = 13$
$x - 2y + 4z = 10$
$3x + y - 3z = 5$

3. $x - 2y - z = 4$
$2x + y + z = 5$
$x - 3y - 2z = 6$

4. $x + 8y - 4z = 9$
$3x + 3y - z = 6$
$6x + 2y - 2z = 7$

5. $x + y + w = 15$
$x + y + z = 18$
$w + y + z = 17$
$w + x + z = 16$

6. $x + y + z = 1$
$ax + by + cz = d$
$a^2x + b^2y + c^2z = d^2$

7. Three towns A, B, C are situated at the vertices of a triangle. The distance from A to B via C is 76 miles; from A to C via B, 79 miles; from B to C via A, 81 miles. Find the distance from A to B; from B to C; from C to A.

8. John, James, and Dick have certain sums of money. If John gives James \$100, they will have the same amount; if John gives Dick \$100, Dick will have twice as much as John; if James gives Dick \$100, Dick will have four times as much as James. How much money has John? James? Dick?

9. The sides of a triangle are all tangent to a circle. The sides of the triangle are 28, 36, and 40 inches in length, respectively. Find the lengths of the segments into which the sides of the triangle are divided by the points of contact of the circle.

10. A grocer sold 6 pounds of sugar and 3 pounds of coffee for 96 cents. He also sold 2 pounds of coffee and 1 pound of tea for 80 cents, and 15 pounds of sugar, 4 pounds of coffee and 3 pounds of tea for \$2.90. Find the price of a pound of sugar, a pound of coffee, and a pound of tea.

11. The sum of the digits of a three digit number is 8. The units' digit exceeds the tens' digit by 3. If 396 is added to the number, the order of the digits is reversed. Find the number.

12. The equation $x^2 + y^2 + Ax + By + C = 0$ is satisfied by $x = 1$, $y = 2$; $x = 2$, $y = 1$; $x = 3$, $y = -1$. Find the values of A, B, and C.

13. The equation $x^2 + y^2 + Mx + Ny + P = 0$ is satisfied by $x = 2$, $y = -1$; $x = 3$, $y = 1$; $x = -1$, $y = 1$. Find the values of M, N, and P.

14. Solve for x, y, and z, $ax + y - z = a^2 + a - 1$; $-x + ay + z = a^2 - a + 1$; $x - y + az = a$.

MASTERY TEST

1. Find the change ratio of the following functions:

a) $3x + 2$
b) $2x - 7$
c) $ax + b$
d) $-px - q$

2. Find the intercepts of the lines with the following equations. Sketch the lines.

a) $2x - y = 4$
b) $3x + y = 6$
c) $-2x + y = 8$
d) $x - 7 = 0$
e) $3y - 5 = 0$
f) $\frac{2x}{3} - \frac{y}{5} = 4$

3. Solve graphically the following pairs of equations:

a) $3x - y = 2$
$2x + y = 3$

b) $3x + 2y = 8$
$x - y = 1$

c) $x - 3 = 0$
$2x - y = 0$

d) $3x - 4 = 0$
$2y + 3 = 0$

4. Solve for x and y:

$$\frac{a}{b + x} = \frac{b}{a - y}$$
$$\frac{a}{b + y} = \frac{b}{a - x}$$

5. Solve for x and y:

$$\frac{3}{4x} - \frac{2}{3y} = 4$$
$$\frac{2}{5x} - \frac{3}{y} = 1$$

6. Solve for A, B, and C:

$$2A - 3B = 21$$
$$3C + 5B = -1$$
$$8A - 5C = -16$$

7. Solve the following sets of equations for x, y, and z:

$$\frac{z - y}{x - y} = -\frac{1}{3}$$
$$\frac{2x + y}{y + x} = 3$$
$$-5\left(\frac{x - 6}{1 - 2z}\right) = 4$$

8. Find A, B, and C if $x^2 + y^2 + Ax + By + C = 0$ is satisfied by $x = 1$, $y = 2$; $x = 2$, $y = -3$; $x = -1$, $y = 2$.

9. A printed page contains 260 words of large type or 370 words of small type. In printing an article of 3670 words the printer used twelve pages. How many pages are in large type?

10. How many ounces of an alloy three-fourths gold should be mixed with an alloy five-twelfths gold in order to produce one hundred ounces two-thirds gold?

11. Smith can do a certain job in 18 days, and Jones can do the same job in 24 days. They worked together for a certain number of days, and then Jones finished the job in 10 days. How many days did Smith help Jones?

12. At what time between 4 and 5 o'clock are the hands of a watch at right angles? separated by 10 minutes?

13. In the Jones family each daughter has as many brothers as sisters, and each son has three times as many sisters as brothers. How many daughters and sons are there in the Jones family?

14. It is now between 3 and 4 o'clock, and in a quarter of an hour the minute hand will be as much ahead of the hour hand as it is now behind it. What time is it?

15. Two presses running together can print an edition of a book in 30 hours. At the end of 18 hours one press breaks down, and it takes the other press 20 hours to complete the work. How many hours would it take each press alone to print the book?

CHAPTER VI

Quadratic Equations

Quadratic equations in one variable

A quadratic function is a function of the second degree in its variables. Thus, $3x^2 - 7x + 1$ is a quadratic function in x; while $3xy$ is a quadratic function in x and y.

The general quadratic function in the variable x is $ax^2 + bx + c$ where a, b, c, are constants and $a \neq 0$. Functions of this type abound in practice. For example, from physics we know that if a baseball is thrown vertically upward with an initial velocity of 50 ft. per second from the top of a tower 100 ft. high, its distance s (in feet) from the ground at the end of t seconds is given approximately by the quadratic function

$$s = 100 + 50t - 16t^2$$

The general quadratic equation in x is

$$ax^2 + bx + c = 0, \quad a \neq 0$$

The following are examples of quadratic equations:

$$3x^2 - 7x - 1 = 0, \quad 2x^2 + 7 = 0, \quad 5x^2 - 3x = 0, \quad 7x^2 = 0$$

In this chapter we shall study methods for finding the roots of the equation $ax^2 + bx + c = 0$, $a \neq 0$, as well as properties of the quadratic function $ax^2 + bx + c$, $a \neq 0$.

EXAMPLE 1. Is $x = 2 + \sqrt{3}$ a root of $x^2 - 4x + 1 = 0$?

Solution. Substituting $x = 2 + \sqrt{3}$ gives

$$(2 + \sqrt{3})^2 - 4(2 + \sqrt{3}) + 1 \stackrel{?}{=} 0$$
$$4 + 4\sqrt{3} + 3 - 8 - 4\sqrt{3} + 1 \stackrel{?}{=} 0$$
$$0 = 0$$

$$\therefore \quad x = 2 + \sqrt{3} \text{ is a root.}$$

EXAMPLE 2. Find k so that 2 is a root of

$$3\,kx^2 + (2\,k - 1)x - 14 = 0$$

Solution. Substituting $x = 2$ gives

$$12\,k + 4\,k - 2 - 14 = 0 \text{ or } k = 1$$

What is the value of the other root?

EXAMPLE 3. Solve for x, $x^2 - 4 = 0$.

Solution. Transposing the constant gives

$$x^2 = 4$$

If we extract the square root of both members, we have

$$\pm x = \pm 2$$

Now $+x = +2$ is the same as $-x = -2$. Why?
And $-x = +2$ is the same as $x = -2$. Why?
Therefore it is not necessary to place the $\pm$ sign in front of both members, and we can say that

if $$x^2 = 4$$

then $$x = \pm 2$$

Check. $x = 2 \qquad (2)^2 = 4$
$x = -2 \qquad (-2)^2 = 4$

EXERCISES

Determine if the roots of the following equations are as stated:

1. $x^2 - 4\,x + 3 = 0;\quad 1, 3$

2. $x^2 - 6\,x = 0;\quad 0, 6$

3. $x^2 + 3\,x - 2 = 0;\quad \dfrac{3 + \sqrt{17}}{2}, \dfrac{3 - \sqrt{17}}{2}$

4. $ax^2 + bx + c = 0; \quad \dfrac{-b + \sqrt{b^2 - 4\,ac}}{2\,a}, \dfrac{-b - \sqrt{b^2 - 4\,ac}}{2\,a}$

Find k so that the number or letter beside the equation is a root:

5. $x^2 + 3\,kx - 5 = 0; \quad 2$
6. $kx^2 - 5\,x + k - 3 = 0; \quad 3$
7. $3\,x^2 + (k - 1)x + 8 - k = 0; \quad 2$
8. $(2\,k - 1)x^2 - 4\,x + 3 = 0; \quad m$
9. $kx^2 + (3\,k - 1)x - 7 = 0; \quad p$
10. $9\,x^2 + (k - 1)x + 2\,k - 3 = 0; \quad r$

Solve the following equations for x:

11. $x^2 - 9 = 0$
12. $a^2x^2 - b^2 = 0$
13. $c^2x^2 - p^2 - 2\,pq - q^2 = 0$
14. $x^2 = 0$
15. $(x - 3)^2 = 0$

The relation $A \cdot B = 0$

In solving equations the following principle is often used: If a product of two or more factors is zero, we may conclude that some one of the factors is zero. In the simplest case this means that if A and B represent algebraic expressions and if $A \cdot B = 0$, we can conclude that either $A = 0$ or $B = 0$ or $A = B = 0$. We must of course be careful to assure ourselves that each of the expressions involved represents a number for the values under consideration. Thus, for example, we cannot conclude from the relation $x \cdot \dfrac{1}{x} = 0$ that either $x = 0$ or $\dfrac{1}{x} = 0$; for when $x = 0$, $\dfrac{1}{x}$ is meaningless. In fact the given relation is impossible, for the equality is not true for any value of x.

We can apply the principle to show the absurdity of some mistakes that careless students often make. For example, a favorite error is to cancel the x's in the expression

$$\frac{a + x}{b + x}$$

This would be justifiable if the equality

$$\frac{a+x}{b+x} = \frac{a}{b}$$

were an identity. If we clear this equality of fractions by multiplying both members by $b(b + x)$, we obtain

$$ab + bx = ab + ax$$

or

$$bx = ax$$

or finally

$$(b - a)x = 0$$

Hence we conclude that either $b - a = 0$; (*i.e.*, $b = a$) or $x = 0$. Therefore the canceling operation mentioned above is unjustified except when $b = a$ or $x = 0$.

EXERCISES

Treat similarly the following equalities to determine under what conditions they are true. Each one is related to an error that careless students sometimes make.

1. Is $\sqrt{a^2 + b^2} = a + b$? (Square both sides.)

2. Is $\dfrac{a}{b} + \dfrac{c}{d} = \dfrac{a+c}{b+d}$?

3. Is $\dfrac{2a+b}{2a+c} = \dfrac{a+b}{a+c}$?

4. Is $(x + y)^2 = x^2 + y^2$?

5. If $x^2 = 4x$, are we justified in concluding that $x = 4$?

Solving by factoring

Solving an equation by factoring depends upon the fundamental principle that *if a product is equal to zero, one or more of its factors is equal to zero.* Hence we shall transpose all terms to one member, factor this member, place each factor equal to zero, and solve the resulting equations.

EXAMPLE. Solve by factoring $x^2 - 6x + 8 = 0$.

Solution. $x^2 - 6x + 8 = (x - 4)(x - 2) = 0$

whence

$$x - 4 = 0$$

or

$$x - 2 = 0$$

That is $$x = 4, \quad x = 2$$

Check. Substituting $x = 2$ in the given equation gives

$$4 - 12 + 8 = 0$$

Similarly $x = 4$ gives

$$16 - 24 + 8 = 0$$

Hence, the roots are 2 and 4.

It is obvious that there can be no roots other than 2 and 4; for if any other value is substituted, neither $x - 4$ nor $x - 2$ is 0; hence, the product $(x - 4)(x - 2)$ is not zero.

EXERCISES

Solve each of the following equations by factoring:

1. $x^2 - 7x = 0$
2. $x^2 + 2x = 15$
3. $12 + x = x^2$
4. $2x^2 + x - 6 = 0$
5. $2x^2 + 5ax + 3a^2 = 0$
6. $6x^2 = x + 2$
7. $36x^2 + 9ax = 10a^2$
8. $3x^2 - 2x = 1$
9. $2x^2 - 7x + 3 = 0$
10. $3x^2 - a^2x = 2a^4$
11. $3x^2 = 10ax - 8a^2$
12. $m^2x^2 + x^2 = m^3x + m^2$
13. $6x^2 - 11ax + 3a^2 = 0$
14. $a^2 - 9 = x^2 - 6x$
15. $3a(x - b) = 2(x - b)(x - a)$
16. $x^2 - a^2 + x - a = 0$
17. $2m(x - 1) + 3(1 - x)(x + 3) = 0$
18. $4ax^2 + 28x^2 = 7a^2 + 2a^2x$
19. $100 = 60x - 9x^2$
20. $(x - 1)^2 - 3(x - 1) - 28 = 0$

Solving by completing the square

The quantity $x^2 + 4ax + 4a^2$ is called a perfect square since it is the square of the binomial $(x + 2a)$. What must one add to the quadratic binomial $x^2 + 4ax$ in order to form a perfect square? Obviously, one must add $4a^2$, which is *the square of half the coefficient of* x. Thus, to complete $x^2 + 10x$ we add 25, which gives $x^2 + 10x + 25$; while to complete $x^2 - 7x$ we add $\frac{49}{4}$, which gives $x^2 - 7x + \frac{49}{4}$. What must one add to $x^2 - \frac{3x}{5}$ to form a perfect square?

The following examples will illustrate the method of solving a quadratic by completing the square.

Example 1. Solve $x^2 - 8x + 7 = 0$ by completing the square.

Solution.

1. Transpose the constant term.	1. $x^2 - 8x = -7$
2. Take $\frac{1}{2}$ the coefficient of x, square it and add it to both members, $(\frac{1}{2})(-8) = -4$ $(-4)^2 = 16$	2. $x^2 - 8x + 16 = 16 - 7$ $= 9$
3. Take the square root of both members.	3. $x - 4 = \pm 3$
4. Solve for x.	4. $x = 4 \pm 3$ $x = 7, 1$

The check is left as an exercise.

EXAMPLE 2. Solve $\quad 3x^2 - 5x + 1 = 0$

Solution. $\quad 3x^2 - 5x = -1$

Dividing by 3 $\quad x^2 - \frac{5}{3}x = -\frac{1}{3}$

Adding to both members $\left[\left(\frac{1}{2}\right)\left(\frac{-5}{3}\right)\right]^2$ or $\frac{25}{36}$,

$$x^2 - \frac{5}{3}x + \frac{25}{36} = \frac{25}{36} - \frac{1}{3} = \frac{13}{36}.$$

Taking the square root of both members gives

$$x - \frac{5}{6} = \pm\frac{\sqrt{13}}{6}$$

Hence $\quad x = \frac{5 \pm \sqrt{13}}{6}$

Check. Substituting in the original equation gives

$$3\left(\frac{5 \pm \sqrt{13}}{6}\right)^2 - 5\left(\frac{5 \pm \sqrt{13}}{6}\right) + 1 \stackrel{?}{=} 0$$

$$3(25 \pm 10\sqrt{13} + 13) - 30(5 \pm \sqrt{13}) + 36 \stackrel{?}{=} 0$$

$$75 \pm 30\sqrt{13} + 39 - 150 \mp 30\sqrt{13} + 36 \stackrel{?}{=} 0$$

$$0 = 0$$

Hence, the roots are

$$x = \frac{5 \pm \sqrt{13}}{6}$$

EXERCISES

Solve each of the following equations by completing the square:

1. $x^2 + 6x - 5 = 0$
2. $x^2 + 8x + 3 = 0$
3. $x^2 - 10x = 1$
4. $x^2 - 4x + 3 = 0$
5. $x^2 + 7x = 1$
6. $x^2 - 3x + 2 = 0$
7. $x^2 + 5x = 3$
8. $x^2 - 11x + 3 = 0$
9. $2x^2 + 3x = 1$
10. $3x^2 = 5x - 2$
11. $7x^2 - 2x = 1$
12. $2 = -3x - 5x^2$
13. $x^2 = q - 2px$
14. $x^2 + 2px - 4r^2 = 0$
15. $x^2 + mx + p = 0$
16. $x^2 = 3mx + 2p$
17. $2x^2 + 5mx = p$
18. $mx^2 - 3x + 2 = 0$
19. $mx^2 = -2px + 5$
20. $ax^2 + bx + c = 0$

Solution by formula

If we solve the general quadratic equation $ax^2 + bx + c = 0$, $a \neq 0$, by completing the square, we obtain a formula which we can use in solving any quadratic equation.

$$ax^2 + bx + c = 0$$

$$ax^2 + bx = -c$$

$$x^2 + \frac{b}{a}x = -\frac{c}{a}$$

$$x^2 + \frac{b}{a}x + \frac{b^2}{4a^2} = \frac{b^2}{4a^2} - \frac{c}{a} = \frac{b^2 - 4ac}{4a^2}$$

$$x + \frac{b}{2a} = \frac{\pm\sqrt{b^2 - 4ac}}{2a}$$

or

$$x = \frac{-b \pm \sqrt{b^2 - 4ac}}{2a}$$

Check.

$$a\left(\frac{-b \pm \sqrt{b^2 - 4ac}}{2a}\right)^2 + b\left(\frac{-b \pm \sqrt{b^2 - 4ac}}{2a}\right) + c \stackrel{?}{=} 0$$

$$a(b^2 \mp 2b\sqrt{b^2 - 4ac} + b^2 - 4ac) + 2ab(-b \pm \sqrt{b^2 - 4ac}) + 4a^2c \stackrel{?}{=} 0$$

$$ab^2 \mp 2ab\sqrt{b^2 - 4ac} + ab^2 - 4a^2c - 2ab^2 \pm 2ab\sqrt{b^2 - 4ac} + 4a^2c \stackrel{?}{=} 0$$

$$0 = 0$$

Hence, the roots of $ax^2 + bx + c = 0$ are

$$x = \frac{-b \pm \sqrt{b^2 - 4ac}}{2a}$$

Query. What are the values of a, b, and c in

$$3x^2 - 5x - 7 = 0? \text{ in } 2x^2 = 5x + 11?$$

EXAMPLE. Solve by the formula $3x^2 = 7x - 4$.

Solution.

Transposing the right hand terms gives $3x^2 - 7x + 4 = 0$.

Hence $a = 3,\ b = -7,\ c = 4$

Substituting in $x = \frac{-b \pm \sqrt{b^2 - 4ac}}{2a}$ gives

$$x = \frac{7 \pm \sqrt{49 - 4(3)(4)}}{6}$$

$$= \frac{7 \pm 1}{6}, \quad \text{or} \quad 1, \frac{4}{3}$$

The check is left as an exercise.

EXERCISES

Solve the following exercises by the formula:

1. $3x^2 = 7x - 2$
2. $4x^2 - 5x - 3 = 0$
3. $z^2 - 2z - 1 = 0$
4. $4m^2 - 3m - 1 = 0$
5. $x^2 - 2ax + a^2 = b^2$
6. $4x^2 - 4ax + b^2 - a^2 = 0$
7. $\frac{x}{a} + \frac{a}{x} = \frac{x}{b} + \frac{b}{x}$
8. $\frac{3}{x} - \frac{2}{x - 1} = 1$
9. $\frac{1}{x - 1} - \frac{3}{x + 1} = \frac{5}{x}$
10. $\frac{x - a}{x + a} + \frac{4ax}{x^2 - a^2} = \frac{2x - a}{x - a}$

11. $p^2x^2 + 4x = -m$
12. $(m - n)x^2 + x = a^2 + b^2$
13. $ax^2 + \frac{3x}{a} = 1$
14. $(a^2 + b^2)x^2 + 2(a^2 - b^2)x = b^2 - a^2$
15. $x^2 + bx + x^2 + a = x + 1$
16. $\frac{3a - b}{x - b} - \frac{2a}{x + b} = 1$
17. $\frac{x(x - 1)}{3} - x + 7 = \frac{x^2 + x - 2}{4}$
18. $m^2x^2 + m(m - p)x - mp = 0$
19. $kx^2 - 5x + k - 1 = 0$
20. $\frac{2a - b}{x - a} + \frac{a - b}{x + a} = 1$

Historical note on quadratic equations

In the Ahmes Papyrus, written approximately 1650 B.C. and now preserved in the British Museum, is found the first reference to the solution of a quadratic equation. The Greeks solved certain quadratic equations, but their solution was geometric and not algebraic. The first algebraic solution of the general equation $ax^2 + bx + c = 0$, $a \neq 0$, showing the roots to be $x = \frac{-b \pm \sqrt{b^2 - 4ac}}{2a}$ was given by a Hindu, Śridhara, about 1020 A.D.

Equations in quadratic form

The equation $ax^{2n} + bx^n + c = 0$, $a \neq 0$, is said to be in quadratic form and may be solved for x^n, from which we can obtain the values of x. Thus, the equation $3x - 5\sqrt{x} + 2 = 0$ is quadratic in terms of $\sqrt{x}$. In terms of what functions are the following equations quadratic?

1. $x^{\frac{1}{2}} + 3x^{\frac{1}{4}} - 2 = 0$
2. $x^2 + 5x + 3\sqrt{x^2 + 5x} - 4 = 0$
3. $x^{-4} - 5x^{-2} + 4 = 0$

EXAMPLE 1. Solve for x, $x^4 + 6x^2 = 55$.

Solution. The equation is quadratic in terms of x^2.

$$\begin{aligned} x^4 + 6x^2 - 55 &= 0 \\ (x^2 + 11)(x^2 - 5) &= 0 \\ x^2 &= -11, 5 \\ x &= \pm\sqrt{-11}, \pm\sqrt{5} \end{aligned}$$

The check is left as an exercise.

EXAMPLE 2. Solve for x, $x^2 - 3x = 6\sqrt{x^2 - 3x - 3} - 2$.

Solution. Adding -3 to both members makes the left hand member the same as the quantity under the radical sign, and the equation is then quadratic in terms of $\sqrt{x^2 - 3x - 3}$.

Hence $\qquad x^2 - 3x - 3 = 6\sqrt{x^2 - 3x - 3} - 5$

Transposing $\qquad (x^2 - 3x - 3) - 6\sqrt{x^2 - 3x - 3} + 5 = 0$

Factoring $\qquad (\sqrt{x^2 - 3x - 3} - 5)(\sqrt{x^2 - 3x - 3} - 1) = 0$

Placing each factor equal to zero gives

$$\sqrt{x^2 - 3x - 3} = 5, \quad \sqrt{x^2 - 3x - 3} = 1$$

Squaring both members gives:

$$\begin{aligned} x^2 - 3x - 3 &= 25 \\ x^2 - 3x - 28 &= 0 \\ (x - 7)(x + 4) &= 0 \\ x = 7, x &= -4 \end{aligned} \qquad \Bigg| \qquad \begin{aligned} x^2 - 3x - 3 &= 1 \\ x^2 - 3x - 4 &= 0 \\ (x - 4)(x + 1) &= 0 \\ x = 4, x &= -1 \end{aligned}$$

It is left as an exercise for the student to prove that these values satisfy the given equation.

EXERCISES

Solve:

1. $x^4 - 13x^2 + 36 = 0$

2. $x^4 - 3x^2 + 2 = 0$

3. $x - 8\sqrt{x} + 16 = 0$

4. $x = 2x^{\frac{1}{2}} + 48$

5. $x^{\frac{2}{3}} - 22x^{\frac{1}{3}} + 21 = 0$

6. $x^{\frac{2}{3}} + 3x^{\frac{1}{3}} = 40$

7. $x^{\frac{2}{5}} + x^{\frac{1}{5}} = 20$

8. $\sqrt[5]{x^2} = \sqrt[5]{x} + 72$

9. $2x^{\frac{2}{3}} - 9x^{\frac{1}{3}} + 4 = 0$

10. $x^{-2} - 2x^{-1} - 8 = 0$

11. $x^{-4} - 10x^{-2} + 9 = 0$

12. $6x^{\frac{1}{2}} - 5x^{-\frac{1}{2}} + 13 = 0$

13. $x^{\frac{2}{3}} - 5\,x^{\frac{1}{3}} + 6 = 0$

14. $x^2 + 1 + 2\sqrt{x^2 + 6\,x} = 25 - 6\,x$

15. $3\,x^2 - 16\,x - 7 + 3\sqrt{3\,x^2 - 16\,x + 21} = 0$

16. $x^2 + 8\,x + 3\sqrt{x^2 + 8\,x + 2} = 8$

17. $\dfrac{x^2}{x+1} - \dfrac{x+1}{x^2} = \dfrac{7}{12}$

18. $x^2 + 5\,x = 10 + \sqrt{x^2 + 5\,x + 2}$

Equations involving radicals

On page 78 we learned that if we square both members of an equation we may get an equation which is not equivalent to the original. For example, the only root of $x = 2$ is 2; while if we square both members we have $x^2 = 4$, which has the roots 2 and -2. The value -2 is called an *extraneous root.*

We shall consider equations containing one, two, and three radicals. The following examples will illustrate the method of solution.

EXAMPLE 1. Solve $\sqrt{x^2 - 7} + 3 = 0$.

Solution. When there is only one radical, we can remove this radical if we place the radical term in one member and all other terms in the other member and then square both members. Will the resulting equation necessarily be equivalent to the original?

Thus,
$$\sqrt{x^2 - 7} = -3$$

Squaring both members, we have
$$x^2 - 7 = 9$$
$$x^2 = 16$$
or
$$x = \pm 4$$

We know these are the only values of x which *may be* roots. We must check to determine if they are.

Check. $x = 4$ gives
$$\sqrt{16 - 7} + 3 = 0$$
$$3 + 3 = 0$$

Hence $x = 4$ is not a root.
In similar manner we see

$$x = -4 \text{ is not a root.}$$

Hence, the equation $\sqrt{x^2 - 7} + 3 = 0$ has no roots.

Query. How can you tell from the form of the original equation that there are no roots?

EXAMPLE 2. Solve $\sqrt{x} + \sqrt{2x + 1} = 1$.

Solution. If we square both members of the equation, we shall reduce it to an equation containing only one radical. This equation can then be solved as in the last example.

Squaring both members gives,

$$x + 2\sqrt{2x^2 + x} + 2x + 1 = 1$$

Is this equation necessarily equivalent to the equation given above?

Transposing $\qquad 2\sqrt{2x^2 + x} = -3x$

Squaring $\qquad 4(2x^2 + x) = 9x^2$

Note that the coefficient 2 in the expression $2\sqrt{2x^2 + x}$ is squared.

Now $\qquad 8x^2 + 4x = 9x^2$

$$x^2 - 4x = 0$$

or $\qquad x(x - 4) = 0$

$$x = 0, x = 4$$

These are the only values which may be roots, and we must check to see if they are.

Check. $x = 0$; $\sqrt{0} + \sqrt{1} = 1$

$$1 = 1$$

Hence $x = 0$ is a root.

$x = 4$; $\sqrt{4} + \sqrt{9} = 1$

$$2 + 3 = 1$$

Hence $x = 4$ is not a root.

EXAMPLE 3. Solve $\sqrt{x+1} + \sqrt{x+16} = \sqrt{x+25}$.

Solution. Squaring both members gives an equation with only one radical. Thus,

$$x + 1 + 2\sqrt{(x+1)(x+16)} + x + 16 = x + 25$$
$$2\sqrt{x^2 + 17x + 16} = -x + 8$$

Squaring both members,

$$4(x^2 + 17x + 16) = x^2 - 16x + 64$$
$$4x^2 + 68x + 64 = x^2 - 16x + 64$$
$$3x^2 + 84x = 0$$
$$x^2 + 28x = 0$$
$$x(x + 28) = 0$$
$$x = 0,\ x = -28$$

Check. $x = 0$

$\sqrt{1} + \sqrt{16} = \sqrt{25}$

$1 + 4 = 5$

$\therefore\ x = 0$ is a root.

$x = -28$.

$\sqrt{-28+1} + \sqrt{-28+16} = \sqrt{-28+25}$

$3\sqrt{-3} + 2\sqrt{-3} = \sqrt{-3}$

$\therefore\ x = -28$ is not a root.

EXERCISES

Solve each of the following equations for x:

1. $\sqrt{x-9} + 1 = \sqrt{x}$
2. $\sqrt{x-7} + \sqrt{3x+1} = 10$
3. $\sqrt{2x-1} + \sqrt{x+4} = 6$
4. $\sqrt{x+3} + \sqrt{x+8} = 5\sqrt{x}$
5. $\sqrt{x+2} + \sqrt{3-x} = 3$
6. $\sqrt{x} + \sqrt{x+7} = 7$
7. $\sqrt{x+2} - \sqrt{x+7} = -1$
8. $\sqrt{x-7} = 7 + \sqrt{x}$
9. $\sqrt{x+3} - \sqrt{4x+1} = \sqrt{2-3x}$
10. $-\sqrt{x+1} + \sqrt{4x-3} = 1$
11. $\sqrt{x-2} + \sqrt{11-x} = 3$
12. $\dfrac{-1}{\sqrt{x+1}} + \dfrac{1}{\sqrt{x-1}} = \dfrac{1}{\sqrt{x^2-1}}$
13. $\sqrt{x+4} + \sqrt{x} = 3$
14. $\sqrt{x+16} + \sqrt{x+1} - \sqrt{x+25} = 0$
15. $\sqrt{x} - \sqrt{x-3} = \dfrac{2}{\sqrt{x}}$
16. $\sqrt{3x+10} - \sqrt{5-10x} = \sqrt{7-x}$

17. $\sqrt{2x-4}+\sqrt{3x+4}=\sqrt{10x-4}$

18. $\frac{6}{\sqrt{x+3}}-\sqrt{x+3}=\sqrt{x}$

19. $\sqrt{x}-\sqrt{x-8}=\frac{2}{\sqrt{x-8}}$

20. $\sqrt{x+5}+\sqrt{x}=\sqrt{4x+9}$

21. $1-\sqrt{2x+1}=2\sqrt{x}$

22. $\sqrt{3-3x}-\sqrt{3-x}=\sqrt{4-2x}$

23. $\sqrt{3x-\frac{1}{2}}-\sqrt{6x+1}=\sqrt{x+\frac{1}{2}}$

24. $\sqrt{x^2+4x+17}=3+\sqrt{x^2+4x-16}$

25. $\sqrt{b+x}+\sqrt{a-x}=\sqrt{2a+2b}$

Nature or character of the roots

The roots of a quadratic equation are—

1. Real or imaginary.
2. Rational or irrational.
3. Equal or unequal.

We shall assume in the equation $ax^2+bx+c=0$, $a \neq 0$, that a, b, and c represent rational numbers. Since the roots of the equation are

$$\frac{-b+\sqrt{b^2-4ac}}{2a} \quad \text{and} \quad \frac{-b-\sqrt{b^2-4ac}}{2a}$$

whether they are real or imaginary depends upon whether the quantity under the radical is positive or negative. Likewise, if the quantity under the radical is a perfect square, the roots are rational; otherwise they are irrational. In order for the roots to be equal, it is obvious that the radical should vanish; otherwise the numerators of the fractions would not be the same. That is, the quantity under the radical should equal zero. Hence, we see that the character of the roots can be determined by examining the value of b^2-4ac which is called the *discriminant*. Thus:

1. If b^2-4ac is zero, each root becomes $\frac{-b}{2a}$ and hence the roots are real, equal, and rational.

2. If $b^2 - 4ac$ is negative, $\sqrt{b^2 - 4ac}$ is imaginary, and hence the roots are unequal and imaginary.
3. If $b^2 - 4ac$ is positive and a perfect square, $\sqrt{b^2 - 4ac}$ is rational and hence the roots are real, unequal, and rational.
4. If $b^2 - 4ac$ is positive but not a perfect square, $\sqrt{b^2 - 4ac}$ is real but irrational, hence the roots are real, unequal, and irrational.

EXAMPLE. Without solving, find the nature of the roots of the following equations:

a) $x^2 - 8x + 7 = 0$
b) $16x^2 - 8x + 1 = 0$
c) $3x^2 - 2x + 11 = 0$
d) $3x^2 - 2x - 11 = 0$

Solution. a) $b^2 - 4ac = 64 - 4(1)(7) = 36$

The roots are real, rational, and unequal.

b) $b^2 - 4ac = 64 - 4(16)(1) = 0$

The roots are real, equal, and rational.

c) $b^2 - 4ac = 4 - 4(3)(11) = -128$

The roots are imaginary and unequal.

d) $b^2 - 4ac = 4 - 4(3)(-11) = 136$

The roots are real, unequal, and irrational.

EXAMPLE 2. Given $(3k + 1)x^2 + (11 + k)x + 9 = 0$. Find the values of k for which:

a) The roots are equal.
b) The roots are real and unequal.
c) The roots are imaginary.

Solution. a) For equal roots, $b^2 - 4ac = 0$.

$$\therefore \quad (11 + k)^2 - 4(3k + 1)\,9 = 0$$

or $$k^2 - 86k + 85 = 0$$
$$(k - 85)(k - 1) = 0$$
$$\therefore \quad k = 85 \text{ and } 1$$

b) For real and unequal roots $b^2 - 4ac > 0$.
$$(k - 85)(k - 1) > 0$$

Hence $$k > 85 \text{ and } k < 1$$

c) For imaginary roots $b^2 - 4ac < 0$.
$$(k - 85)(k - 1) < 0$$

Hence $$1 < k < 85$$

EXERCISES

Without solving, find the nature of the roots of the following equations:

1. $3x^2 - 7x + 1 = 0$
2. $2x^2 + 8x + 11 = 0$
3. $4x^2 - 4x + 1 = 0$
4. $25x^2 - 30x + 9 = 0$
5. $3x^2 - 2 = 0$
6. $14x^2 = 3x + 11$
7. $2x^2 + 8x + 15 = 0$
8. $3x^2 = 7x + 11$
9. $x^2 + x + 1 = 0$
10. $x^2 - x = 0$

For what values of k are the roots of the following equations equal? real and unequal? imaginary?

11. $x^2 - kx + 9 = 0$
12. $kx^2 - 12x + 9 = 0$
13. $3x^2 + 2kx - 2k = 0$
14. $(3k + 1)x^2 + 2(k + 1)x + k = 0$
15. $(k - 1)x^2 - kx = -1$
16. $x^2 + 2(k + 1)x + k^2 = 0$
17. $2kx^2 + (5k + 2)x + 4k + 1 = 0$
18. $(k - 3)x^2 = (k - 6)x + 4$
19. $(2k - 1)x^2 + (1 - 3k)x + (2 - k) = 0$
20. $3kx^2 = 2kx - 2x^2 + 1$

Relations between roots and coefficients

Let r_1 and r_2 stand for the roots of $ax^2 + bx + c = 0, a \neq 0$. Thus,

$$r_1 = \frac{-b + \sqrt{b^2 - 4ac}}{2a}, \qquad r_2 = \frac{-b - \sqrt{b^2 - 4ac}}{2a}$$

Now $r_1 + r_2 = \dfrac{-b + \sqrt{b^2 - 4\,ac}}{2\,a} + \dfrac{-b - \sqrt{b^2 - 4\,ac}}{2\,a} = -\dfrac{b}{a}$

$$r_1 r_2 = \frac{(-b + \sqrt{b^2 - 4\,ac})(-b - \sqrt{b^2 - 4\,ac})}{4\,a^2}$$

$$= \frac{b^2 - (b^2 - 4\,ac)}{4\,a^2} = \frac{c}{a}$$

If we divide both members of the equation $ax^2 + bx + c = 0$, $a \neq 0$, by a, it takes the form

$$x^2 + \frac{b}{a}x + \frac{c}{a} = 0$$

We now see that in a quadratic equation in which the coefficient of x^2 is unity and all terms are in the same member, *the sum of the roots is the coefficient of x with its sign changed; whereas the product of the roots is the constant term.*

EXAMPLE 1. Given $3\,x^2 - 7\,x + 2 = 0$. Without solving find the sum and the product of the roots.

Solution. $3\,x^2 - 7\,x + 2 = 0$.

Sum of the roots is $-\dfrac{b}{a} = \dfrac{7}{3}$.

Product of the roots is $\dfrac{c}{a} = \dfrac{2}{3}$.

EXAMPLE 2. Form the equation whose roots are

$$\frac{3 + \sqrt{7}}{4}, \quad \frac{3 - \sqrt{7}}{4}$$

Solution. Sum of roots is $\dfrac{3 + \sqrt{7}}{4} + \dfrac{3 - \sqrt{7}}{4} = \dfrac{6}{4} = \dfrac{3}{2}$.

Product of roots is $\dfrac{(3 + \sqrt{7})(3 - \sqrt{7})}{4 \times 4} = \dfrac{9 - 7}{16} = \dfrac{1}{8}$.

Hence the equation is

$$x^2 - \tfrac{3}{2}\,x + \tfrac{1}{8} = 0 \qquad \text{or} \qquad 8\,x^2 - 12\,x + 1 = 0$$

EXAMPLE 3. Find k so that one root of $2x^2 - 16x + k = 0$ is twice the other root.

Solution. If one root is p, the other root is $2p$. Sum of roots is $-\frac{b}{a} = 8 = 3p$.

$$\therefore \quad p = \tfrac{8}{3}$$

Product of roots is $\frac{c}{a} = \frac{k}{2} = 2p^2$,

and $$k = 4p^2 = 4(\tfrac{8}{3})^2 = \tfrac{256}{9}$$

EXERCISES

Without solving, find the sum and product of the roots of each of the following equations:

1. $2x^2 - 3x + 5 = 0$
2. $7x^2 = 2x + 1$
3. $4x^2 = 6x - 1$
4. $x^2 - 7 = 0$
5. $2x^2 = 3x - 5$
6. $9x^2 = 8x - 1$
7. $2kx^2 - (7 + k)x + 1 = 0$
8. $(3k - 1)x^2 - mx + (a - b) = 0$
9. $2kx^2 = 3bx - c$
10. $\frac{k}{x} = \frac{x}{k} + 1$

Form the equations with the following roots:

11. $2, 3$
12. $-4, 7$
13. $1 + \sqrt{3}, 1 - \sqrt{3}$
14. $2 + \sqrt{3}, 2 - \sqrt{3}$
15. $\sqrt{a}, -\sqrt{a}$
16. $\frac{2 + \sqrt{3}}{5}, \frac{2 - \sqrt{3}}{5}$
17. $\frac{3 - \sqrt{2}}{2}, \frac{3 + \sqrt{2}}{2}$
18. $\frac{a + \sqrt{b}}{2}, \frac{a - \sqrt{b}}{2}$
19. $\frac{3 + \sqrt{2}}{3}, \frac{3 - \sqrt{2}}{3}$
20. $\frac{1 + \sqrt{-3}}{2}, \frac{1 - \sqrt{-3}}{2}$

21. Given the equation $(k - 2)x^2 + (k - 5)x - 5 = 0$. Find k so that:

a) One root is 2.
b) The sum of the roots is 3.
c) The product of the roots is -4.
d) The roots are equal.
e) The roots are numerically equal but opposite in sign.

22. Given the equation $(k - 1)x^2 = kx - 1$. Find k so that:
a) One root is -3.
b) The sum of the roots is 2.
c) The product of the roots is -3.
d) The roots are equal.
e) The roots are numerically equal but opposite in sign.

23. Prove that the roots of $x^2 + mx + m^2 = 0$ are imaginary for any real value of m.

24. Prove that the roots $ax^2 + bx + a = 0$ are reciprocals of each other.

25. Prove that the roots of $ax^2 + bx + c = 0$ are reciprocals of the roots of $cx^2 + bx + a = 0$.

26. If R and r are the roots of $ax^2 + bx + c = 0$, find in terms of a, b, and c the value of:

a) $\frac{1}{r} + \frac{1}{R}$ c) $\frac{1}{r^2} + \frac{1}{R^2}$ e) $\frac{1}{r^3} + \frac{1}{R^3}$

b) $r^2 + R^2$ d) $r^3 + R^3$ f) $\frac{(R + r)^2}{R^2 + r^2}$

27. Find k so that the difference between the roots of $x^2 - 4x + k = 0$ is 2.

28. Find k so that one root of $2kx^2 - 20x + 21 = 0$ exceeds the other by 2.

29. Find the equation whose roots are twice the roots of $3x^2 - 5x + 1 = 0$.

30. Find the equation whose roots are n times the roots of $x^2 + px + q = 0$.

31. Find the relation between p and q if one root of $x^2 + px + q = 0$ is 37 times the other root.

32. Find the relation among the letters, a, b, c, n, if one root of $ax^2 + bx + c = 0$ is n times the other root.

33. Find the equation whose roots are larger by 2 than the roots of $x^2 - 3x + 2 = 0$.

34. If the constant term in a quadratic equation is zero, prove that one root is zero.

Graph of the quadratic function $ax^2 + bx + c$ $(a \neq 0)$

On page 96 we drew the graph of certain quadratic functions. We shall presently show that the graph of $y = ax^2 + bx + c$, $a > 0$, is concave upward; whereas when $a < 0$, it is concave downward. (See Fig. 23.) The curve in either case is called a *parabola*. The real roots of the equation $ax^2 + bx + c = 0$, $a \neq 0$, are given by the abscissas of the points the curve has in common with the x axis. Why? If the curve is tangent to the x axis (*i.e.*, touches the x axis) the roots are real and equal; while if the curve has no points in common with the x axis,

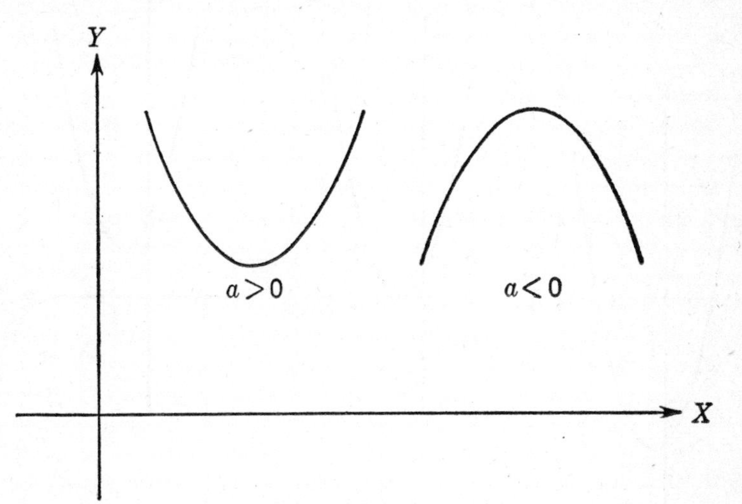

FIGURE 23

the roots of the given equation are imaginary. These three cases are illustrated in Fig. 24, where are plotted respectively the functions $x^2 - x - 6$, $x^2 - 2x + 1$, $x^2 - 2x + 3$.

It is easy to verify that $y = ax^2 + bx + c$ can be written in the form

$$y = a\left[\left(x + \frac{b}{2a}\right)^2 + \frac{4ac - b^2}{4a^2}\right]$$

If $a > 0$, what value of x gives the smallest or minimum value of y? We see this value is $x = -\frac{b}{2a}$ and that the minimum value of the function is $\frac{4ac - b^2}{4a}$. If $a < 0$, it is evident that y has its maximum value when $\left(x + \frac{b}{2a}\right)^2$ has its minimum value. This occurs when $x = -\frac{b}{2a}\cdot$ Hence the maximum value of the function is $\frac{4ac - b^2}{4a}$, which occurs when $x = -\frac{b}{2a}\cdot$

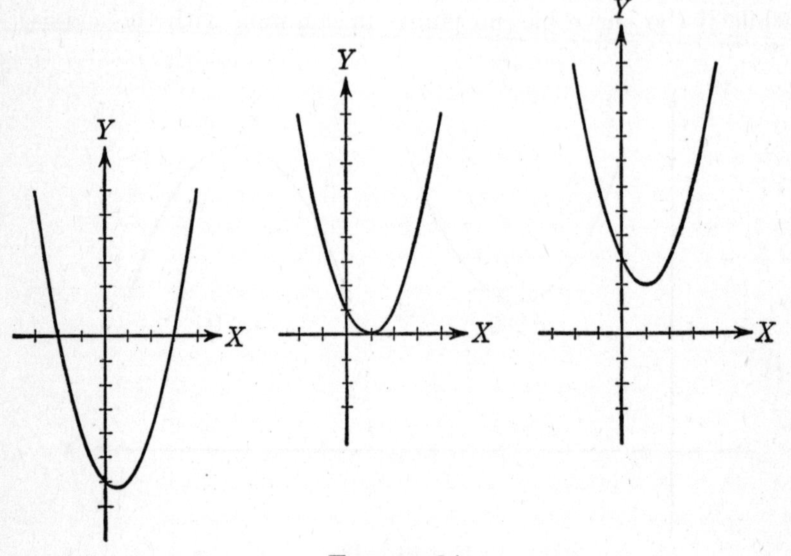

FIGURE 24

EXAMPLE. Find the minimum value of the function $2x^2 - 8x + 3$. Draw the graph.

Solution. When $x = -\frac{b}{2a} = \frac{8}{4} = 2$, the function has its minimum value, namely, $2(2)^2 - 8(2) + 3$ or -5. Therefore the minimum point on the curve is $(2, -5)$. Assigning values to x and computing the corresponding value of the function, we construct the table

x	-1	0	1	2	3	4	5
function	13	3	-3	-5	-3	3	13

Plotting these points gives the graph in Fig. 25.

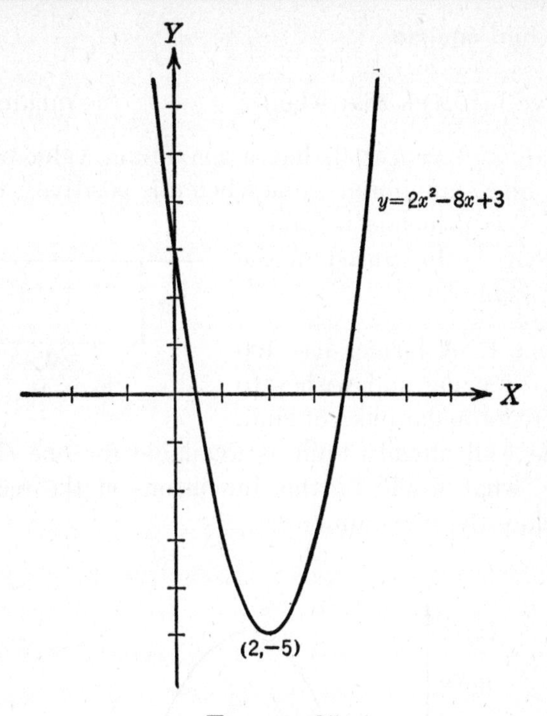

FIGURE 25

EXERCISES

Construct the graphs of the functions in the following equations. In each example determine the curve's maximum or minimum point (as the case may be) as well as the real roots of the equation.

1. $x^2 + 2x - 3 = 0$ from $x = -4$ to $x = 2$
2. $x^2 - 2x - 3 = 0$ from $x = -2$ to $x = 4$
3. $x^2 + x - 6 = 0$ from $x = -4$ to $x = 3$
4. $x^2 - 6x + 9 = 0$ from $x = 0$ to $x = 6$
5. $6 - x - x^2 = 0$ from $x = -4$ to $x = 3$
6. $4 - 5x - x^2 = 0$ from $x = -6$ to $x = 2$
7. $5 - 2x - x^2 = 0$ from $x = -3$ to $x = 2$
8. $4 - 4x + x^2 = 0$ from $x = 0$ to $x = 4$
9. $10 - 4x - x = 0$ from $x = -4$ to $x = 2$

Maxima and minima

We have just seen that when $x = -\frac{b}{2a}$ the quadratic function $ax^2 + bx + c$, $a \neq 0$, has a maximum value when a is negative, and a minimum value when a is positive. The application of this principle to practical problems is illustrated in the following examples.

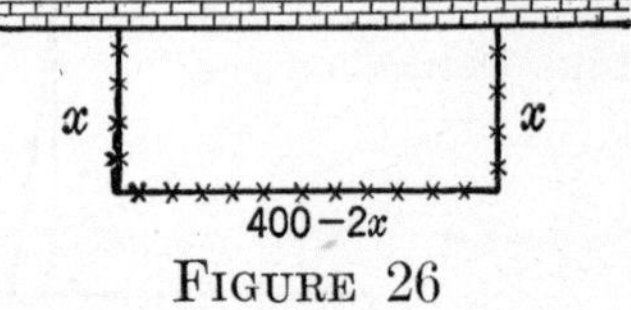

FIGURE 26

EXAMPLE 1. A farmer has 400 ft. of wire fencing and wishes to enclose a rectangular piece of land. If a stone wall already built is available for one side of the rectangle, what would be the dimensions of the rectangle so as to enclose the maximum area?

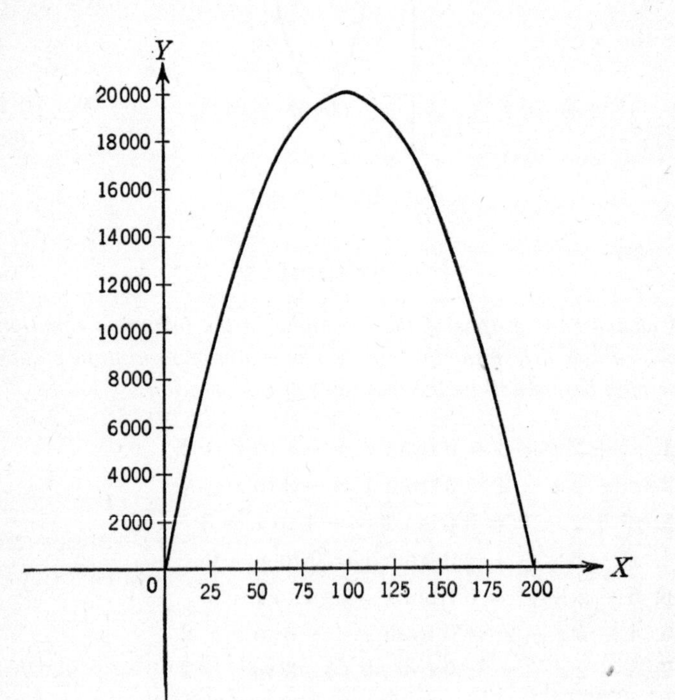

FIGURE 27

Solution. Suppose the rectangle is of width x (Fig. 26). Its length then is $400 - 2x$. If we call the area y, then

$$y = x(400 - 2x)$$

or

$$y = -2x^2 + 400x$$

If we plot this function, we have the curve in Fig. 27. We wish to find the value of x corresponding to the greatest value of y. This value is

$$x = -\frac{b}{2a} = -\frac{400}{-4} = 100$$

$\therefore$ The width is $x = 100$ ft. The length is

$$400 - 2x = 200 \text{ ft.}$$

Corresponding to $x = 100$, $y = 20{,}000$. The maximum area of 20,000 sq. ft. is therefore obtained when the width is 100 ft. and the length is 200 ft.

EXAMPLE 2. Three streets intersect so as to enclose a triangular lot ABC. The frontage on BC is 180 ft., and point A

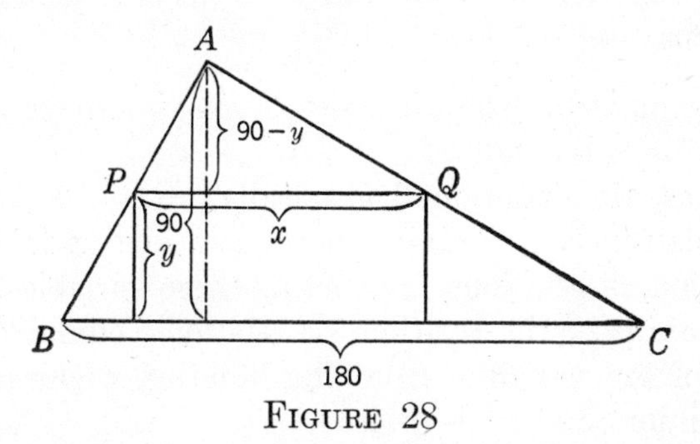

FIGURE 28

is 90 ft. back of BC. What are the dimensions of the ground plan of a rectangular building having the maximum floor area and facing BC?

Solution. Let x and y (Fig. 28) be the dimensions of the floor plan. Neglecting the thickness of the walls, the area A is

$$A = xy \tag{1}$$

In order to find the maximum value of A, we must express A as a function of either x or y. To do this we must find a relation between x and y and then eliminate one of the variables in (1). Triangles ABC and APQ are similar; hence,

$$\frac{x}{180} = \frac{90 - y}{90}$$

Whence $$y = -\tfrac{1}{2}x + 90 \qquad (2)$$

Substituting in (1) gives

$$A = 90x - \tfrac{1}{2}x^2$$

The floor area A is now expressed as a function of the side x. The value $x = -\dfrac{b}{2a} = \dfrac{-90}{-1} = 90$ gives the largest value of A, namely, $A = 4050$. The value of y is found from (2) to be 45. That is, the maximum floor area is 4050 sq. ft. and is obtained by erecting a building 90 ft. long and 45 ft. deep.

To solve a maximum or minimum problem which involves a quadratic function it is necessary to keep in mind the following steps.

1. Determine for what function a maximum or minimum value is to be found.
2. Express this function algebraically.
3. If this function contains more than one variable, find a relation, or relations, connecting these variables.
4. By means of the relation, or relations, eliminate all but one of the variables from the function whose maximum or minimum value is desired.
5. Proceed with the algebraic computation.

EXERCISES

1. Separate 40 into two parts such that the product of these parts shall be a maximum.

2. Find the rectangle of maximum area whose perimeter is 100 ft.

3. Separate 40 into two parts such that the sum of the squares of these parts is a minimum.

4. If a farmer digs his potatoes today, he will have 100 bushels, worth $2 a bushel. Every week he waits the crop increases 10 bushels and the price drops 10¢ a bu. When should he dig?

5. The base of a triangle is $2b$, and its altitude is $2a$. What are the dimensions of the greatest rectangle that can be inscribed with one side along the base?

6. Find the area of the largest rectangle with perimeter $2p$.

7. Divide 10 into two parts such that the sum of the double of one and square of the other is a minimum.

8. The perimeter of a rectangle is 64 ft. Find the dimensions so that the area will be a maximum.

MASTERY TEST

1. Find k so that $2 + \sqrt{3}$ is a root of $x^2 - 4x + k = 0$.

2. Is $\dfrac{3 + \sqrt{7}}{2}$ a root of $x^2 + 3x = 2$?

3. Solve by factoring: $6x^2 + x = 35$

4. Solve by completing the square: $7x^2 = 3x - 5$

5. Solve for x by the formula: $3a^2x^2 - 4ax = 1$

6. Solve for x by any method:

a) $7x^2 = 3x$

b) $mx^2 - 2px = q$

c) $4x^2 = 8x - 1$

7. Solve for x: $6x + 5\sqrt{x} - 4 = 0$

8. Solve for x: $8 + x + 15x^{-1} = 0$

9. Solve for x: $\left(x + \dfrac{1}{x}\right)^2 = 3\left(x + \dfrac{1}{x}\right) - 2$

10. Solve for x: $x^2 - 5x - 4\sqrt{x^2 - 5x + 5} = -8$

11. Solve for x: $\sqrt{3x + 2} - \sqrt{x - 2} = \sqrt{x + 6}$

12. Without solving, find the nature of the roots of:

a) $7x^2 = 2x - 1$

b) $16x^2 - 8x + 1 = 0$

c) $3x^2 = -2x + 7$

13. Find k so that the roots of

$$(7k + 2)x^2 - (3k + 3)x + 1 = 0$$

are equal.

14. Find k so that the roots of

$$(6k + 3)x^2 - 6x + (2k - 1) = 0$$

are imaginary; real and unequal.

15. Solve for x:

$$\frac{3x-1}{x^2-3x+2} - \frac{2x-1}{x-1} = \frac{3}{2(x-2)}$$

16. Given the equation $3x^2 - 7x + 5 = 0$; without solving, find:

a) The sum of the squares of the roots.

b) The square of the sum of the roots.

17. Find k so that one root of $3kx^2 - 2x + 5 = 0$ exceeds the other by $\frac{8}{3}$.

18. Find the relation between p and q if one root of $3px^2 + 2qx + 7 = 0$ is five times the other.

19. Sketch the graph of $y = x^2 - 8x + 1$. What are the coordinates of the minimum point?

20. Solve graphically the equations:

a) $x^2 + x - 6 = 0$

b) $5x - 3 = 2x^2$

21. Find to the nearest hundredth the roots of $3x^2 - 7x - 1 = 0$.

22. Solve for x: $2\sqrt{x+7} - \sqrt{x+2} = \sqrt{7x+2}$

23. Find to the nearest tenth the roots of $\frac{2}{x} + \frac{3}{4} = x$.

24. Divide $ax^2 + bx + c$ by $x - r$ and prove that the remainder is $ar^2 + br + c$.

25. Assuming the result of exercise 24, find the remainder when $7x^2 - 3x - 8$ is divided by $x - 2$.

26. If r_1 and r_2 are the roots of $ax^2 + bx + c = 0$, prove that $ax^2 + bx + c = a(x - r_1)(x - r_2)$.

27. Form the equation whose roots are three less than the roots of $x^2 - 8x - 1 = 0$.

28. Form the equation whose roots are two more than the roots of $x^2 - 6x + 2 = 0$.

29. Given the equation $ax^2 + bx + c = 0$, $a \neq 0$, find:

a) The difference of the squares of the roots.

b) The square of the difference of the roots.

30. A ball is thrown vertically upward with an initial velocity of 64 ft. a second from the top of a building 80 ft. high. Its distance s (in ft.) above the ground at the end of t seconds is given approximately by the formula $s = 80 + 64t - 16t^2$.

a) At what time does the ball reach its greatest height?

b) How high does the ball go?

c) How long is the ball in the air?

31. Form the equation whose roots are twice the roots of

$$\frac{2}{x-1} - \frac{1}{x} = 1$$

32. Form the equation whose roots are

$$\frac{2+\sqrt{-7}}{3}, \frac{2-\sqrt{-7}}{3}$$

33. Given that the equation $ax^2 + bx + c = 0$, $a \neq 0$, has real coefficients. Prove that if one root is imaginary the second root is also imaginary.

34. Find the equation whose roots are k greater than the roots of $x^2 + px + q = 0$.

35. Given the equation $(3p + 1)x^2 + (2p + 2)x + p = 0$. Find p so that:

a) One root is 2.
b) One root is 0.
c) The roots are numerically equal but opposite in sign.
d) The sum of the roots is 4.
e) The product of the roots is -3.
f) One root is twice the other.

36. If a ball is thrown vertically upward, its height s in feet at the end of t seconds is given approximately by the formula

$$s = -\tfrac{1}{2}gt^2 + v_0t$$

where $g = 32$ and v_0 is the initial velocity.

If the ball is tossed with an initial velocity of 80 ft. a second,

a) How high will it go in 3 seconds?
b) When will it reach its greatest height?
c) What is its greatest height?
d) When will it be 96 ft. above the ground?

37. If the radii of two concentric circles are R and r, the area A between the circles is given by the formula $A = \pi(R^2 - r^2)$.

a) Find the area between two concentric circles of radii 80 ft. and 83 ft. respectively.
b) If the area between two concentric circles is 44π sq. ft., and the diameter of the larger circle is 24 ft., what is the diameter of the smaller circle?

38. Engineers use the formula

$$H = \frac{62.56\,Ch}{33{,}000}$$

for computing the horse power of a stream passing over a dam, where h = height of the dam in feet and C = number of cubic feet of water flowing over the dam in one minute.

a) Find the horse power of a stream flowing 7000 cu. ft. per minute over a dam 25 ft. high.

b) Find the stream flow that produces 4000 horse power over a dam 30 ft. high.

39. If a retaining wall rectangular in shape, is h ft. high and t ft. thick, and built to retain loam, the quantities h and t are connected by the relation $t^2 + .14\,th = .13\,h^2$.

Find the thickness of a wall 5 ft. high.

40. From physics comes the formula $v^2 = \frac{g}{l}(s^2 - s_1^2)$.

a) Find v in terms of the other letters.

b) Find s in terms of the other letters.

c) Find s_1 if $v = 8$, $l = 2$, $g = 32$, $s = 10$.

41. From physics comes the formula $\frac{1}{T} = \frac{1 + c(n - n')^2}{b(n - n')}$. Find the value of $n - n'$ in terms of the other letters.

42. If E is the effective area of a chimney, then $E = A - 0.6\sqrt{A}$, where A is the actual area.

a) Find E when $A = 64$.

b) Find A when $E = 18$.

c) Find A in terms of E.

43. From physics comes the formula $s = v_0t + \frac{1}{2}gt^2$. Find t when $v_0 = 50$, $g = 32$, $s = 1000$.

44. If the number of vibrations of a pendulum of length l is n, then $n = \frac{k}{\sqrt{l}}$ when k is a constant.

a) Find l if $n = 4$, $k^2 = 39.1$.

b) Find l in terms of n and k.

CHAPTER VII

Systems of Quadratic Equations

The graph of a quadratic equation in two variables

Any quadratic equation in terms of x and y which is satisfied by pairs of real values of the variables can be graphed. To construct the graph we can proceed as follows:

1. Solve the equation for one variable in terms of the other.
2. If the equation is solved for y, assign values to x and compute the corresponding values of y. If the equation is solved for x, assign values to y and compute the corresponding values of x.
3. Plot the points corresponding to the values of x and y just found and draw a smooth curve through them.

EXAMPLE 1. Plot $x^2 - xy = 4$.

Solution. Solving the equation for y gives

$$y = \frac{x^2 - 4}{x}$$

Assigning values to x and computing the corresponding values for y gives

x	-5	-4	-3	-2	-1	0	1	2	3	4	5
y	$-4\frac{1}{5}$	-3	$-\frac{5}{3}$	0	3	No value	-3	0	$\frac{5}{3}$	3	$4\frac{1}{5}$

It should be noted that as x approaches zero negatively, y is positive and increases without limit. Thus, if $x = -.1$,

$y = 39.9$; $x = -.01$, $y = 399.99$; etc. On the other hand, if x approaches zero positively, y is negative and increases in

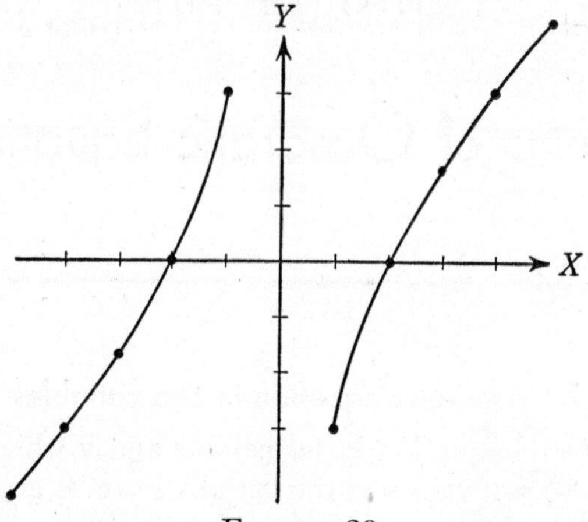

FIGURE 29

absolute value without limit. Thus, if $x = .1$, $y = -39.9$; $x = .01$, $y = -399.99$; etc. The curve is said to be discontinuous at $x = 0$.

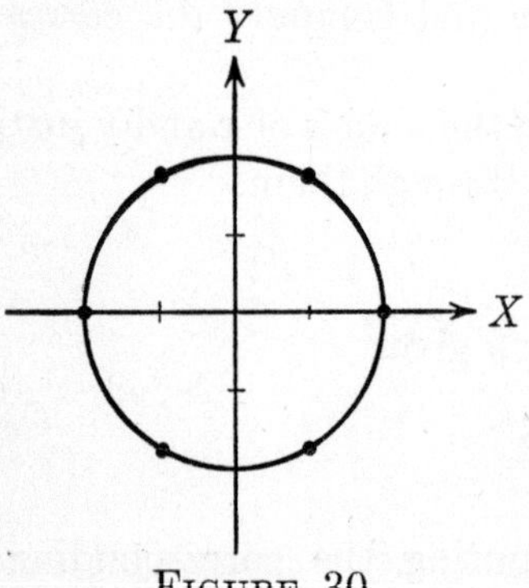

FIGURE 30

Plotting these points and drawing a smooth curve through them gives the curve in Fig. 29.

EXAMPLE 2. Sketch $x^2 + y^2 = 4$.

Solution. Solving for y gives $y = \pm\sqrt{4 - x^2}$.

What is the largest value x can have? the smallest? Assigning values to x and computing the corresponding values for y gives

x	-2	-1	0	1	2
y	0	$\pm\sqrt{3}$	± 2	$\pm\sqrt{3}$	0

Plotting these points and drawing a smooth curve through them gives the curve in Fig. 30.

EXAMPLE 3. Sketch $x^2 - y^2 = 4$.

Solution. Solving for x gives $x = \pm\sqrt{4 + y^2}$.

Are there any values of y which must be excluded? Assigning values to y and computing the corresponding values of x gives

y	-4	-3	-2	-1	0	1	2	3	4
x	$\pm\sqrt{20}$	$\pm\sqrt{13}$	$\pm\sqrt{8}$	$\pm\sqrt{5}$	± 2	$\pm\sqrt{5}$	$\pm\sqrt{8}$	$\pm\sqrt{13}$	$\pm\sqrt{20}$

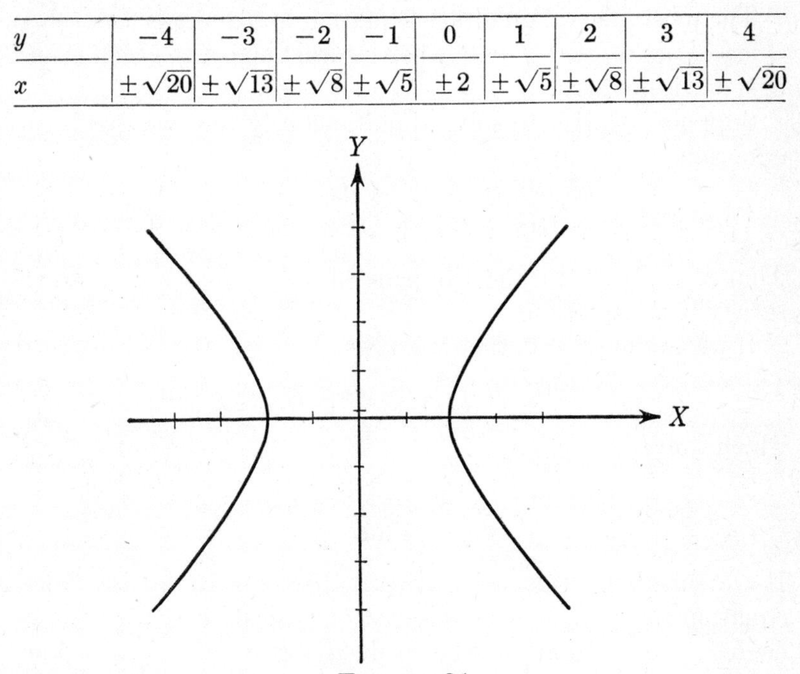

FIGURE 31

Plotting these points and drawing a smooth curve through them gives the curve in Fig. 31.

EXERCISES

Sketch:

1. $x^2 + y^2 = 16$
2. $x^2 + y^2 = 9$
3. $y = x^2$
4. $y = x^2 - 2x + 3$
5. $x^2 + 4y^2 = 16$
6. $4x^2 + y^2 = 16$
7. $x^2 - y^2 = 1$
8. $x^2 - y^2 = 4$
9. $xy = 4$
10. $xy = 2$
11. $xy = -4$
12. $xy = -2$
13. $y = -x^2 + 4x + 3$
14. $y = -2x^2 - x + 7$

15. $y = 4x^2 + 9y - 36$
16. $y^2 - x^2 = 4$
17. $4x^2 - y^2 = 4$
18. $xy + y = 4$
19. $xy - x = 4$
20. $x^2 + xy = 4$

Algebraic solution of systems of quadratic equations

The most general quadratic equation in x and y is $ax^2 + bxy + cy^2 + dx + ey + f = 0$, where at least one of the coefficients a, b, or c is not zero.

Suppose we wish to solve simultaneously the two quadratic equations

$$ax^2 + bxy + cy^2 + dx + ey + f = 0 \quad (1)$$
$$Ax^2 + Bxy + Cy^2 + Dx + Ey + F = 0 \quad (2)$$

That is, we wish to find the pairs of values of x and y which satisfy both equations.

If we assume $c \neq 0$, then we have

$$cy^2 + (bx + e)y + (ax^2 + dx + f) = 0$$

which, solved for y, gives

$$y = \frac{-(bx + e) \pm \sqrt{(bx + e)^2 - 4c(ax^2 + dx + f)}}{2c}$$

If we substitute this value in (2), there results an irrational equation in x which when cleared of radicals is of the fourth degree. This equation when solved for x gives four values (See page 285). In like manner if we should eliminate y we would find four values for x. If we group the four values of x and the four values of y in pairs, we shall have sixteen pairs but not all of these pairs of values will satisfy both (1) and (2). By substitution we can show that but four pairs of values satisfy the given equations.

Inasmuch as we are unable at present to solve a fourth degree equation, we shall confine ourselves to the solution of certain special cases which involve only quadratic equations.

Case 1. One linear and one quadratic equation.

EXAMPLE. Solve:

$$x^2 - y^2 = 7 \quad (1)$$
$$3x - 2y = 6 \quad (2)$$

Solution. If we solve the linear equation for one variable in terms of the other and then substitute this value in the second degree equation, we shall have a quadratic equation in one variable. The values found from this quadratic equation can then be substituted in the *linear* equation to find the corresponding values of the other variable.

Solving $3x - 2y = 6$ for x, gives $x = \frac{6 + 2y}{3}$.

Substituting this value in (1) gives

$$\left(\frac{6 + 2y}{3}\right)^2 - y^2 = 7$$

or
$$5y^2 - 24y + 27 = 0$$

Hence
$$(5y - 9)(y - 3) = 0$$

or
$$y = \tfrac{9}{5},\ y = 3$$

If $y = 3$, then from (2) $x = 4$; if $y = \frac{9}{5}$ then from (2) $x = \frac{16}{5}$. These results must be correctly paired and for a check substituted in both of the given equations. Thus

$$\begin{cases} x = 4 \\ y = 3 \end{cases} \qquad \begin{cases} x = \frac{16}{5} \\ y = \frac{9}{5} \end{cases}$$

Check. $x = 4,\ y = 3$ $\qquad$ $x = \frac{16}{5},\ y = \frac{9}{5}$

In (1) $4^2 - 3^2 = 7$
$16 - 9 = 7$
$7 = 7$

In (1) $(\frac{16}{5})^2 - (\frac{9}{5})^2 = 7$
$\frac{256}{25} - \frac{81}{25} = 7$
$\frac{175}{25} = 7$
$7 = 7$

In (2) $12 - 6 = 6$
$6 = 6$

In (2) $\frac{48}{5} - \frac{18}{5} = 6$
$\frac{30}{5} = 6$
$6 = 6$

Let us interpret these solutions geometrically (Fig. 32, page 162). Since any point whose co-ordinates satisfy an equation lies on its graph, it follows that the solutions of the two equations are the co-ordinates of the points of intersection of the graphs. Hence the points (4, 3) and $(\frac{16}{5}, \frac{9}{5})$ are the points of intersection of the curve $x^2 - y^2 = 7$ (called a hyperbola) and the line $3x - 2y = 6$.

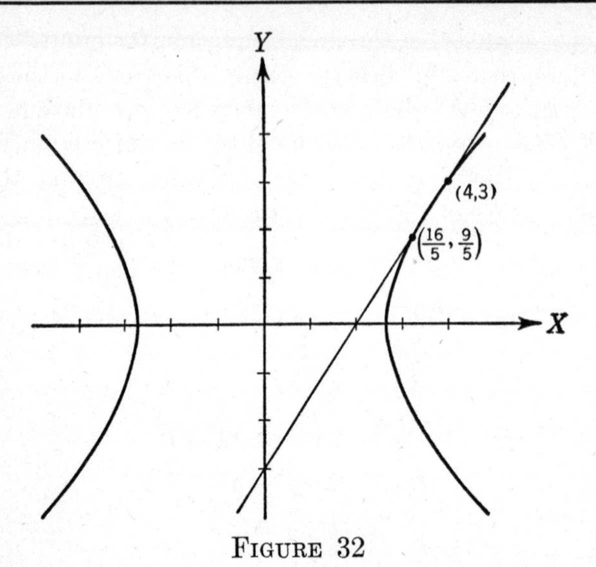

FIGURE 32

Query. Can you now tell why after finding the values of y we substitute in the linear equation to find the corresponding values of x and not in the quadratic equation?

EXERCISES

Solve the following sets of equations:

1. $x^2 + y^2 = 13$
$y + 3 = 3x$

2. $x - 2y^2 = 0$
$y + 5 = 3x$

3. $3x^2 - y^2 = 47$
$3x - y = 11$

4. $xy = 4$
$x + y = 5$

5. $x^2 + y^2 = 40$
$y = x + 4$

6. $x^2 + y^2 + xy = 7$
$x - y = 1$

7. $9x^2 + 4y^2 = 36$
$3x + 2y = 6$

8. $16x^2 + 9y^2 = 25$
$4x + 3y = 7$

9. $16x^2 - 26y^2 = 400$
$4x = 20 + 5y$

10. $\frac{1}{x} + \frac{1}{y} = 3$
$y + x = 1.5$

11. $x^2 + y^2 = 2a^2 + 2b^2$
$x + y = 2a$

12. $x^2 + 2y^2 = 5 + y$
$2x = 7 - 3y$

Case 2. Both equations are of the form $ax^2 + by^2 = c$. The following example will illustrate the method of solution.

EXAMPLE. Solve:

$$5x^2 - y^2 = 8 \quad (1)$$
$$2x^2 + y^2 = 6 \quad (2)$$

Equations of this form can be solved like two linear simultaneous equations.

Solution. Adding (1) and (2)

$$7x^2 = 14$$
$$x^2 = 2$$
$$x = \pm\sqrt{2}$$

Substituting in (2) gives $y = \pm\sqrt{2}$. Therefore the solutions are

$$\begin{cases} x = \sqrt{2} \\ y = \sqrt{2} \end{cases} \quad \begin{cases} x = \sqrt{2} \\ y = -\sqrt{2} \end{cases} \quad \begin{cases} x = -\sqrt{2} \\ y = \sqrt{2} \end{cases} \quad \begin{cases} x = -\sqrt{2} \\ y = -\sqrt{2} \end{cases}$$

The check is left as an exercise for the student.

EXERCISES

Solve the following sets of equations:

1. $x^2 + y^2 = 15$
   $x^2 - y^2 = 3$
2. $x^2 + y^2 = 16$
   $16x^2 + 9y^2 = 144$
3. $4x^2 + 9y^2 = 36$
   $9x^2 + 4y^2 = 36$
4. $7x^2 + 3y^2 = 27$
   $8x^2 - 4y^2 = 16$
5. $5x^2 - 2y^2 = 18$
   $2x^2 + y^2 = 9$
6. $3x^2 - y^2 = 2$
   $x^2 + 2y^2 = 3$
7. $4x^2 + 9y^2 = 81$
   $x^2 - y^2 = 4$
8. $x^2 + y^2 = 36$
   $4x^2 + y^2 = 144$

Case 3. Both equations are of the form $ax^2 + bxy + cy^2 = d$. Note that all terms except the constant are of the second degree with respect to the variables.

EXAMPLE. Solve:

$$x^2 + 3xy + 2y^2 = 3 \quad (1)$$
$$4x^2 - 5xy + 11y^2 = 58 \quad (2)$$

Solution. We shall first eliminate the constant term between the two equations and then solve the resulting equation for one variable in terms of the other. Our problem is now reduced to two examples of Case 1. If we multiply both members of (1) by 58 and both members of (2) by 3 and subtract, we have

$$\begin{aligned} 58\,x^2 + 174\,xy + 116\,y^2 &= 174 \\ 12\,x^2 - 15\,xy + 33\,y^2 &= 174 \\ \hline 46\,x^2 + 189\,xy + 83\,y^2 &= 0 \\ (2\,x + y)(23\,x + 83\,y) &= 0 \end{aligned}$$

$$y = -2\,x,\ y = -\tfrac{23}{83}\,x$$

Each of these equations may be solved with (1) or (2). Solving with (1) gives

$y = -2x$	$y = -\frac{23}{83}\,x$
$x^2 + 3\,xy + 2\,y^2 = 3$	$x^2 + 3\,xy + 2\,y^2 = 3$
Eliminating y, we have	Eliminating y, we have
$x^2 - 6\,x^2 + 8\,x^2 = 3$	$x^2 - \frac{69}{83}\,x^2 + \frac{1058}{6889}\,x^2 = 3$
$x^2 = 1$	$x^2 = \frac{6889}{740}$
$x = \pm 1$	$x = \pm\frac{83}{370}\sqrt{185}$

Hence the following pairs of values may satisfy the given equations.

$$\begin{cases} x = 1 \\ y = -2 \end{cases} \quad \begin{cases} x = -1 \\ y = 2 \end{cases} \quad \begin{cases} x = \frac{83}{370}\sqrt{185} \\ y = -\frac{23}{370}\sqrt{185} \end{cases} \quad \begin{cases} x = -\frac{83}{370}\sqrt{185} \\ y = \frac{23}{370}\sqrt{185} \end{cases}$$

It is left as an exercise for the student to check these results.

EXERCISES

Solve the following sets of equations:

1. $x^2 + 3\,xy + y^2 = 61$
$x^2 - xy + y^2 = 13$

2. $x^2 + 5\,xy + y^2 = 43$
$x^2 + 5\,xy - y^2 = 25$

3. $x^2 + 3\,xy = 7$
$xy + 4\,y^2 = 2$

4. $2\,x^2 - 2\,xy = 5 - 5\,y^2$
$3\,x^2 - 4\,xy = 2 - 3\,y^2$

5. $x^2 + 3\,xy + y^2 = 11$
$3\,x^2 - xy + 3\,y^2 = 13$

6. $x^2 + xy + y^2 = 7$
$x^2 + y^2 = 10$

7. $x^2 - xy = 3$
$2\,xy + 4\,y^2 = 28$

8. $2\,x^2 + y^2 = 3(1 + xy)$
$x^2 + 2\,xy = 5 + 3\,y^2$

9. $x^2 + xy + y^2 = 37$
$x^2 + y^2 = 25$

10. $2\,x^2 + y^2 = 3(1 + xy)$
$3\,x^2 = 2 + xy$

Case 4. Symmetrical equations. If an equation is unchanged when the variables are interchanged, the equation is called *symmetrical*. Thus $ax^2 + bxy + ay^2 = c$ is a symmetrical equation. We shall now consider the case of solving simultaneously two such equations. The following example will illustrate the method.

EXAMPLE. Solve:

$$x^2 + x + y + y^2 = 8 \qquad (1)$$
$$x + y + xy = 5 \qquad (2)$$

Solution. Let $x = u + v$ and $y = u - v$.

Substitute these values in (1) and (2). Then

(1) becomes $$u^2 + u + v^2 = 4$$

(2) becomes $$u^2 + 2u - v^2 = 5$$

Eliminating v gives $$2u^2 + 3u - 9 = 0$$

$$(2u - 3)(u + 3) = 0$$

or $$u = \tfrac{3}{2} \quad \text{and} \quad u = -3$$

Substituting $u = \frac{3}{2}$ in $u^2 + u + v^2 = 4$, gives $v = \pm\frac{1}{2}$, while substituting $u = -3$ gives $v = \pm\sqrt{-2}$.

Hence $$\begin{cases} u = \frac{3}{2} \\ v = \frac{1}{2} \end{cases} \quad \begin{cases} u = \frac{3}{2} \\ v = -\frac{1}{2} \end{cases} \quad \begin{cases} u = -3 \\ v = -\sqrt{-2} \end{cases} \quad \begin{cases} u = -3 \\ v = \sqrt{-2} \end{cases}$$

By adding and subtracting the values of u and v in each pair, we have

$$\begin{cases} x = 2 \\ y = 1 \end{cases} \quad \begin{cases} x = 1 \\ y = 2 \end{cases} \quad \begin{cases} x = -3 - \sqrt{-2} \\ y = -3 + \sqrt{-2} \end{cases} \quad \begin{cases} x = -3 + \sqrt{-2} \\ y = -3 - \sqrt{-2} \end{cases}$$

It is left as an exercise for the student to check these results.

EXERCISES

Solve the following sets of equations:

1. $x^2 + y^2 = 5$
$xy = 2$

2. $x^2 + y^2 + x + y = 4$
$xy = -2$

3. $x^3 + y^3 = 28$
$x + y = 4$

4. $x^4 + x^2y^2 + y^4 = 243$
$x^2 - xy + y^2 = 9$

5. $x^4 + y^4 = 82$
$x + y = 4$

6. $x^2 + y^2 + x + y = 18$
$xy = 6$

7. $x^3 + y^3 = 9$
$y + x = 3$

8. $x^2 + xy + y^2 = 7$
$xy = 2$

VERBAL PROBLEMS

1. The sum of two numbers is 15, and the difference of their squares is 15. What are the numbers?

2. Find two numbers whose difference is 7 and the difference of whose positive square roots is 1.

3. The perimeter of a rectangle is 136 ft., and a diagonal is 52 ft. Find the area of the rectangle.

4. Two men A and B working together can do a piece of work in twelve days. It takes B twice as long as A to do the work alone. How long does it take each to do the work alone?

5. The sides of two squares differ by 25 in., while the sum of their areas is 2425 sq. in. Find the length of the side of each square.

6. If a two digit number is multiplied by the sum of its digits, the product is 252. The tens' digit exceeds the units' digit by 2. Find the number.

7. The sum of the lengths of the legs of a right triangle is 28 in. If the hypotenuse of the triangle is 20 in., find the lengths of the two legs.

8. Find two numbers whose difference is 11 and the sum of whose squares is 901.

9. A rectangular flower garden containing 1000 sq. ft. is surrounded by a path 5 ft. wide the area of which is 750 sq. ft. What are the dimensions of the garden?

10. The sum of the radii of two circles is 113 in., while the sum of the areas of the two circles is equal to the area of a circle of radius 85 in. Find the radii of each circle. [Area of circle $= \pi R^2$; $\pi = \frac{22}{7}$].

11. A rectangle is 16 ft. wide and 20 ft. long. How much must be added to its width, and how much must be taken from its length, so as to increase its perimeter by 2 ft. and its area by 22 sq. ft?

12. The edge of a cube exceeds the edge of a smaller cube by 1 in. The volumes of the two cubes differ by 61 cu. in. Find the edges of the two cubes.

13. Two trains starting at the same time from towns A and B meet at town C, which is 20 miles nearer B than A. After the trains pass each other, the one from A reaches B in 96 minutes, and the other one reaches A in 2 hr. 30 min. Find the rate of each train.

Honor problems

14. A number is expressed by three digits, of which the first and last are alike. By interchanging the digits in the units' and tens' places the number is increased by 54; but if the digits in the tens' and hundreds' places are interchanged, 9 must be added to four times the resulting number to make it equal to the original number. What is the number?

15. A number is formed by three digits, the third or units' digit being the sum of the other two; the product of the first and third digits exceeds the square of the second by 5. If 396 be added to the number, the order of the digits will be reversed. Find the number.

16. A besieged garrison had enough bread to last them 11 days. If there had been 400 more men, each man would have received 2 ounces less per day; if there had been 600 fewer men, each man's daily share could have been increased by 2 ounces, and the garrison would have had enough bread to last them 12 days. How many pounds of bread did the garrison have, and what was each man's daily share?

MASTERY TEST

1. Find the intercepts of the following lines. Draw the lines.

a) $3x + 2y = 6$ c) $3x - 4y = 12$

b) $4x - y = 4$ d) $5x - y = 10$

2. Solve the following pairs of simultaneous equations and illustrate your solution with a graph:

a) $3x + 2y = 5$, $4x - y = 1$ b) $3x - y = 6$, $3x - y = 2$ c) $x - 2y = 4$, $4y - 2x = -8$

3. Solve the following simultaneous equations:

a) $13x = 131 + 11y$, $19x - 33 = 24y$

b) $\dfrac{3m + 1}{4 - 2p} = \dfrac{4}{3}$, $m + p = 1$

c) $\dfrac{3x - y + 1}{x - y + 3} = 5$, $\dfrac{3y - x}{2x - y + 1} = 1$

4. A man 35 years old has a son 15 years old. In how many years will the son be half as old as his father?

5. John can build a wall in 8 days and William can do it in 10 days. How long will it take them working together?

6. Mr. Robinson invested \$8000. On part of it he received 4 per cent interest and on the balance 3 per cent. How much was in each investment if his income was \$295?

7. How much water must I add to 10 oz. of a 70 per cent solution so as to reduce it to a 40 per cent solution?

8. If the formula $P = aX + bY$ gives $P = 10$ when $X = 1$, and $Y = 3$; $P = 20$ when $X = -3$, $Y = 4$, find the values of a and b.

9. If the formula $x^2 + y^2 + ax + by + c = 0$ is satisfied by $x = 2$, $y = 1$; $x = -1$, $y = 1$; $x = 1$, $y = 3$, find the values of a, b, and c.

10. How many ounces of pure gold and 10-carat gold must be mixed with 24 oz. of 14-carat gold to make 54 oz. of 16-carat gold?

11. Sketch each of the following curves and find the co-ordinates of the maximum or minimum point as the case may be:

a) $y = -x^2 + 4x + 1$ c) $y = -2x^2 + 8x - 1$
b) $y = 2x^2 + 8x - 1$ d) $y = 3x^2 - 12x + 1$

12. Find the area of the greatest rectangle with a perimeter of 40 in.

13. Divide the number 10 into two parts such that the sum of the cube of one part and three times the square of the other part shall be a minimum.

14. Find k so that 3 is a root of $3x^2 + (2k + 1)x - 5 = 0$.

15. Find k so that -2 is a root of $\frac{(k+1)x}{5} = \frac{3x - 1}{x}$.

16. Write the equation $x^2 + 6x + y^2 - 8y = 4$ in the form $(x - h)^2 + (y - k)^2 = c$, when h, k, and c are constants.

17. Solve $7x^2 - 4x = 3$:

a) By factoring.
b) By completing the square.
c) By formula.

18. Solve: a) $x - 6\sqrt{x} = 7$
b) $x^{\frac{2}{3}} + 7x^{\frac{1}{3}} = -12$

19. Solve: a) $\sqrt{x} + \sqrt{x - 3} = \frac{2}{\sqrt{x}}$

b) $\frac{2}{\sqrt{x}} - \sqrt{x} = \sqrt{x - 1}$

c) $\sqrt{x} = \frac{2}{\sqrt{1 + x}} - \sqrt{1 + x}$

d) $\sqrt{3x - 5} + \sqrt{3x + 3} = \sqrt{10x - 4}$

e) $\sqrt{x + 2} - \sqrt{3x + 10} + \sqrt{10x + 16} = 0$

20. Without solving find the nature of the roots of:

a) $7x^2 - 3x + 1 = 0$

b) $16x^2 - 32x + 5 = 0$

c) $9x^2 + 6x + 1 = 0$

d) $\frac{x+3}{2} = \frac{4x+1}{x-3}$

21. Find the equation whose roots are $\frac{3+\sqrt{7}}{2}, \frac{3-\sqrt{7}}{2}$.

22. Given $(2k + 1)x^2 + (k + 2)x + 1 = 0$. Find k so that:

a) One root is 2.

b) The sum of the roots is -5.

c) The product of the roots is 3.

d) The roots are equal.

e) The roots are numerically equal but opposite in sign.

f) The roots are imaginary.

23. If a grocer lowers the price of oranges 3 cents per dozen, he can sell 5 more for 90 cents. What was the original price per dozen?

24. A gives B a 10 minute start in a 24 mile race and beats him by 2 minutes. If A runs $\frac{1}{2}$ mile faster than B, find the rate of each man.

25. A man bought a certain number of pounds of meat for $8. If he had paid two cents more per pound he would have purchased 20 lb. less for the same money. How many pounds did he buy?

CHAPTER VIII

Ratio Proportion Variation

Ratio

A *ratio* is the indicated division of two numbers. The ratio of a to b is written $a{:}b$ or $\frac{a}{b}$. In dealing with ratios of quantities of the same kind, it is necessary to express both terms of the ratio in *the same unit.* Thus the ratio of 2 ft. to 5 yd. is $\frac{2}{15}$. What is the ratio of 3 in. to $1\frac{1}{2}$ ft.?

Proportion

A *proportion* is an equality between two ratios. Thus

$$\frac{a}{b} = \frac{c}{d}, \quad \frac{x}{4} = \frac{7}{3}, \quad \frac{p+q}{r} = \frac{s-t}{v}$$

are proportions.

The proportion $\frac{a}{b} = \frac{c}{d}$ may be written in the form $a{:}b{::}c{:}d$ or in the form $a{:}b = c{:}d$ and is read "a is to b as c is to d". For computation purposes it is always better to use the form $\frac{a}{b} = \frac{c}{d}$.

In the proportion $\frac{a}{b} = \frac{c}{d}$, a is called the first term, b the second, c the third, and d the fourth. The first and fourth terms are called the *extremes,* the second and third the *means.*

If the second and third terms of a proportion are equal, *i.e.*, if the means are equal, the proportion is called a *mean proportion*. Thus $\frac{a}{b} = \frac{b}{c}$ is a mean proportion, and b is said to be a *mean proportional* between a and c.

If we clear the proportion $\frac{a}{b} = \frac{b}{c}$ of fractions we have

$$b^2 = ac$$

and hence

$$b = \pm\sqrt{ac}$$

Therefore, if neither a nor c is zero, there are two mean proportionals between them. If a and c have opposite signs, the mean proportionals between them are imaginary.

In the proportion $\frac{a}{b} = \frac{c}{d}$, d is said to be a *fourth* proportional to a, b, and c.

In the mean proportion $\frac{a}{b} = \frac{b}{c}$, c is said to be the *third* proportional to a and b.

EXERCISES

Express in simplest fractional form:

1. Ratio 3 ft. to 7 yd.
2. Ratio 1 mi. to 300 ft.
3. Ratio 3 pints to 1 gallon.
4. Ratio $3\,xy$ to $-\,6\,xy$.

Solve the following equations for x:

5. $x:2 = 7:3$
6. $3\,x:(1 + x) = 2:3$
7. $5:x = 4:(1 + x)$
8. $(3\,x + 1):(x + 1) = (3\,x - 2):(x - 5)$

Find the mean proportionals between each of the following pairs of numbers:

9. 9 and 4
10. $\frac{1}{2}$ and 32
11. -2, -32
12. $\frac{a + b}{a - b}$, $a^2 - b^2$
13. $9\,x^{-2}$, x^2

Find the third proportional to each of the following pairs of numbers:

14. 7, 2 **15.** a, b **16.** $3x, \frac{x}{3}$

Find the fourth proportional to each of the following sets of numbers:

17. 3, 4, 7 **18.** 2, −5, −6 **19.** a, b, ab

20. $a^2 - b^2, a + b, a^3 - b^3$

21. If $\frac{a}{b} = \frac{c}{d}$, prove that $ad = bc$.

22. If $mn = pq$, prove that $\frac{m}{p} = \frac{q}{n}$.

23. If $\frac{a}{b} = \frac{c}{d}$, prove that $\frac{a+b}{b} = \frac{c+d}{d}$.

24. If $\frac{a}{b} = \frac{c}{d}$, prove that $\frac{a+b}{a-b} = \frac{c+d}{c-d}$.

Variation

If the ratio of two variables is constant, either one is said to *vary directly* as the other. Thus if y varies directly as x, then $\frac{y}{x} = k$ or $y = kx$ where k is a constant called the *constant of variation* or the factor of proportionality.

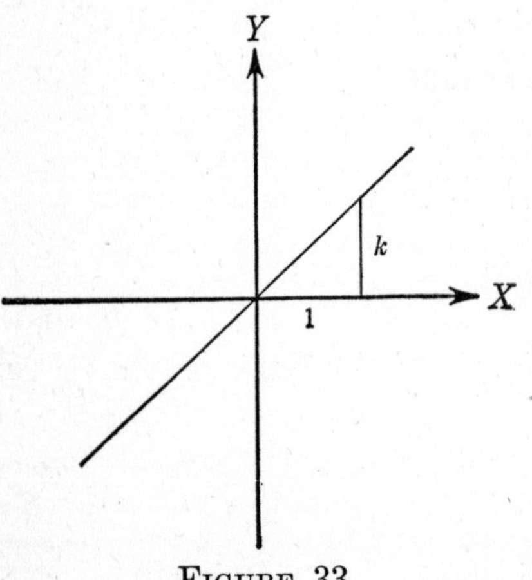

FIGURE 33

Each of the statements "y varies as x", "y varies directly as x", "y is proportional to x", "y is directly proportional to x", means the same thing, namely, that

$$\frac{y}{x} = k \quad \text{or} \quad y = kx$$

In direct variation y increases as x increases, when $k > 0$. This is readily illustrated by the graph of $y = kx$ which is a straight line through the origin whose change ratio is k. This means that for an increase in x of 1 unit there is a corresponding increase in y of k units.

Often the expression "y varies as x" is written

$$y \propto x$$

The area of a circle varies as the square of its radius. If its area is represented by A and its radius by r, then $A = kr^2$ where $k = \pi$. The area of a square varies as the square of its side. If its area is represented by A and its side by x, then $A = kx^2$ and k has what value?

EXAMPLE. The distance a body falls from rest varies as the square of the time. If the body falls 64 ft. in 2 seconds, how far will it fall in 4 seconds?

Solution. Symbolically $D = kT^2$

Now $D = 64$ when $T = 2$

$$\therefore \quad 64 = k\,4$$

or

$$16 = k$$

Hence to find D when $T = 4$, we have

$$D = 16(4)^2$$
$$= 256 \text{ ft.}$$

Inverse variation

The statements "y varies inversely as x," "y is inversely proportional to x," mean that

$$y = \frac{k}{x}$$

where k is the constant of variation.

In inverse variation y decreases as x increases, if $k > 0$; while when x decreases, y increases. This is readily illustrated by the graph of $y = \frac{k}{x}$.

From physics we know that the volume of a gas varies inversely as the pressure. If v represents the volume and p the pressure, then

$$v = \frac{k}{p}$$

EXAMPLE. When air is pumped into an automobile tire, the pressure varies inversely as the volume. If there is a pressure of 30 pounds when the volume is 100 cubic inches, what is the pressure when the volume is 150 cubic inches?

Solution. Symbolically $P = \frac{k}{V}$.

Now $$P = 30 \text{ when } V = 100$$

$$\therefore \quad 30 = \frac{k}{100}$$

or $$k = 3000$$

Hence to find P when $V = 150$ we have

$$P = \tfrac{3000}{150}$$
$$= 20 \text{ lb.}$$

Joint variation

If the three variables z, x, and y are so related that the ratio of z to the product xy is constant, then z is said to vary jointly as x and y. That is,

$$\frac{z}{xy} = k$$

or $$z = kxy$$

EXAMPLE. Suppose y varies directly as x and inversely as z. If $y = 10$ when $x = 2$ and $z = 3$, find y when $x = 3$ and $z = 5$.

Solution. $$y = \frac{kx}{z}$$

Given $y = 10$, $x = 2$, and $z = 3$. Hence

$$10 = \frac{2\,k}{3}$$

and $$k = 15$$

$$\therefore \quad y = \frac{15\,x}{z}$$

When $x = 3$, $z = 5$, we have

$$y = \frac{15(3)}{5} = 9$$

EXERCISES

1. If $y \propto x$ and $y = 10$ when $x = 2$, find y when $x = 5$.

2. If y varies directly as x^2, find y when $x = 3$, if $y = 7$ when $x = 2$.

3. Given that y varies jointly as x and z. If $y = 20$ when $x = 2$, $z = 3$, find y when $x = 3$ and $z = 5$.

4. If y varies directly as x and inversely as z, find x when $y = 3$ and $z = 2$, if $y = 5$ when $x = 1$ and $z = 2$.

5. A ball is allowed to roll down an inclined plane. If the distance traversed varies as the square of the time, how far will the ball go in 4 seconds if in the first second it goes 6 ft.?

6. The distance in feet a body falls from rest varies directly as the square of the number of seconds occupied in falling. If the body falls 16 ft. the first second, how far will it fall in 8 seconds? How far will it fall during the eighth second?

7. Pressure of gas in a tank varies jointly as the density and absolute temperature. If the pressure is 20 lb. per sq. in. when the density is 1 and temperature is 275°, what is the pressure when the density is 3 and temperature is 300°?

8. The illumination I from a source of light varies inversely as the square of the distance d from this source. How far must the screen be placed from the source of light so as to receive 9 times as much illumination as when the light is 10 ft. from the screen?

9. The horsepower P required to operate a boat varies as the cube of the velocity V. If the horsepower is 1125 when the speed is 15 mi. per hr., find the horsepower when the speed is 12 mi. per hr.

10. The area of a circle varies as the square of its radius. If the area of a circle is $100\,\pi$ sq. ft. when the radius is 10 ft., find the area when the radius is 7 ft.

11. The volume of a sphere varies as the cube of its diameter. If the volume is $36\,\pi$ cu. in. when the radius is 3 in., find the volume when the diameter is 10 in.

12. The volume of a gas varies as the absolute temperature and inversely as the pressure. If the volume is 100 cu. in. when the pressure is 30 lb. and the temperature is 300°, find the volume when the pressure is 40 lb. and the temperature is 250°.

13. When air is pumped into an automobile tire, the pressure varies inversely as the volume. If the pressure is 30 lb. when the volume is 120 cu. in., what is the pressure when the volume is 150 cu. in.?

14. The time required for a pendulum to make a vibration varies directly as the square root of its length. If a pendulum 100 cm. long makes a vibration in 1 second, how long does it take a pendulum 64 cm. long to make a vibration?

15. The cost of doing a piece of work varies jointly as the number of men engaged and the number of days they work. If 10 men working 8 days earn $320, how long will it take 15 men to earn $450?

16. Engineers know that the safe load of a horizontal beam supported at both ends, varies jointly as the breadth and square of the depth, and inversely as the length between the supports. If a white pine joist 2×6 in. and 10 ft. long between supports, safely holds 800 lb., what is the safe load of a 4×6 beam of the same material 15 ft. long?

17. The pressure of wind on a billboard varies jointly as the area of the billboard and the square of the wind's velocity. When the wind is 15 miles per hour, the pressure on a square foot is one pound. What is the velocity of the wind when the pressure on a square yard is 25 lb.?

18. The velocity of the rim of a pulley varies directly as its diameter. If at a certain moment a 16-in. pulley has a rim velocity of 150 ft. per min., what is the rim velocity at the same moment, of a 10-in. pulley on the same shaft?

19. Ohm's law states that the current I in an electric wire varies directly as the electromotive force E and inversely as the resistance R. The resistance of a wire varies directly as its length and inversely as the square of its diameter. If the current is 40 amperes when an electromotive force of 100 volts is applied to a wire 1000 ft. long and .06 in. in diameter, what current will flow when 80 volts are applied to a wire of the same material 1500 ft. long and .05 in. in diameter?

CHAPTER IX

Progressions

Arithmetic progression

An *arithmetic progression* (A.P.) is a sequence of numbers, called terms, in which each term after the first is formed from the preceding term by adding to it a fixed number called the *common difference.*

The first of the following arithmetic progressions has a common difference of $+5$ and the second a common difference of -3.

$$3, 8, 13, 18, \cdots$$
$$7, 4, 1, -2, -5, \cdots$$

What is the common difference in the progression $2\frac{2}{3}$, $2\frac{1}{2}$, $2\frac{1}{3}, \cdots$?

To determine if a progression is arithmetic, subtract from each term except the first, the preceding term. If the differences are equal, the progression is arithmetic.[1] Let us test the following progression:

$$(3a + b), (5a - 2b), (7a - 5b), \cdots$$

Now $\qquad (5a - 2b) - (3a + b) = 2a - 3b$

and $\qquad (7a - 5b) - (5a - 2b) = 2a - 3b$

Therefore the progression is arithmetic.

[1] We assume that the law exhibited by the first three terms is the law of formation.

Is $1 + x$, $1 + 3x$, $1 + 5x$, $\cdots$ an A.P.? If so, what is the common difference?

If the first term is a and the common difference is d, the terms of the arithmetic progression are

$$a, a + d, a + 2d, a + 3d, \cdots$$

What is the coefficient of d in the 20th term? the 47th term? the 97th term?

Since the coefficient of d in any term is one less than the number of the term, the nth term is $a + (n - 1)d$.

If we represent *the nth term by l*, then

$$\boldsymbol{l = a + (n - 1)d}$$

Sum of n terms of an A.P.

If the first term of the progression is a, the common difference is d, the nth term is l, and the sum is s, then

$$s = a + (a + d) + (a + 2d) + \cdots + (l - 2d) + (l - d) + l$$

Writing these terms in reverse order gives

$$s = l + (l - d) + (l - 2d) + \cdots + (a + 2d) + (a + d) + a$$

Adding the two expressions, we have

$$2s = (a + l) + (a + l) + (a + l) + \cdots + (a + l) + (a + l) + (a + l)$$

$$= n(a + l)$$

$$\therefore \quad \boldsymbol{s = \frac{n}{2}(a + l)}$$

Substituting the value $a + (n - 1)d$ for l gives

$$\boldsymbol{s = \frac{n}{2}[2a + (n - 1)d]}$$

From the three equations:

$$l = a + (n - 1)d$$

$$s = \frac{n}{2}(a + l)$$

$$s = \frac{n}{2}[2a + (n - 1)d]$$

any two of the five letters l, a, n, d, s can be found when the other three are known. Note that the five letters spell "lands".

EXAMPLE 1. Find the sum of the first 100 terms of the progression 8, 6, 4, · · ·.

Solution.

$l =$
$a = 8$
$n = 100$
$d = -2$
$s = ?$

Of the five letters note that we know the value of three, namely, a, n, and d. We desire to find the value of a fourth, namely, s.

Substituting in $s = \frac{n}{2}[2a + (n - 1)d]$ gives

$$s = 50[16 + (99)(-2)] = -9100$$

EXAMPLE 2. How many terms of the progression 3, 5, 7 · · · must be taken in order that the sum will be 2600? In this case we know the values of a, d, and s and desire the value of n.

Solution.

$l =$
$a = 3$
$n = ?$
$d = 2$
$s = 2600$

We note the formula $s = \frac{n}{2}[2a + (n - 1)d]$ contains only the unknown n. Substituting we have $2600 = \frac{n}{2}[6 + (n - 1)2]$ or $n^2 + 2n - 2600 = 0$.

Hence $$(n + 52)(n - 50) = 0$$

and $$n = 50$$

EXERCISES

1. Find the 20th term of 8, 5, 2, $\cdots$.
2. Find the 35th term of 3, 8, 13, $\cdots$.
3. Find the 24th term of 2.5, $1\frac{5}{6}$, $1\frac{1}{6}$, $\cdots$.
4. Find the $3x$ term of 4, 8, 12, $\cdots$.
5. Find the $(2k + 3)$ term of -3, 1, 5, $\cdots$.
6. Find the sum of 26 terms of 3, 8, 13, $\cdots$.
7. Find the sum of 12 terms of 4, 8, 12, $\cdots$.
8. Find the sum of 100 terms of $2\frac{1}{2}$, $1\frac{5}{6}$, $1\frac{1}{6}$, $\cdots$.
9. Find the sum of 84 terms of $2\frac{1}{4}$, $1\frac{5}{6}$, $1\frac{5}{12}$, $\cdots$.
10. Find the sum of $(5k + 3)$ terms of -2, 1, 4, $\cdots$.
11. Find the sum of the first 100 even integers.
12. Prove that the sum of the first n odd integers is the square of an integer.
13. Prove that the sum of the first n even integers is the product of two consecutive integers.
14. If $s = 594$, $n = 12$, $d = 7$, find a and l.
15. If $s = 623$, $d = 5$, $l = 77$, find a and n.

Arithmetic mean

The *arithmetic mean* between two numbers is the number which when placed between them makes with them an arithmetic progression. If the given numbers are a and b and the arithmetic mean is x, then a, x, and b form an arithmetic progression. By the definition of an arithmetic progression the differences $x - a$ and $b - x$ must be equal. That is,

$$x - a = b - x$$

or

$$x = \frac{a + b}{2}$$

Hence the arithmetic mean between two numbers is their average.

If we wish to insert several arithmetic means; *i.e.*, numbers which when inserted between the given numbers form with them an arithmetic progression, we merely have to find the common difference d, add it to the first term for the first mean, add it to the first mean to get the second mean, and so on.

EXAMPLE. Insert six arithmetic means between 3 and 17.

Solution.

$l = 17$

$a = 3$ We know the first term is 3, the last term is 17, and

$n = 8$ the number of terms is 8, being made up of the num-

$d = ?$ bers 3 and 17, and 6 arithmetic means.

$s =$

Substituting in the formula $l = a + (n - 1)d$

$$17 = 3 + 7d$$

$$d = 2$$

Then 3, {5, 7, 9, 11, 13, 15}, 17 is the series, and the terms in the brackets are the required means.

When we are given an odd number of terms in A.P., it is convenient to call the middle one x, and to use y for the common difference. Thus, for 3 terms, we use

$$x - y, x, x + y$$

for 5 terms, we use

$$x - 2y, x - y, x, x + y, x + 2y$$

If we have an even number of terms, say four, we use

$$x - 3y, x - y, x + y, x + 3y$$

EXAMPLE. The sum of three numbers in A.P. is 33, and the sum of their squares is 461. Find the numbers.

Solution. Let the three numbers be

$$x - y, x, x + y$$

Then $x - y + x + x + y = 33$

and $(x - y)^2 + x^2 + (x + y)^2 = 461$

Simplifying, $x = 11$

and $3x^2 + 2y^2 = 461$

Solving, $x = 11, \quad y = \pm 7$

The numbers are 4, 11, 18.

EXERCISES

1. If $d = 3$, $n = 20$, $s = 67$, find l and a.

2. If $l = 55$, $a = 15$, $n = 13$, find d and s.

3. If $l = 38$, $d = 2$, $s = 410$, find a and n.

4. Insert four arithmetic means between 3 and 18.

5. Insert five arithmetic means between p and q.

6. Insert two arithmetic means between $2x + y$ and $2x - y$.

7. Insert six arithmetic means between 12 and -3.

8. The first term of an arithmetic progression is 5, and the third term is 11. Find the eighth term. Find the sum of eight terms.

9. Arithmetic means are inserted between 8 and 32. If the sum of the first two means is to the sum of the last two means as 7 is to 25, find how many means are inserted. What is the sum of the means?

10. The sum of five numbers in arithmetic progression is 45. If the product of the first and last is $\frac{5}{8}$ of the product of the second and fourth, find the numbers.

11. Four numbers are in A.P. Their sum is 12, and the sum of their squares is 116. Find the numbers.

12. Starting from a basket there are placed in a straight line on a lawn 12 potatoes 3 ft. apart, the first potato being 10 ft. from the basket. A boy starts from the basket, picks up a potato, and deposits it in the basket. If he picks up all of the potatoes in this manner, how far does he travel?

13. A man is hired at $1500 for the year. His employer agrees to increase his salary $150 a year up to and including the eighth year. How much will the man earn his eighth year? How much will he earn in eight years?

14. The tenth term of an A.P. is 24, the fifteenth term is 39. Find the twenty-third term.

15. To dig a well costs $1.50 for the first yard, $1.75 for the second, $2.00 for the third, and so on. How deep a well can be dug for $84.00?

16. How many arithmetic means must be inserted between 4 and 25 if the sum of the means is 87?

17. Three numbers are in A.P. If their sum is 18 and the sum of their squares is 110, what are the numbers?

18. Find three numbers in A.P. if their sum is 21 and the sum of their squares is 155.

19. How many terms of the series $1, 4, 7, \cdots$ must be taken so that the ratio of the sum of the first half of the terms to the sum of the second half is $7:22$?

20. A body falls 16.1 ft. the first second, 48.3 ft. the second second, 80.5 ft. the third second and so on. How many feet will it fall in the seventh second? How far does it fall in seven seconds?

21. If k arithmetic means are inserted between a and l, prove that $d = \frac{l-a}{k+1}$.

Harmonic progression

A *harmonic progression* (H.P.) is a sequence of numbers whose reciprocals form an A.P. Thus, $1, \frac{1}{5}, \frac{1}{9}, \frac{1}{13}, \cdots$ is a harmonic progression because the reciprocals of its terms are $1, 5, 9, 13, \cdots$, which is an A.P.

Problems involving harmonic progressions are generally solved by making use of the properties of the corresponding A.P. There is no general formula for the sum of n terms of a H.P.

EXAMPLE. Find the harmonic mean between a and b.

Solution. Let the harmonic mean be x. Then,

$$\frac{1}{a}, \frac{1}{x}, \frac{1}{b} \quad \text{form an A.P.}$$

Hence,

$$\frac{1}{x} - \frac{1}{a} = \frac{1}{b} - \frac{1}{x} \qquad \text{Why?}$$

$$\frac{2}{x} = \frac{1}{a} + \frac{1}{b}$$

and

$$x = \frac{2\,ab}{a+b}$$

EXERCISES

1. In the following progressions find the terms indicated:

a) $\frac{1}{\sqrt{a}}, \frac{1}{2\sqrt{a}}, \frac{1}{3\sqrt{a}}, \cdots$ (10th term).

b) $\frac{1}{a-2\,b^2}, \frac{1}{2\,a-b^2}, \frac{1}{3\,a}, \cdots$ (8th term).

c) $-\frac{2}{a}, -\frac{1}{a}, -\frac{2}{3\,a}, \cdots$ (11th term).

2. If a, b, c are in H.P. prove that

$$\frac{a}{a-b} = \frac{a+c}{a-c}$$

3. Insert 5 harmonic means between -3 and 2.

4. Find the 28th term of a H.P. if its 6th term is $\frac{1}{3}$ and its 17th term is $\frac{2}{17}$.

5. If the difference between two numbers is 2, and their arithmetical mean exceeds their harmonic mean by $\frac{1}{3}$, what are the numbers?

6. If the mth term of a H.P. is n and the nth term is m, prove that the $(m + n)$th term is $\frac{mn}{m+n}$.

7. If x is the harmonic mean between a and b, prove that

$$\frac{1}{x-a} + \frac{1}{x-b} = \frac{1}{a} + \frac{1}{b}$$

8. Write the 5th term of the H.P. in which the 6th term is $\frac{1}{6a - 4b}$ and the 12th term is $\frac{1}{12a - 10b}$.

9. A man walks up a hill at a rate of a miles an hour and then back down at a rate of b miles an hour. Prove that his average rate is the harmonic mean between a and b.

Geometric progression

A *geometric progression* (G.P.) is a sequence of numbers, called terms, in which each term after the first is formed by multiplying the preceding term by a fixed number called the *ratio.*

In the progression 3, 6, 12, 24, $\cdots$ the common ratio is 2, while in the progression 7, $-\frac{14}{3}$, $\frac{28}{9}$, $-\frac{56}{27}$, $\cdots$ the common ratio is $-\frac{2}{3}$.

How would you test a progression to determine if it is a G.P.?

Test $$a, \sqrt{a}, 1, \cdots$$

If the first term is called a, and the ratio r, the series is

$$a, ar, ar^2, ar^3, \cdots$$

What is the exponent of r in the 27th term? in the 48th term? in the 97th term?

Since the exponent of r in any term is one less than the number of the term, the nth term is ar^{n-1}. The nth term is denoted by l, hence

$$l = ar^{n-1}$$

Geometric means

In a geometric progression the first and last terms are called the *extremes*, while the remaining terms are called *geometric means*. If a, x, b, form a geometric progression, then x is a geometric mean between a and b. By the definition of a geometric progression

$$\frac{x}{a} = \frac{b}{x}$$

or

$$x^2 = ab$$

and

$$x = \pm\sqrt{ab}$$

If 4, x, 9 are in geometric progression, what values may x have?

Sum of n terms of a G.P.

If l represents the nth term, a the first term, n the number of terms, r the common ratio, and s the sum of n terms, then

$$s = a + ar + ar^2 + \cdots + ar^{n-1}$$

Multiplying by r

$$sr = ar + ar^2 + \cdots + ar^{n-1} + ar^n$$

Subtracting the members of the first equation from the corresponding members of the second, we have

$$sr - s = ar^n - a$$
$$s(r - 1) = ar^n - a$$
$$s = \frac{ar^n - a}{r - 1}$$

provided $r \neq 1$.

Since $l = ar^{n-1}$, then $rl = ar^n$.

$$\therefore \qquad s = \frac{rl - a}{r - 1}$$

provided of course that $r \neq 1$.

If $r = 1$, the terms are equal, and $s = a + a + \cdots + a$ to n terms. Hence,

$$s = na$$

From the three equations

$$l = ar^{n-1} \qquad s = \frac{ar^n - a}{r - 1} \qquad s = \frac{rl - a}{r - 1}$$

when three of the letters s, n, a, r, l are known, the remaining two can be found. Note that the five letters spell "snarl".

EXAMPLE 1. Given the progression 8, −4, 2 · · ·. Find (a) the 10th term; (b) the sum of the first 10 terms. We know that the first term is 8, the ratio is $-\frac{1}{2}$, and the number of terms is 10.

Solution.

$s = ?$
$n = 10$
$a = 8$
$r = -\frac{1}{2}$
$l = ?$

$$\begin{aligned} l &= ar^{n-1} \\ &= (8)(-\tfrac{1}{2})^9 \\ &= 2^3\left(\frac{-1}{2}\right)^9 \\ &= \frac{-1}{2^6} = -\frac{1}{64} \end{aligned}$$

$$\begin{aligned} s &= \frac{rl - a}{r - 1} \\ &= \frac{\frac{1}{128} - 8}{-\frac{1}{2} - 1} \\ &= \tfrac{341}{64} \end{aligned}$$

EXAMPLE 2. The sum of the first and fourth terms of a G.P. is 195, and the sum of the second and third terms is 60. Find the four terms.

Solution.

$$\begin{aligned} a + ar^3 &= 195 \\ ar + ar^2 &= 60 \end{aligned}$$

Dividing corresponding sides of these equations gives

$$\frac{a(1+r^3)}{ar(1+r)} = \frac{195}{60}$$

$$\frac{1-r+r^2}{r} = \frac{13}{4}$$

or $$4r^2 - 17r + 4 = 0$$

Hence $$(4r-1)(r-4) = 0$$

$$r = \tfrac{1}{4},\ r = 4$$

Substituting these values in the second equation, we find

when $$r = \tfrac{1}{4},\ a = 192$$
$$r = 4,\ a = 3$$

Hence the required numbers are 3, 12, 48, 192.

EXAMPLE. 3. Insert three geometric means between 2 and 162.

Solution. From the statement of the problem $a = 2, l = 162, n = 5$. Substituting these values in the formula $l = ar^{n-1}$, we have $162 = 2r^4$ or $r = \pm 3$.

If $r = 3$, the series is $2, 6, 18, 54, 162$
If $r = -3$, the series is $2, -6, 18, -54, 162$

EXERCISES

1. Find the 8th term of $2, 4, 8, \cdots$.
2. Find the 10th term of $12, 6, 3, \cdots$.
3. Find the 10th term of $\frac{1}{2}, 1, 2, \cdots$.
4. Find the 8th term of $\frac{3}{4}, \frac{3}{2}, 3, \cdots$.
5. Find the 10th term of $\frac{1}{12}, -\frac{1}{4}, \frac{3}{4}, \cdots$.
6. Find the sum of 8 terms of $16, 8, 4, \cdots$.
7. Find the sum of 12 terms of $1, 3, 9, \cdots$.
8. Find the sum of 7 terms of $\frac{15}{8}, \frac{3}{8}, \frac{3}{40}, \cdots$.
9. Find the sum of $2p$ terms of $3, -4, \frac{16}{3}, \cdots$.
10. Find the sum of 9 terms of $-\frac{1}{3}, \frac{1}{2}, -\frac{3}{4}, \cdots$.
11. Insert four geometric means between 1 and 243.
12. Insert six geometric means between 3 and 384.

13. Insert five geometric means between $\frac{1}{4}$ and 16.

14. Find the sum of a geometric progression of four terms in which the first term is 6 and the last term is $\frac{2}{9}$.

15. Find x so that $2x + 1$, $4x + 2$, and $7x + 5$ form a geometric progression.

16. A bacterium entered a human body, and at the end of 36 hours it divided into 2 bacteria. At the end of another 36 hours each of these bacteria divided into two, and so on. Find the number of bacteria at the end of 6 weeks.

17. A farmer sowed $\frac{1}{8}$ bushel of wheat and used the whole crop for seed the following year and so on to the fourth crop which amounted to 8192 bushels. Assuming r to be constant, find the amount of the second crop.

18. The sum of the first and fourth terms of a G.P. is 27, and the sum of the second and third terms is 18. Find the four terms.

Infinite geometric progression

If r is numerically less than 1 and n increases without limit, what value does l approach? Since l approaches zero as n becomes infinite, the fraction $\frac{rl - a}{r - 1}$ approaches $\frac{-a}{r - 1}$ or $\frac{a}{1 - r}$. This result is usually stated as the sum of an infinite number of terms of a geometric progression in which $|r| < 1$. Stated more briefly, the sum to infinity is $\frac{a}{1 - r}$. Symbolically we write

$$S_\infty = \frac{a}{1 - r}$$

EXAMPLE. Find the sum to infinity of the progression 1, $\frac{1}{3}$, $\frac{1}{9}$, $\frac{1}{27}$, $\cdots$.

Solution. We see that $a = 1$ and $r = \frac{1}{3}$. We are required to find S_∞.

$$S_\infty = \frac{a}{1 - r}$$

$$= \frac{1}{1 - \frac{1}{3}}$$

$$= \frac{3}{2}$$

Repeating decimals

The formula on page 188 can be used for evaluating a repeating decimal.

There are two ways of writing a repeating decimal. For example, 0.343434 · · · may be written as $.\dot{3}\dot{4}$. When dots are placed over figures in a repeating decimal, it is understood that these figures together with those between them compose the repeating part of the decimal. Thus

$$0.\dot{3}\dot{4} = 0.343434 \cdots$$
$$0.\dot{2}1\dot{7} = 0.217217217 \cdots$$
$$0.7\dot{5}1\dot{2} = 0.7512512 \cdots$$

EXAMPLE. Find the value of the repeating decimal $.2\dot{3}\dot{4}$.

Solution.

$$\begin{aligned} .2\dot{3}\dot{4} &= .2343434 \cdots \\ &= .2 + (.034 + .00034 + .0000034 + \cdots) \\ &= .2 + \frac{0.034}{1 - .01} \\ &= .2 + \tfrac{34}{990} \\ &= \tfrac{116}{495} \end{aligned}$$

The fraction $\frac{116}{495}$ is called the generating fraction of the repeating decimal $.2\dot{3}\dot{4}$.

EXERCISES

1. Find the sum to infinity of 16, −8, 4, · · ·.
2. Find the sum to infinity of $\frac{1}{2}, \frac{1}{3}, \frac{2}{9}, \cdots$.
3. Find the sum to infinity of $\frac{1}{3}, \frac{1}{6}, \frac{1}{12}, \cdots$.
4. Find the sum to infinity of $1, -\frac{3}{5}, \frac{9}{25}, \cdots$.
5. Find the sum to infinity of $5, -3, 1\frac{4}{5}, \cdots$.

Find the generating fraction for each of the following repeating decimals:

6. $0.\dot{1}\dot{5}$
7. $0.\dot{2}\dot{4}$
8. $2.\dot{3}\dot{4}$
9. 0.123123 · · ·
10. $4.5\dot{3}$
11. $2.\dot{1}0\dot{3}$
12. $0.2\dot{1}0\dot{1}$
13. $0.5\dot{6}\dot{7}$
14. $0.00\dot{1}\dot{0}$

MASTERY TEST

1. Make a table like the following and fill in the blank spaces where l, a, n, d, s, are symbols in an A.P.

	a	*b*	*c*	*d*	*e*	*f*
l					11	23
a	-3	-7		10		
n	8		19			29
d	2	3	$\frac{2}{3}$	-1	1	
s		430	38	55	66	58

2. How many numbers between 10 and 500 are divisible by 7?

3. How many strokes does an ordinary clock make during a day in striking the hours?

4. The payments in a Christmas savings fund are made for 50 weeks. The first payment is 5 cents, the second 10 cents, the third 15 cents, etc. What will be the 28th payment? the 50th payment? How much will be in the fund after the 50th payment has been made?

5. A pile of fence posts has 50 posts in the first layer, 49 in the second, 48 in the third, etc. If there are 20 layers, how many posts are there in the pile?

6. Make a table like the following and fill in the blank spaces where s, n, a, r, l, are symbols in a G.P.

	a	*b*	*c*	*d*	*e*
s				600	49
n		3	3		3
a	2		4	15	7
r	4	4		3	
l	32	80	64		

7. A cask contains 40 gallons of alcohol. If 10 gallons are drawn out and the cask is filled with water, and if this procedure is repeated five times, find how much alcohol remains in the cask.

8. A tennis ball is dropped from a height of 21 ft. Each time it strikes the ground it rebounds one-third the height from which it fell.

How far has it gone when it strikes the ground the 8th time? How far does it go before coming to rest?

9. The second term of a G.P. is 54, and its sum to infinity is 216. Find the 10th term.

10. Find the generating fraction of $4.\dot{3}1\dot{2}$.

11. A square is formed by connecting the mid-points of the sides of another square 10 inches on a side. A third square is formed in like manner from the second square. If this is done so there are six squares, find the sum of their areas.

12. Three numbers are in A.P., and their sum is 48. If the second number is increased by 2 and the third by 13, the three numbers will be in G.P. Find the numbers.

13. The sum of two numbers is 20. The ratio of their arithmetic mean to their positive geometric mean is 1.25. Find the numbers.

14. Between the numbers 9 and 2 there are inserted two numbers, x and y such that 9, x, and y form a G.P. and x, y, and 2 form an A.P. Find x and y.

15. Find the G.P. in which the sum of the third and fifth terms is 90 and the sum of the sixth and eighth terms is 2430.

16. Find the generating fraction of $3.\dot{2}1\dot{3}$.

17. Find the generating fraction of $0.12\dot{3}\dot{4}$.

18. Find the sum to infinity of the series $\frac{1}{2}, \frac{1}{6}, \frac{1}{18}, \cdots$.

19. Given four numbers the first three of which are in A.P., while the first, third, and fourth are in G.P. The fourth number is three times the sum of the first two, and the third exceeds the fourth by 18. Find the numbers.

20. Insert five arithmetic means between a and b.

21. Insert four geometric means between a and b.

22. If $a = 2$, $r = 3$, $l = 162$, find n.

23. If $a = 3$, $r = 2$, $n = 10$, find s.

24. If the fifth term of a G.P. is 48 and the second term 6, find the sixth term.

25. Insert three geometric means between -9 and -144.

26. Insert four geometric means between 1024 and 1.

27. Find a geometric mean between x and y. How many solutions are there?

28. The first term of a G.P. is 5. Find r when the sum to infinity is $\frac{50}{11}$.

29. The sum to infinity of a G.P. is 243. The second term is 54. Find the 10th term.

30. The eighth term of a G.P. is -384, the third term is 12. Find the series.

31. Four numbers are in G.P. The sum of the first two numbers is 16, the sum of the last two is 144. Find the numbers.

32. The sum of three numbers in A.P. is 15. If 1, 4, and 19 are added respectively to these numbers, the results are in G.P. Find the numbers.

33. The sum of four numbers is 13, the fourth being 3 times the second. Find the numbers if the first three are in G.P. and the last three are in A.P.

34. Given x, y, z, and w in geometric progression. Prove that

$$(x^2 + y^2 + z^2)(y^2 + z^2 + w^2) = (xy + yz + zw)^2$$

CHAPTER X

Logarithms

The fundamental principle

Many of the computations of insurance, engineering, astronomy, etc., require a prohibitive amount of labor. That it is possible to effect such computations is due largely to the invention of *logarithms* by John Napier (1550–1617), Baron of Merchiston, in Scotland. Like many epoch-making inventions, the fundamental principle is very simple.

Consider the function $y = 2^x$ from which we can readily obtain the following table:

x	-9	-8	-7	-6	-5	-4	-3	-2	-1	0	1	2	3	4	5	6	7	8	9
y	.001953125	.00390625	.0078125	.015625	.03125	.0625	.125	.25	.5	1	2	4	8	16	32	64	128	256	512

Since $2^u \cdot 2^v = 2^{u+v}$, it is clear that if we wish the product of two numbers in the lower line of the above table, we have only to add the two corresponding numbers in the upper line (the exponents) and then find the number in the lower line corresponding to this sum. For example, to find $.0078125 \times 128$, we find from the table the numbers corresponding to .0078125 and 128 to be -7 and 7, whose sum is 0. The number in the lower line corresponding to 0 is 1. Hence

$$.0078125 \times 128 = 1$$

Since $\frac{2^u}{2^v} = 2^{u-v}$, what is the quotient of $\frac{4}{.015625}$? of $\frac{.0625}{8}$?

Although the fundamental idea just described is simple, considerable insight was required to make the idea practicable. The above table can only be used when the numbers in question and their product or quotient can be found in the lower line. In order for the table to be practical, it is necessary that it contain every number, or that at least from it the corresponding exponent of any number can be obtained, either exactly or with a high degree of approximation. In short, Napier's problem was to fill in the gaps.

An examination of the table reveals the following two properties:

1. The values of x form an arithmetic progression.
2. The values of y form a geometric progression.

In the first place the table can be readily extended in either direction by writing out more terms of the progressions. In the second place, we can find new numbers to fill the gaps by inserting arithmetic means between successive values of x and geometric means between successive values of y. Thus, if we take the following portion of the preceding table

-2	-1	0	1	2	3	4
$.25 = \frac{1}{4}$	$.50 = \frac{1}{2}$	1	2	4	8	16

and insert between every two successive numbers in the upper line their arithmetic mean and between every two successive numbers of the lower line their geometric mean, we obtain the following table in which the results of the G.P. have been expressed to two decimal places.

x	-2.0	-1.5	-1.0	-0.5	0	0.5	1.0	1.5	2	2.5	3	3.5	4
y	0.25	0.35	0.50	0.72	1.00	1.41	2.00	2.83	4.00	5.66	8.00	11.31	16.00

This process, if continued indefinitely, enables us to make any number appear among the values of y to as high a degree of approximation as we desire.

We define the terms of the arithmetic series as being logarithms of the corresponding terms in the geometric series. The common ratio of the geometric series is called the *base* of the logarithms. Thus $\log_2 16 = 4$ is read, "The logarithm of 16 to the base 2 is 4," and means $2^4 = 16$.

A formal definition of a logarithm is as follows: The logarithm of a number N to a base b ($b > 0, \neq 1$) is the exponent x of the power to which the base b must be raised to produce the number N. That is, if $b^x = N$, then $x = \log_b N$. One should always keep in mind the fact that if one of these expressions is given the other is implied.

EXERCISES

1. Write as powers of 2:

a) 64
b) 2048
c) .25
d) .03125

2. Using the table on page 193, find the value of:

a) $.125 \times 8$
b) $\dfrac{512}{.0625}$
c) $.001953125 \times 16$
d) $.015625 \times 32$

3. Find the following logarithms:

a) $\log_2 16$
b) $\log_3 9$
c) $\log_5 125$
d) $\log_5 1$
e) $\log_7 7$
f) $\log_4 64$
g) $\log_p p$
h) $\log_x 1$

4. Find the following logarithms:

a) $\log_2 \frac{1}{8}$
b) $\log_3 \frac{1}{27}$
c) $\log_5 \frac{1}{125}$
d) $\log_4 \frac{1}{16}$
e) $\log_2 \frac{1}{64}$
f) $\log_6 \frac{1}{216}$

5. Write the following equations in logarithmic notation. Be sure to indicate the base.

a) $2^5 = 32$
b) $3^2 = 9$
c) $5^3 = 125$
d) $3^4 = 81$
e) $10^3 = 1000$
f) $10^{-2} = .01$
g) $10^{-1} = .1$
h) $5^{-2} = .04$
i) $x^n = p$
j) $p^3 = 4$
k) $\left(\dfrac{1}{x}\right)^p = q$

The three fundamental laws of logarithms

Law I. *The logarithm of a product equals the sum of the logarithms of its factors.* Symbolically

$$\log_b MN = \log_b M + \log_b N$$

Proof. Let
$$\log_b M = x$$
$$\log_b N = y$$

Then
$$b^x = M$$
$$b^y = N$$

Multiplying
$$MN = b^{x+y}$$

Hence
$$\log_b MN = x + y$$

or
$$\log_b MN = \log_b M + \log_b N$$

Law II. *The logarithm of a quotient equals the logarithm of the dividend minus the logarithm of the divisor.* Symbolically

$$\log_b \frac{M}{N} = \log_b M - \log_b N$$

Proof. Let
$$\log_b M = x$$
$$\log_b N = y$$

Then
$$b^x = M$$
$$b^y = N$$

Dividing
$$\frac{M}{N} = b^{x-y}$$

Hence
$$\log_b \frac{M}{N} = x - y = \log_b M - \log_b N$$

Law III. *The logarithm of the pth power of a number equals p times the logarithm of the number.* Symbolically

$$\log_b M^p = p \log_b M$$

Proof. Let
$$\log_b M = x$$

Then
$$b^x = M$$

Raising both sides to the pth power gives

$$b^{px} = M^p$$

Hence $$\log_b M^p = px = p \log_b M$$

EXAMPLE 1. Given $\log_{10} 2 = 0.3010$, $\log_{10} 7 = 0.8451$; find $\log_{10} 14$.

Solution.
$$\begin{aligned}\log_{10} 14 &= \log_{10} (2 \times 7) \\ &= \log_{10} 2 + \log_{10} 7 && \text{(Rule I)} \\ &= 0.3010 + 0.8451 = 1.1461\end{aligned}$$

EXAMPLE 2. Given $\log_{10} 2 = 0.3010$, $\log_{10} 3 = 0.4771$; find $\log_{10} \sqrt{\frac{3}{2}}$.

Solution.
$$\begin{aligned}\log_{10} \sqrt{\tfrac{3}{2}} &= \log_{10} (\tfrac{3}{2})^{\frac{1}{2}} \\ &= \tfrac{1}{2} \log \tfrac{3}{2} && \text{(Rule III)} \\ &= \tfrac{1}{2}(\log 3 - \log 2) && \text{(Rule II)} \\ &= \tfrac{1}{2}(0.4771 - 0.3010) \\ &= \tfrac{1}{2}(.1761) = .0880\end{aligned}$$

EXERCISES

1. Given $\log_{10} 2 = 0.3010$, $\log_{10} 3 = 0.4771$, $\log_{10} 7 = 0.8451$. Find:

a) $\log_{10} 21$
b) $\log_{10} 4$
c) $\log_{10}\sqrt{7}$
d) $\log_{10}\sqrt{\frac{7}{3}}$
e) $\log_{10} 49$
f) $\log_{10} \frac{7}{2}$
g) $\log_{10}\sqrt{2^3 \times 3^5}$
h) $\log_{10}\sqrt{42}$

2. What is the value of $\log_{10} 10$? $\log_{17} 17$? $\log_a a$?

3. Given $\log_{10} 2 = 0.3010$, find $\log_{10} 5$. [*Hint.* $\log_{10} 5 = \log_{10} \frac{10}{2}$]

4. Using the three logarithms given in example 1, find the following logarithms:

a) $\log_{10} \dfrac{4 \times 7}{3 \times 5}$
b) $\log_{10} 2^{25}$
c) $\log_{10} \dfrac{2048}{\sqrt{14}}$
d) $\log_{10} (2)^3 \frac{1}{9}$
e) $\log_{10} 3^3 \cdot 5^6 \cdot 7^4$
f) $\log_{10}(\frac{3}{2})^{100}$

Systems most frequently used

From the definition of a logarithm any positive number except 1 can be used as the base. The numbers most generally used are—

1. A certain irrational number which is approximately equal to 2.71828 and is called e.
2. The number 10.

Logarithms to the base e are used in many theoretical problems; such logarithms are called *natural logarithms.* For numerical computation the base 10 has numerous advantages; such logarithms are called *common logarithms.* In this book when no base is written, 10 is assumed to be the base. Thus, $\log M$ means $\log_{10} M$.

Logarithms to the base 10

Henry Briggs (1556–1631) was the first person to call attention to the advantages of 10 as a base. These advantages appear below.

If the base is 10, $\log 10 = 1$, $\log 100 = 2$, $\log 1000 = 3$, etc. Hence it follows that if a number is multiplied by 10 or by any positive integral power of 10 the logarithm of the number is increased by an *integer.* That is to say, shifting the decimal point to the right or left in a number changes only the integral part of the logarithm and leaves unchanged the decimal part of the logarithm. For example, if

$$\log 2 = 0.3010$$

then $$\log 20 = 1.3010$$

and $$\log 2000 = 3.3010$$

Or again, if $$\log 27.32 = 1.4365$$

then $$\log 2732 = 3.4365$$

and $$\log 273200 = 5.4365$$

From these examples it should be clear that the decimal part of a logarithm of a number greater than 1, when the base is 10, depends only on the succession of figures composing the number irrespective of where the decimal point is located. On the other hand, the integral part of the logarithm of the number depends simply on the position of the decimal point.

The decimal part of a logarithm is called its *mantissa;* the integral part, its *characteristic.* From the above discussion it is obvious that only the mantissas of logarithms to the base 10 need be tabulated, for the characteristic can be found by inspection, as we shall show. First let us consider numbers greater than 1. Since

$$\begin{aligned} 10^0 &= 1 \\ 10^1 &= 10 \\ 10^2 &= 100 \\ 10^3 &= 1000 \end{aligned}$$

it follows that a number with one digit in its integral part lies between 10^0 and 10^1; a number with two digits in its integral part lies between 10^1 and 10^2; and so on. Hence a number with n digits in its integral part lies between 10^{n-1} and 10^n. Therefore:

The characteristic of the logarithm of a number greater than 1 is one less than the number of digits at the left of the decimal point. For example, the characteristic of log 27.37 is 1, of log 727.34 is 2, of log 700273.732 is 5.

Let us now consider numbers less than 1. Since

$$\begin{aligned} 10^0 &= 1 \\ 10^{-1} &= .1 \\ 10^{-2} &= .01 \\ 10^{-3} &= .001 \end{aligned}$$

it follows that a decimal with one zero between the decimal point and the first significant figure, such as .0725, lies between 10^{-2} and 10^{-1}, and hence the characteristic of the logarithm of this number is -2. A number with two zeros between the decimal point and the first significant figure, such as .00235, lies between 10^{-3} and 10^{-2} and its logarithm has a characteristic of -3. Likewise a decimal with n zeros between the decimal point and the first significant figure lies between $10^{-(n+1)}$ and 10^{-n}, and its logarithm has the characteristic $-(n + 1)$.

Thus the characteristic of log 0.002 is -3, while the characteristic of log 0.0003 is -4. We may write

$$\begin{aligned} \log 0.002 &= 0.3010 - 3 \\ \log 0.0003 &= 0.4771 - 4 \end{aligned}$$

For convenience, if $n < 10$, we write $-n - 1$ as $(9 - n) - 10$; *i.e., count the number of zeros between the decimal point and the first significant figure, subtract this number from 9 and add -10.* This characteristic is written in two parts. The first part $9 - n$ is written to the left of the mantissa and the -10 at the right.

Thus,
$$\log 0.002 = 7.3010 - 10$$
$$\log 0.0003 = 6.4771 - 10$$

Another form of writing a negative characteristic is to write a minus sign over the characteristic.

Thus,
$$\log 0.002 = \bar{3}.3010$$
$$\log 0.0003 = \bar{4}.4771$$

The first two methods for writing a negative characteristic are preferable to the third method.

Note, we cannot write log 0.002 as -3.3010 as this would mean the entire logarithm is negative, whereas only the characteristic is negative.

A second method for determining characteristics

If a number has a decimal point at the right of the first significant figure, reading from left to right, we say the decimal point is in standard position. Thus in the numbers 5.672 and 3.0214 the decimal point is in standard position, and the characteristic of the logarithms of all such numbers is 0.

Moreover, any positive number can be expressed as the product of a number whose decimal point is in standard position and some integral power of 10. For example,

$$567.2 = 5.672 \times 10^2$$

and

$$0.0005672 = 5.672 \times 10^{-4}$$

If we take the logarithm of both members of these equations, we have

$$\log 567.2 = \log 5.672 + 2 \log 10 = \log 5.672 + 2$$
$$\log 0.0005672 = \log 5.672 - 4 \log 10 = \log 5.672 - 4$$

Since the characteristic of log 5.672 is 0, we see that the characteristic of log 567.2 is 2, and -4 for log 0.0005672. But 2 is the number of places the decimal point must be moved to the left in 567.2 to bring the decimal point in standard position, and 4 is the number of places the decimal point must be moved to the right in 0.0005672 to bring the decimal point in standard position.

These examples illustrate the rule: *If N is the number of places the decimal point is removed from standard position, the characteristic of a number greater than 1 is N, and the characteristic of a number less than 1 is $-N$.*

Use of tables

A table of logarithms contains only the mantissas since the characteristics are found by inspection. A table of logarithms should be so arranged that we can find:

a) The logarithm of any given number.

b) The number corresponding to a given logarithm.

Tables of logarithms vary as to the number of decimal places to which the mantissas are given and also in incidental details. However, the principles governing their use are identical and will be explained for a four-place table.

Problem I. *To find the logarithm of a given number.*

EXAMPLE 1. Find log 37.2

Solution. The characteristic is 1. Why? In the column headed **N** (page 358) we find 37; and if we follow this row across to the column headed 2, we read 5705, which is the desired mantissa. Hence

$$\log 37.2 = 1.5705$$

EXAMPLE 2. Find log 0.07234

Solution. The characteristic is 8 − 10. Why? The mantissa cannot be found in our table, but it can be found by a process called *interpolation* which assumes that to a small change in the number there corresponds a proportional change in the mantissa. Schematically we have:

	Number	Mantissa	
Difference 10 (4)	7230	8591	
	7234	?	6 = Difference
	7240	8597	

Our mantissa is $8591 + \frac{4}{10}(6) = 8593$.

Hence $\log 0.07234 = 8.8593 - 10$

Problem II. *To find the number corresponding to a given logarithm.*

EXAMPLE 1. Find x when $\log x = 7.8893 - 10$.

Solution. Since the characteristic is $7 - 10$, there are two zeros between the decimal point and the first significant figure. Why? From our table we find the mantissa 8893 corresponds to 775. Hence

$$x = 0.00775$$

EXAMPLE 2. Find x when $\log x = 0.7727$

Solution. We cannot find this mantissa in our table, but we can find 7723 and 7731 which correspond to 5920 and 5930 respectively. Reversing the process of Example 2 in Problem I, we have schematically:

	Number	Mantissa	
	5920	7723 (4)	
Difference 10	?	7727	8 = Difference
	5930	7731	

Hence the significant figures in our required number are $5920 + \frac{4}{8} \cdot 10 = 5925$.

Since the characteristic is 0, our number is 5.925.

EXERCISES

Find the logarithms of the following numbers:

1. 72.73
2. 873.4
3. 602500.0
4. 0.5937
5. 0.007373
6. 0.00007007
7. 920000
8. 7.234000
9. 0.87240000000

Find the numbers corresponding to the following logarithms:

10. 7.2342 − 10
11. 2.8765
12. 0.7895
13. 9.1234 − 10
14. 4.6789
15. 6.9873 − 10
16. 3.2794
17. 1.6784
18. 5.7234 − 10

Four epoch-making inventions aiding calculations

The first and greatest invention made to aid calculation was the Hindu notation, introduced sometime during the fifth or sixth century, using the base 10. To appreciate the importance of this system, try multiplying the numbers MCXI and DCLXV in Roman notation. The second great invention was made by Stevin (1585) when he extended the Hindu system to include decimals. In 1614 Napier made the third big contribution when he gave the world logarithms. Henry Briggs, who was Professor of Mathematics at Gresham College, became much interested in Napier's work and in 1624 brought out a system of logarithms using the base 10. The fourth and latest big invention is the calculating machine which is used so extensively in modern business.

Rounded numbers and significant figures

When the result of a measurement is expressed in the decimal notation, it is customary to write no more digits than are (probably) correct. If a distance is measured and expressed as 14.1 ft., it means the measure is correct to the nearest tenth of a foot. On the other hand, if the measure is found correctly to the nearest hundredth of a foot, we write 14.10 ft. In other words, $x = 14.1$ means that the exact value of x lies between 14.05 and 14.15, whereas if $x = 14.10$ the exact value of x lies between 14.095 and 14.105.

It is important to note that 14.1, 14.10, 14.100 *do not mean the same thing when they express the result of a measurement.* Do they represent the same amount if they represent dollars?

Sometimes we are furnished with numbers expressing measures which are given with greater accuracy than we can use, or care to use. Thus suppose we want to express a measured length of 3.5 in. in terms of centimeters. We find in a table of equivalent lengths that 1 in. = 2.54001 cm. It would be obviously absurd to use this expression as it stands. We accordingly round it off to 2.54 or even to 2.5 and find that 3.5 in. = 8.9 cm. If, on the other hand, we wish to express 3.50000 in. in centimeters, we should have to use the value 2.54001.

A number is rounded off by dropping one or more digits at the right, and, if the last digit dropped is 5+, 6, 7, 8, or 9, increasing the preceding digit by 1. Thus the successive approximations to π obtained by rounding off 3.14159 · · · are 3.1416, 3.142, 3.14, 3.1, 3.

The significant figures of a number may now be defined as the digits 1, 2, 3, · · ·, 9 together with such zeros as occur between them or as have been properly retained in rounding them off. Thus 34.96 and 3,496,000 are both numbers of four significant figures. On the other hand, 3,496,000.0 has eight significant figures, since the 0 in the first decimal place according to the convention adopted means that the number is exact to the nearest tenth. This zero is then essentially a digit properly retained in rounding off, and should be counted as one of the significant figures.

Confusion can arise in only one case. For example, if the number 3999.7 were rounded by dropping the 7, we should write it as 4000 which, according to the rule just given, we would consider as having only one significant figure, whereas in reality we know from the way in which the number was obtained, that all five of the figures are significant. When such a case arises in practice we may simply remember the fact, or we can indicate that the zeros are significant by underscoring them, or by some other device. Computers adopt devices of their own to avoid errors in such cases.

Any result obtained by using approximate numbers may be no more accurate than the least accurate number used in the computation. To illustrate this fact, suppose we measured the sides of a rectangle and found them to be 12.3 ft. and 11.5 ft. respectively. If we multiply these values we might be inclined to say the area is 12.3×11.5 or 141.45 sq. ft. but this is not correct as will be presently shown. Recalling the meaning of approximate numbers we see the area of the rectangle lies between $12.25 \times 11.45 = 140.2625$ sq. ft. and $12.35 \times 11.55 = 142.6425$ sq. ft. Hence to claim the area is 141.45 sq. ft. is obviously not correct. If we round off this number to the same number of significant digits as there are in the given numbers, namely three, the area equals 141 sq. ft. The first two figures in this answer are correct and the last figure is an approximation.

Computations

In the following computations we shall use a four-place table of logarithms. Any number of less than four places we shall assume to be exact; numbers with more than four significant digits we shall round off to four digits. A few devices, often necessary, or at least desirable, will be introduced. Reference is made to them here in order that one may be sure to use them when the need arises.

EXAMPLE 1. Find the value of $23.46 \times 1.273 \times 0.8738$.

Solution. We find the logarithm of each factor, add them, and then find the number corresponding to this logarithm. The work is best arranged as follows:

Numbers		Logarithms
23.46	$\longrightarrow$	1.3703
1.273	$\longrightarrow$	0.1048
0.8738	$\longrightarrow$	9.9414 − 10
		11.4165 − 10
26.09 Ans.	$\longleftarrow$	1.4165

EXAMPLE 2. Find the value of $73.26 \div 89.14$.

Solution.

Numbers		Logarithms
73.26	$\longrightarrow$	11.8649 − 10
89.14	$\longrightarrow$	1.9501
.8228 Ans.	$\longleftarrow$	9.9148 − 10

The logarithm of 73.26 is 1.8649 but we write it as 11.8649 − 10 to make the subtraction easier.

EXAMPLE 3. Find the value of $(1.357)^5$.

Solution.

Number		Logarithm
1.357	→	0.1325
		5
4.597 Ans.	←	0.6625

EXAMPLE 4. Find the cube root of -0.007632.

Solution.

Number		Logarithm
0.007632	→	7.8826 − 10
	3	27.8826 − 30
0.1969	←	9.2942 − 10

When a logarithm with a negative characteristic is to be divided by any integer, it is best first to add and subtract such a multiple of 10 that, after dividing there will be −10 at the right.

Since the cube root of a negative number is negative, the desired result is −0.1969.

EXERCISES

Find by logarithms the value of each of the following expressions:

1. 35.97×4.68

2. $318.7 \times 9.02 \times .0573$

3. $\dfrac{0.5785}{0.3215}$

4. $\dfrac{5.006 \times 2.494}{6.533 \times 1.111}$

5. $(34.17 \times .383)^2$

6. $8.75 \times (.721)^3 \times 1.837$

7. $\sqrt[3]{\dfrac{473}{(21.4)^2}}$

8. $\sqrt{\frac{1379}{4581}}$

9. $\sqrt{\dfrac{\pi \times 2.876}{8.14}}$

10. $\sqrt[3]{\dfrac{4.723 \times 17.53}{2175 \times 18.75}}$

11. $\dfrac{\sqrt{0.007561}}{(385)^2}$

12. $(21.12)^{\frac{1}{5}}$

13. 3^{100}

14. $\dfrac{3^{100}}{2^{50}}$

15. $(0.07072)^{\frac{1}{5}}$

16. The time t of oscillation of a pendulum of length l centimeters is given in seconds by the formula

$$t = \pi\sqrt{\frac{l}{980}}$$

Find the time of oscillation of a pendulum 75.24 centimeters in length.

17. The crushing weight P in pounds of a wrought iron column is given by the formula

$$P = 299{,}600 \frac{d^{3.55}}{l^2}$$

where d is the diameter in inches and l is the length in feet. What weight will crush a wrought iron column 10 ft. long and 2.7 in. in diameter?

18. The weight W in grams of a cubic meter of saturated aqueous vapor at 17° C. is given by the formula

$$W = \frac{1293 \times 12.7 \times 5}{(1 + \frac{17}{273})(760 \times 8)}$$

Find W to four significant figures.

Exponential equations

An equation in which the unknown is contained in an exponent is known as an *exponential equation*. Some equations of this type can be solved by taking the logarithm of both sides after the equation has been properly transformed.

EXAMPLE 1. Solve for x,

$$2^{3x+1} + 5 = 11$$

Solution.

$$\begin{aligned} 2^{3x+1} + 5 &= 11 \\ 2^{3x+1} &= 6 \\ \log 2^{3x+1} &= \log 6 \\ (3\,x + 1) \log 2 &= \log 6 \\ 3\,x + 1 &= \frac{\log 6}{\log 2} \\ x &= \frac{1}{3}\left[\frac{\log 6}{\log 2} - 1\right] \\ &= \frac{1}{3}\left[\frac{.7782}{.3010} - 1\right] \\ &= .5284 \end{aligned}$$

The student should note that $\frac{\log 6}{\log 2}$ is the quotient of two logarithms and not the logarithm of a quotient.

EXAMPLE 2. Solve for x,

$$3^x = .2$$

Solution. Taking the logarithm of both members gives

$$x \log 3 = \log .2$$

$$x = \frac{\log .2}{\log 3}$$

$$= \frac{9.3010 - 10}{.4771}$$

$$= \frac{-.6990}{.4771}$$

$$= -1.465$$

EXERCISES

1. Solve for x the equation $3^x = 6$.

2. Solve for x the equation $2^x = 5$.

3. Solve for x the equation $3^x + 2 = 11$.

4. Solve for x and y the equations $3^{x+y} = 5$, $2^{x-y} = 4$.

5. Solve for x and y the equations $2^{x+y} = 3^y$, $3^{x-1} = 2^{y+1}$.

6. If $A = P(1 + i)^n$, prove that

$$n = \frac{\log A - \log P}{\log (1 + i)}$$

7. If $P = A(1 + i)^{-n}$, prove that

$$n = \frac{\log A - \log P}{\log (1 + i)}$$

8. Solve for n the equation $S = \dfrac{ar^n - a}{r - 1}$.

9. Solve for n the equation $S = \dfrac{(1 + i)^n - 1}{i}$.

10. Solve for n the equation $A = \dfrac{1 - (1 + i)^{-n}}{i}$.

11. In a table of natural logarithms would you expect to find the characteristics tabulated? Give a reason for your answer.

MASTERY TEST

1. Using a four-place table of logarithms, find the value of the following expressions:

a) 0.07834×10.27

b) $273.1 \div 4.764$

c) $\dfrac{27.43}{11.73 \times 25.83}$

d) $\dfrac{22.7 \times (-3.72) \times 72.5}{-0.72 \times (-47.3) \times (-0.007)}$

e) $\sqrt[3]{0.7563}$

f) $\sqrt{\frac{3}{4}}$

g) $\dfrac{\sqrt[5]{0.007654}}{\sqrt[3]{0.03456}}$

h) $\left(\dfrac{0.39 \times 14.27}{9.32 \times 473.1}\right)^{\frac{1}{5}}$

2. In the formula $H = \dfrac{PLAN}{33{,}000}$, find H when $P = 80.5$, $L = 3.2$, $A = 240.5$, $N = 120$

3. Heron's formula for the area of a triangle is

$$K = \sqrt{s(s-a)(s-b)(s-c)}$$

where $2s = a + b + c$.

Find K if $a = 70.4$, $b = 36.6$, and $c = 48.2$.

4. Solve for x, $\quad 3^x = 8^{x-1}$

5. The formula

$$n = \frac{1}{2l}\sqrt{\frac{Mg}{m}}$$

gives the number of vibrations n made by a stretched string of length l (in centimeters), where M is the weight (in grams) stretching the string and m is the weight (in grams) of one centimeter of the string. Compute n, if

$$\begin{aligned} M &= 4572 \text{ grams} \\ l &= 80.63 \text{ centimeters} \\ m &= .0072 \text{ grams} \\ g &= 980 \end{aligned}$$

6. P dollars at compound interest at r per cent compounded m times a year, will in n years amount to A dollars where

$$A = P\left(1 + \frac{r}{m}\right)^{mn}$$

Find A if $P = 3500$, $r = .04$, $m = 4$, $n = 15$.

7. If $T = \pi\sqrt{\dfrac{l}{g}}$, find T if $l = 5$, $g = 32$.

8. If $f = \dfrac{mv^2}{r}$, find r if $m = 16.3$, $v = 32.5$, $f = 15{,}400$.

9. Find x if $\log_{10}(x - 1) - \log_{10} x = \log_{10} 2$.

10. In the formula $R = \sqrt[3]{\dfrac{HT}{V^2}}$, find V if $R = 12.8$, $H = 25$, $T = 12$.

TRUE-FALSE TEST

Tell whether each of the following statements is true or false:

1. The ratio of 1 yard to 1 rod is $\frac{1}{5}$.

2. The average of a and b is their arithmetic mean.

3. The only geometric mean between 1 and 4 is 2.

4. The series 4, 9, 16, 25, $\cdots$ is a geometric progression.

5. It is possible by use of the formula $s = \dfrac{a}{1 - r}$ to find the sum of an infinite number of terms of the series 1, 2, 4, 8, $\cdots$.

6. In every A.P. of n terms, s is always greater than 1.

7. Since $3^4 = 81$, then $\log_3 81 = 4$.

8. $\text{Log}\,\dfrac{x}{y} = \dfrac{\log x}{\log y}$.

9. The characteristic of log 0.0000078 is -6.

10. If $3^x = 5$ then $x = \dfrac{\log 5}{\log 3}$.

11. $2 \log x - 3 \log (y + 1) = \log \dfrac{x^2}{(1 + y)^3}$.

12. The equation $\sqrt{x + 1} + \sqrt{x + 2} + \sqrt{x + 3} = 0$ has a real positive root.

13. The log of 1 to any base is 0.

14. If $xy = k$, then y varies inversely as x.

15. In the formula $F = \frac{9}{5}C + 32$, if $C = 10$, then $F = 40$.

16. $\text{Log}\sqrt[3]{x^2\dfrac{(y - z)}{t^5 m}} = \dfrac{1}{3}[2 \log x - 5 \log t + \log (y - z) - \log m]$.

CHAPTER XI

The Theory of Investment

Compound interest

In this chapter we shall explain how the solution of certain problems which involve interest, discount, annuities, etc., may be simplified by the means of algebraic formulas.

When one borrows money, he has to pay for its use; and the money paid is called *interest.* The amount of money borrowed or placed at interest is called the *principal.* If the interest is added to the principal each time the interest is computed, we say that the interest has been *compounded.* The time between successive conversions of interest is called the *conversion period.* The sum to which the principal accumulates is called the *amount.* The interest earned by one unit of capital, in one unit of time, is called the *rate.* Even though interest may be compounded more than once a year, it is customary to quote it on an annual basis. For example, a rate of 4 per cent semiannually means a rate of 2 per cent every half year.

Suppose that a sum of P dollars is placed at compound interest for n equal conversion periods at the rate of i per cent per conversion period. Then the amount A_1 at the end of the first period is

$$A_1 = P + Pi = P(1 + i)$$

At the end of the second period the amount A_2 is

$$\begin{aligned} A_2 &= P(1 + i) + P(1 + i)i \\ &= P(1 + i)^2 \end{aligned}$$

Continuing this process, we see that the amount A_n at the end of n periods is

$$A_n = P(1 + i)^n$$

The factor $(1 + i)^n$ is called the *accumulation factor*. Thus, if money is invested at 4 per cent semiannually for ten years, the rate used each time interest is computed is $\frac{.04}{2}$ or 2 per cent, while n, the number of periods, is 10×2 or 20. Hence, the accumulation factor is $(1.02)^{20}$.

If any three of the four quantities A_n, P, i, and n are known, the fourth quantity can be found. The following examples will illustrate how this is done except in the case when A_n, i, and n are given and P is desired. This case will be discussed in the next article.

EXAMPLE 1. What sum will \$1000 amount to in 10 years at 4 per cent compound interest?

Solution. Method I. By logarithms.

$$A_n = P(1 + i)^n$$
$$P = 1000, \quad i = .04, \quad n = 10$$

Hence $$A_n = 1000(1.04)^{10}$$

Now
$$\begin{aligned} \log A_n &= \log 1000 + 10 \log 1.04 \\ &= 3.0000 + 10(0.0170) \\ &= 3.1700 \\ A_n &= \$1479 \text{ (approximately)} \end{aligned}$$

Method II. From the table on page 360.

$$\begin{aligned} (1.04)^{10} &= 1.4802 \\ A_n &= 1000(1.04)^{10} \\ &= 1000(1.4802) \\ &= \$1480 \text{ (approximately)} \end{aligned}$$

EXAMPLE 2. Find the amount of \$500 in 5 years compounded quarterly at 4 per cent.

Solution. Method I. By logarithms.

$$P = 500,\ i = \frac{.04}{4} = .01,\ n = 5 \times 4 = 20$$

Hence $$A_n = 500(1.01)^{20}$$

Now
$$\begin{aligned} \log A_n &= \log 500 + 20 \log 1.01 \\ &= 2.6990 + 20(0.0043) \\ &= 2.7850 \\ A_n &= \$609.60 \text{ (approximately)} \end{aligned}$$

Method II. From the table on page 360.

$$\begin{aligned} (1.01)^{20} &= 1.2202 \\ \therefore \quad A_n &= 500(1.01)^{20} \\ &= 500(1.2202) \\ &= \$610.20 \text{ (approximately)} \end{aligned}$$

EXAMPLE 3. At what rate of interest will money double itself in 12 years?

Solution. If the principal is P, then the amount will be $2P$.

Hence
$$\begin{aligned} 2P &= P(1 + i)^{12} \\ (1 + i)^{12} &= 2 \\ 1 + i &= \sqrt[12]{2} \\ i &= \sqrt[12]{2} - 1 \end{aligned}$$

Using logarithms to compute the value of $\sqrt[12]{2}$ gives

$$i = 1.059 - 1 = .059$$

Hence the rate is 5.9 per cent.

EXAMPLE 4. How long will it take \$10 to amount to \$18 at 4 per cent interest compounded annually?

Solution. Now $18 = 10(1.04)^n$

Then
$$\begin{aligned} (1.04)^n &= 1.8 \\ n \log 1.04 &= \log 1.8 \\ n &= \frac{\log 1.8}{\log 1.04} = \frac{.2553}{.0170} \\ &= \text{approximately 15 years} \end{aligned}$$

EXERCISES

1. Find the amount of $100 for five years at 2 per cent interest compounded (a) annually; (b) semiannually.

2. Find the amount of $300 for ten years at 4 per cent interest compounded quarterly.

3. Find the amount of $1000 for six years at 3 per cent interest compounded semiannually.

4. How long will it take $100 to double itself at interest compounded annually at 4 per cent?

5. How long will it take $100 to amount to $146.85 at interest compounded at 3 per cent annually?

6. If $100 placed at compound interest computed annually amounts in 15 years to $180.10, what is the rate?

7. If the population of a town is 10,000 and is increasing at the rate of 2 per cent per year, what will be the population in 20 years?

8. In how many years will it take P dollars to treble itself at compound interest computed at 6 per cent annually?

9. In what time will $100 amount to $300 with interest compounded semiannually at 3 per cent?

10. In 5 years $1000 placed at compound interest converted quarterly amounts to $1,346.85. What is the rate?

Present value

We call P the *present value* of A_n, for it represents the amount of money which invested today will amount to A_n dollars in n periods at i per cent. If A_n, n, and i are given, then

$$P = \frac{A_n}{(1 + i)^n} = A_n(1 + i)^{-n}$$

The factor $(1 + i)^{-n}$ is called the *discount factor.*

EXAMPLE 1. Find the present value of a note of $200 due in 5 years with interest compounded at 4 per cent semiannually.

Solution. Method I. By logarithms.

$$P = A_n(1 + i)^{-n}$$

$$A_n = 200, \; i = \frac{.04}{2} = .02, \; n = 5 \times 2 = 10$$

Hence $\quad P = 200(1.02)^{-10}$

Now
$$\begin{aligned} \log P &= \log 200 - 10 \log (1.02) \\ &= 2.3010 - 10(.0086) \\ &= 2.2150 \\ P &= \$164.10 \text{ (approximately)} \end{aligned}$$

Method II. From the table on page 361.

$$\begin{aligned} (1.02)^{-10} &= .82035 \\ \therefore \quad P &= 200(1.02)^{-10} \\ &= 200(.82035) \\ &= \$164.07 \text{ (approximately)} \end{aligned}$$

EXAMPLE 2. The present value of a note of $400 due in 10 years is $270.23. What is the rate of interest?

Solution.
$$\begin{aligned} 270.23 &= 400(1 + i)^{-10} \\ +10 \log (1 + i) &= +\log 400 - \log 270.23 \\ +10 \log (1 + i) &= 2.6021 - 2.4318 \\ \log (1 + i) &= .0170 \\ 1 + i &= 1.04 \\ i &= .04 \end{aligned}$$

EXAMPLE 3. The present value of a note of $400 bearing interest of 4 per cent is $300. In how many years will the note be due?

Solution.
$$\begin{aligned} 300 &= 400(1.04)^{-n} \\ +n \log (1.04) &= +\log 400 - \log 300 \\ +n(.0170) &= +2.6021 - 2.4771 \\ +n (.0170) &= +.1250 \\ n &= \frac{.1250}{.0170} = 7.4 \end{aligned}$$

or approximately $7\frac{1}{2}$ years.

EXERCISES

1. How much money placed in a bank paying 2 per cent compound interest will amount to $1000 in 10 years?

2. For what amount should a note of $1000, due in 8 years and bearing compound interest at 4 per cent, sell for today?

3. What is the present value of a note of $1000, due in 10 years, bearing interest of 4 per cent payable semiannually?

4. If a note of $1000 bearing interest of 4 per cent is worth $600 today, in how many years will the note be due?

5. A man wishes to deposit in a savings bank at the time of the birth of a son enough money so that the boy will have $2000 on his eighteenth birthday. If the bank pays 3 per cent interest compounded annually, how much money should he deposit?

6. How much money must one deposit in a bank paying 3 per cent interest compounded annually, so as to be able to withdraw $1000 in 2 years and $2000 in 5 years?

7. A man borrowed $10,000 at 5 per cent. He paid $4000 at the end of the first year and the balance at the end of the second year. What was the value of the last payment?

8. How much money must a man deposit in a bank paying 3 per cent interest so that his son will have $1000, 10 years from now?

Annuity

In many business transactions one has to make equal payments at equal intervals of time, such as making interest payments on a mortgage or paying for insurance. The series of these payments is called an *annuity*.

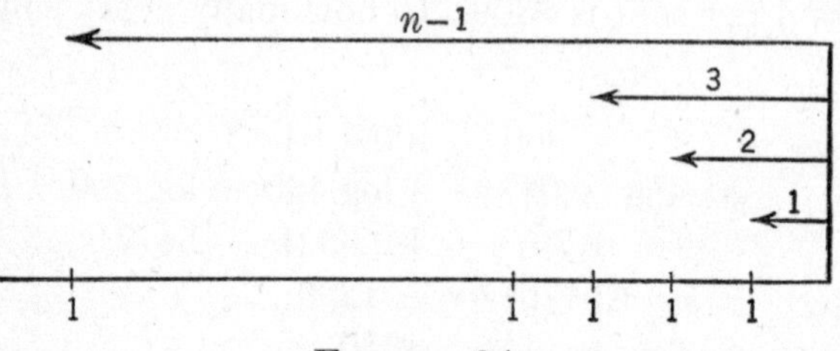

FIGURE 34

Unless otherwise stated, it is assumed that the payment interval and the interest interval are equal and that the first payment is made at the *end* of the first interval. Each payment is called *rent* and is denoted by R.

The amount of an annuity $s_{\overline{n}|}$ is the total amount which would be accumulated at the end of the term if each payment as it is made is placed at compound interest. Suppose the payments are $1 each. At the end of the term the last payment of

\$1 will have just been made, and hence its value is \$1; the next to the last payment will have been at interest for one period; hence its amount will be $(1 + i)$. The payment before this has been at interest for two periods; hence its amount is $(1 + i)^2$. Continuing this process, we arrive at the first payment which has been at interest for $n - 1$ periods, and its amount is $(1 + i)^{n-1}$. Therefore, $s_{\overline{n|}}$ is the sum of the geometric progression,

$$1 + (1 + i) + (1 + i)^2 + \cdots + (1 + i)^{n-1}$$

Since $a = 1$, $r = (1 + i)$, $l = (1 + i)^{n-1}$ and $s = \dfrac{rl - a}{r - 1}$, then,

$$s_{\overline{n|}} = \frac{(1 + i)^n - 1}{i} \tag{1}$$

The present value of an annuity, denoted by $a_{\overline{n|}}$, is the sum of the present values of all the payments at the beginning of the term. Obviously,

$$a_{\overline{n|}} = s_{\overline{n|}}(1 + i)^{-n}$$

$$= \frac{(1 + i)^n - 1}{i}(1 + i)^{-n}$$

$$\therefore \quad a_{\overline{n|}} = \frac{1 - (1 + i)^{-n}}{i} \tag{2}$$

EXAMPLE 1. Find the amount of an annuity of \$2000 a year, for 5 years, at 4 per cent.

Solution. Method I. By logarithms,

$$\text{the sum} = Rs_{\overline{n|}} = R\frac{(1 + i)^n - 1}{i}$$

$$= 2000\frac{(1.04)^5 - 1}{.04}$$

We can find the value of $(1.04)^5$ by logarithms.

$$\log (1.04)^5 = 5 \log 1.04$$
$$= 5(.0170)$$
$$= 0.0850$$
$$\therefore \quad (1.04)^5 = 1.216$$

Hence, $$Rs_{\overline{5}|} = 2000\,\frac{1.216 - 1}{.04} = 2000\frac{.216}{.04}$$

$$= 2000(5.4) = \$10{,}800 \text{ (approximately)}$$

Method II. From the table on page 362,

$$\text{the sum} = 2000\,\frac{(1.04)^5 - 1}{.04} = 2000(5.4163)$$

$$= \$10{,}832.60 \text{ (approximately)}$$

EXAMPLE 2. What should one pay for an annuity of $1000 a year payable annually for 20 years, if money is worth 3 per cent?

Solution. Method I. By logarithms,

$$\text{the present value} = Ra_{\overline{n}|}$$

$$= 1000\frac{1 - (1.03)^{-20}}{.03}$$

It is left as an exercise for the student to prove by logarithms that $(1.03)^{-20} = .5546$.
Hence the present value = $14,846 (approximately).

Method II. Using the table on page 363, we have

$$\text{the present value} = 1000\frac{1 - (1.03)^{-20}}{.03}$$

$$= 1000(14.8775)$$

$$= \$14{,}877.50 \text{ (approximately)}$$

EXERCISES

1. Find the amount of an annuity of $200 a year for 5 years at 2 per cent.

2. Find the present value of an annuity of $500 a year for 8 years at 3 per cent annually.

3. A man deposits $500 a year in a bank paying 2 per cent compound interest. How much will be on deposit at the end of 10 years?

4. A man deposits $500 every 6 months in a bank paying compound interest of 2 per cent semiannually. How much will he have on deposit at the end of 10 years?

5. Find the present value of an annuity of $200 payable every three months for 5 years, if money is worth 4 per cent quarterly.

6. I wish to accumulate $1000 in $2\frac{1}{2}$ years. How much should I deposit every 6 months in a savings bank paying interest of 3 per cent compounded semiannually?

7. I can buy a house for $10,000 or I can pay $3000 cash and make ten equal payments at the end of each year. Find the amount of these payments if money is worth 4 per cent.

8. In how many years will an annuity whose rent is $100 payable annually, accumulate to $3,245.29 if interest is compounded at 3 per cent annually?

9. At the time of the birth of a son, a man deposits $4000 in a bank paying compound interest at 3 per cent annually. The money is to be paid to the boy in 4 equal annual installments, the first to be on the boy's eighteenth birthday. Find the amount of each installment.

10. A man deposits $400 at the end of each year for 6 years in a bank paying $2\frac{1}{2}$ per cent interest compounded annually. The fund is then allowed to accumulate for 4 years more without any additional payments. How much will be on deposit at the end of 10 years?

11. Prove $s_{\overline{1}|} = 1$.

12. Prove $a_{\overline{1}|} = (1 + i)^{-1}$.

13. Find the present value of 20 semiannual payments of $1000, interest at 4 per cent convertible semiannually.

14. Find the present value of an annuity of quarterly payments of $200 each for 12 years, money worth 4 per cent quarterly.

Perpetuities

If the payments of an annuity are made for an unlimited period, the annuity is called a *perpetuity*. We shall now find the present value of a perpetuity whose payments of 1 unit each are made at the end of every k years. Discounting each payment to today, we see that the present value is the sum of the series

$$(1 + i)^{-k},\ (1 + i)^{-2k},\ (1 + i)^{-3k},\ \cdots$$

What kind of a series is it? Is the ratio numerically less than 1? Since it is a geometric series with the ratio numerically less than 1, we know that the sum to infinity can be found by the formula $\frac{a}{1-r}$. Hence the sum is

$$\frac{(1+i)^{-k}}{1-(1+i)^{-k}}$$

If we multiply the numerator and denominator by $(1+i)^k$, we have

$$\frac{1}{(1+i)^k-1}$$

If we multiply the numerator and denominator by i, we have

$$\frac{1}{i}\frac{i}{(1+i)^k-1} \tag{3}$$

or

$$\frac{1}{i}\cdot\frac{1}{s_{\overline{k|}}}$$

When $k = 1$, formula (3) reduces to

$$\frac{1}{i} \tag{4}$$

EXAMPLE 1. If money is worth 4 per cent, how much is a business worth whose net yearly income is $12,000?

Solution. The value is $(12{,}000)\left(\frac{1}{.04}\right) = \$300{,}000.$

EXAMPLE 2. A road costing $250,000 has to be rebuilt every thirty years. What sum should be set aside at the time the road is built, in order to provide for an indefinite number of renewals on the supposition that the cost of renewal remains constant, and that money remains at 4 per cent?

Solution.

$$\begin{aligned}\frac{R}{i}\frac{1}{s_{\overline{k|}}} &= \frac{250{,}000}{.04}\frac{1}{s_{\overline{30|}}}\\ &= \frac{250{,}000}{.04}(.0178301)\\ &= \$111{,}437.50\end{aligned}$$

EXERCISES

Find the present value of each of the following perpetuities:

1. Annual payments of $1000, interest at 5 per cent.

2. Payments of $1000 every two years, interest at 4 per cent.

3. Payments of $1000 every five years, interest at 3 per cent.

4. A railroad pays $1000 a year to guard a crossing. If money is worth 4 per cent, how much can they afford to pay to abolish the crossing?

5. Every two years a farm yields a crop whose net value is $2000. What is a reasonable value for the farm immediately after a crop has been harvested, and money is worth 4 per cent?

6. How much money must a man give a college to build a dormitory costing $100,000, to pay for janitor service of $1200 a year, and to renovate the building every 20 years at a cost of $20,000, if money is worth 4 per cent?

CHAPTER XII

Mathematical Induction
Binomial Theorem

Proof by induction

The following exercises will aid in familiarizing one with the terminology used in this chapter.

In the series

$$1 + 3 + 5 + \cdots + (2n - 1)$$

the first term is 1, the second term is 3, the nth term is $2n - 1$. What is the $(n - 4)$th term? the $(n + 6)$th term?

The nth term of a series is called the *general term*. Let us find the general term of the series

$$2 + 2^3 + 2^5 + \cdots .$$

The exponents form the series $1, 3, 5, \cdots$. What kind of a progression is this? What is the nth term of this progression? Show that it is $2n - 1$. Hence the general term of the given series is 2^{2n-1}.

EXERCISES

Find the general term in each of the following series:

1. $2 + 4 + 6 + \cdots$
2. $2^0 + 2^3 + 2^6 + 2^9 + \cdots$
3. $\frac{1}{2} + \frac{1}{2^2} + \frac{1}{2^3} + \cdots$
4. $\frac{1}{3^2} + \frac{1}{3^3} + \frac{1}{3^4} + \cdots$
5. $y + \frac{y^2}{2} + \frac{y^3}{3} + \frac{y^4}{4} \cdots$
6. $\frac{1}{1 \cdot 2} + \frac{1}{2 \cdot 3} + \frac{1}{3 \cdot 4} + \cdots$
7. $1 + \frac{1}{3} + \frac{1}{5} + \frac{1}{7} + \cdots$
8. $\frac{1}{2^2} + \frac{1}{2^3} + \frac{1}{2^4} + \cdots$

Sometimes students are prone to draw erroneous conclusions concerning the validity of formulas. For example, suppose we were given the expression $n = x^2 - x + 41$ and noticed that n is prime when $x = 1, 2, 3, 4, 5, 6$. Thus when

$$x = 1, n = 41 \qquad x = 4, n = 53$$
$$x = 2, n = 43 \qquad x = 5, n = 61$$
$$x = 3, n = 47 \qquad x = 6, n = 71$$

We might be tempted to say "n is a prime number for every integral value of x." In fact, n is prime until we reach $x = 41$ when $n = 1681$ which is 41^2. Hence n is not prime for every integral value of x.

Induction is the process of discovering or proving a general law or proposition from particular cases. In algebra the method of *mathematical induction* is often used in proving the validity of certain mathematical formulas which involve n, the number of terms. There are three distinct steps to the process.

1. We prove the formula is true for particular values of n, usually $n = 1$ or $n = 2$.
2. We assume the formula to be true for any fixed integral value of n, for example $n = r$.
3. We then prove that *if* the formula is true for $n = r$ it is also true for $n = r + 1$.

Therefore, since the formula is true for $n = 1$ (step 1), it is true for $n = 2$ (step 3). Since it is true for $n = 2$, it is true for $n = 3$. Continuing this process, we know that the formula is true for all integral values of n.

EXAMPLE. Prove by mathematical induction that the sum of the first n odd integers is n^2. That is, prove

$$1 + 3 + 5 + \cdots + (2n - 1) = n^2 \qquad (1)$$

Proof. 1. The formula we know is true for $n = 1$, for $1 = 1^2$.

2. We now wish to prove that if the formula is true for any integral value of n; for example, $n = r$, it is also true for the next integral value of n, namely $n = r + 1$.

Assume the formula to be true for $n = r$. That is, assume that

$$1 + 3 + 5 + \cdots + (2r - 1) = r^2 \qquad (2)$$

Adding $2r + 1$ to both members of (2) gives

$$1 + 3 + 5 + \cdots + (2r - 1) + (2r + 1) = r^2 + (2r + 1)$$
$$= (r + 1)^2 \qquad (3)$$

Hence, if formula (1) is true for $n = r$, it is true for $n = r + 1$. But (1) is true for $n = 1$; hence it is true for $n = 2$; since it is true for $n = 2$, it is true for $n = 3$. Continuing this process, we see that it must hold for any positive integral value of n.

EXERCISES

Prove by mathematical induction:

1. $1 + 2 + 3 + \cdots + n = \dfrac{n(n+1)}{2}$

2. $3 + 6 + 9 + \cdots + 3n = \dfrac{3n(n+1)}{2}$

3. $2 + 4 + 6 + \cdots + 2n = n(n+1)$

4. $2^0 + 2^1 + 2^2 + \cdots + 2^{n-1} = 2^n - 1$

5. $1^3 + 2^3 + 3^3 + \cdots + n^3 = \dfrac{n^2(n+1)^2}{4}$

6. $1^2 + 2^2 + 3^2 + \cdots + n^2 = \frac{1}{6}n(n+1)(2n+1)$

7. $2^2 + 4^2 + 6^2 + \cdots + (2n)^2 = \dfrac{2n(n+1)(2n+1)}{3}$

8. $2 + 2^2 + 2^3 + \cdots + 2^n = 2^{n+1} - 2$

9. $\dfrac{1}{1 \cdot 2} + \dfrac{1}{2 \cdot 3} + \dfrac{1}{3 \cdot 4} + \cdots + \dfrac{1}{n(n+1)} = \dfrac{n}{n+1}$

10. $a - b$ is a factor of $a^n - b^n$ if n is any positive integer.

Hint. Note $a^{r+1} - b^{r+1} = a(a^r - b^r) + b^r(a - b)$

11. $1 \cdot 3 + 2 \cdot 4 + 3 \cdot 5 + \cdots + n(n+2) = \frac{1}{6}n(n+1)(2n+7)$

12. $\dfrac{1}{2} + \dfrac{1}{2^2} + \dfrac{1}{2^3} + \cdots + \dfrac{1}{2^n} = \dfrac{2^n - 1}{2^n}$

13. $\dfrac{1}{1 \cdot 3} + \dfrac{1}{3 \cdot 5} + \dfrac{1}{5 \cdot 7} + \cdots + \dfrac{1}{(2n-1)(2n+1)} = \dfrac{n}{2n+1}$

14. $1^3 + 2^3 + 3^3 + \cdots + n^3 = (1 + 2 + \cdots + n)^2$

15. $1^3 + 3^3 + 5^3 + \cdots + (2n-1)^3 = n^2(2n^2 - 1)$

16. $a + ar + ar^2 + \cdots + ar^n = \dfrac{a - ar^n}{1 - r}$

17. $a + (a + d) + (a + 2d) + \cdots + [a + (n - 1)d]$

$$= \frac{n}{2}[2a + (n - 1)d]$$

Factorial notation

The product of n positive consecutive integers starting with 1 is called factorial n and is designated by the symbol $n!$ Thus

$$1 \cdot 2 \cdot 3 \cdot \cdots \cdot n = n!$$

Which would you prefer to have, factorial ten dollars or a million dollars?

EXERCISES

1. Simplify: a) $\dfrac{n!}{(n-1)!}$ b) $\dfrac{(n-r-1)!}{(n-r+1)!}$

2. Prove that $\dfrac{k(k-1) \cdots (k-r+2)}{(r-1)!}$

$$+ \frac{k(k-1) \cdots (k-r+3)}{(r-2)!} = \frac{(k+1)k \cdots (k-r+3)}{(r-1)!}$$

3. Prove that $\dfrac{n(n-1)(n-2) \cdots (n-r+1)}{r!} = \dfrac{n!}{r!(n-r)!}$

Binomial theorem

Let us consider the expansion of $(a + x)^n$ where n is a positive integer. By actual multiplication show that:

$$(a + x)^1 = a + x$$
$$(a + x)^2 = a^2 + 2ax + x^2$$
$$(a + x)^3 = a^3 + 3a^2x + 3ax^2 + x^3$$
$$(a + x)^4 = a^4 + 4a^3x + 6a^2x^2 + 4ax^3 + x^4$$

In the above expansion of $(a + x)^n$ where $n = 1, 2, 3, 4$, note the following properties:

a) The number of terms is $n + 1$.

b) The first term is a^n; the second is $na^{n-1}x$.

c) The exponents of a decrease by 1, while the exponents of x increase by 1. Their sum in each term is n.

d) If in any term the coefficient is multiplied by the exponent of a and the product is divided by one more than the exponent of x, the result is the coefficient of the next term.

Assuming the above properties to hold for every positive integral value of n, it appears that

$$(a + x)^n = a^n + \frac{n}{1!}a^{n-1}x + \frac{n(n-1)}{2!}a^{n-2}x^2 + \cdots$$
$$+ \frac{n(n-1)\cdots(n-r+2)}{(r-1)!}a^{n-r+1}x^{r-1} + \cdots + x^n$$

This formula is called the *binomial formula.* We shall now prove by mathematical induction that this formula is true for every positive integral value of n.

1. The formula, we know, is true for $n = 1$, $n = 2$.

2. We now wish to prove that if the formula is true for any value of n, for example, $n = k$, it is true for $n = k + 1$. Assume

$$(a + x)^k = a^k + ka^{k-1}x + \frac{k(k-1)}{2!}a^{k-2}x^2 + \cdots$$
$$+ \frac{k(k-1)\cdots(k-r+2)}{(r-1)!}a^{k-r+1}x^{r-1} + \cdots + x^k$$

Multiplying * both members by $a + x$ and combining like terms gives

$$(a + x)^{k+1} = a^{k+1} + (k+1)a^kx + \frac{(k+1)ka^{k-1}x^2}{2!} + \cdots$$
$$+ \frac{(k+1)k\cdots(k-r+3)}{(r-1)!}a^{k-r+2}x^{r-1}\cdots + (k+1)ax^k + x^{k+1}$$

---

* $a^k + ka^{k-1}x + \frac{k(k-1)}{2!}a^{k-2}x^2 + \cdots + \frac{k(k-1)\cdots(k-r+2)}{(r-1)!}a^{k-r+1}x^{r-1} + \cdots + x^k$

$a + x$

$a^{k+1} + ka^kx + \frac{k(k-1)}{2!}a^{k-1}x^2 + \cdots + \frac{k(k-1)\cdots(k-r+2)}{(r-1)!}a^{k-r+2}x^{r-1} + \cdots + ax^k$

$a^kx + ka^{k-1}x^2 + \cdots + \frac{k(k-1)\cdots(k-r+3)}{(r-2)!}a^{k-r+2}x^{r-1} + \cdots + kax^k + x^{k+1}$

$a^{k+1} + (k+1)a^kx + \frac{(k+1)k}{2!}a^{k-1}x^2 + \cdots + \frac{(k+1)k\cdots(k-r+3)}{(r-1)!}a^{k-r+2}x^{r-1} + \cdots + (k+1)ax^k + x^{k+1}$

This expansion is identical to what we would obtain if we replaced k by $k + 1$ in the expansion of $(a + x)^k$. Hence, if the expansion is true for $n = k$, it is true for $n = k + 1$. Since we know it to hold for $k = 2$, it holds for $k = 3$ and so on. Therefore, the formula is true for any positive integral value of n.

It should be noted that the rth term of the expansion $(a + x)^n$ is

$$\frac{n(n-1)\cdots(n-r+2)}{(r-1)!}a^{n-r+1}x^{r-1}$$

EXAMPLE 1. Expand and simplify the first four terms of $\left(2x - \frac{y}{3}\right)^5$.

Solution. In the expansion we shall first place $2x$ and $\frac{y}{3}$ in parentheses in order to determine the proper coefficients and exponents in each term of the expansion. We shall then remove the parentheses.

$$\left(2x - \frac{y}{3}\right)^5 = (2x)^5 - 5(2x)^4\left(\frac{y}{3}\right) + 10(2x)^3\left(\frac{y}{3}\right)^2 - 10(2x)^2\left(\frac{y}{3}\right)^3 + \cdots$$

$$= 32x^5 - \tfrac{80}{3}x^4y + \tfrac{80}{9}x^3y^2 - \tfrac{40}{27}x^2y^3 + \cdots$$

EXAMPLE 2. Find the 8th term of $(x - 2y)^{11}$.

Solution. $n = 11$, $r = 8$, $a = x$, $b = -2y$.

Hence the 8th term is

$$\frac{11\cdot 10\cdot 9\cdot 8\cdot 7\cdot 6\cdot 5}{1\cdot 2\cdot 3\cdot 4\cdot 5\cdot 6\cdot 7}(x)^4(-2y)^7$$

or

$$-42240\,x^4y^7$$

Pascal's triangle

If we write the binomial coefficients in rows, we obtain the following arrangement of the coefficients which is known as Pascal's triangle.

$n = 0$							1						
$n = 1$						1		1					
$n = 2$					1		2		1				
$n = 3$				1		3		3		1			
$n = 4$			1		4		6		4		1		
$n = 5$		1		5		10		10		5		1	
$n = 6$	1		6		15		20		15		6		1

etc.

It will be noted that the first and last numbers in each row are 1 and that any other number can be obtained by adding the two numbers in the preceding row that are just at the left and just at the right of the given number.

EXAMPLES

Expand and simplify:

1. $(a - b)^5$
2. $(a - 2b)^5$
3. $(2a - 3b)^5$
4. $(a + 2b)^6$
5. $(2a - b)^6$
6. $\left(\frac{a}{2} - b\right)^6$
7. $(x^{-1} + x^{-2})^4$
8. $\left(\frac{a}{\sqrt{b}} - \frac{\sqrt{b}}{a}\right)^6$
9. $(\sqrt{x} - \sqrt{y})^4$
10. $\left(x + \frac{1}{x}\right)^6 - \left(x - \frac{1}{x}\right)^6$

11. Find the 6th term of $(x - y)^{11}$.
12. Find the middle term of $(2x + y)^{14}$.
13. Find the 20th term of $(2x - y)^{22}$.
14. Use the binomial theorem and find the value of $(.9)^3$.
[*Hint.* $.9^3 = (1 - .1)^3$].
15. Find by the binomial theorem the value of $(1.1)^8$, correct to four significant figures.
16. Find the coefficient of x^7 in the expansion of $(x^3 - 2x^{-1})^5$.
17. Expand by the binomial theorem $(a + b - c)^3$.
18. Find the coefficient of x^{11} in $\left(\frac{a^2}{x} - \frac{1}{x^{-2}}\right)^7$.

CHAPTER XIII

Inequalities

If $a - b$ is a positive quantity, then a is greater than b. We express this fact symbolically as $a > b$. If $a - b$ is negative, then a is less than b; symbolically we write $a < b$. In the

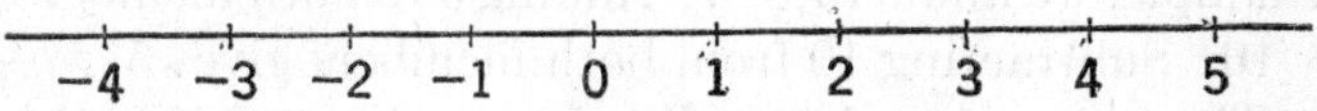

−4 −3 −2 −1 0 1 2 3 4 5

FIGURE 35

algebraic scale in Fig. 35, $a > b$ means that a is to the right of b, while if $a < b$, it means a is to the left of b. Such expressions are called inequalities, and *they refer only to real numbers a and b.*

Two inequalities are said to have the *same sense* if their signs of inequality point in the same direction; thus, $a > b$ and $m > p$ have the same sense; likewise do $p < l$ and $s < r$.

Two inequalities are said to be *opposite in sense* if their signs of inequality point in opposite directions; thus, $a > b$ and $p < q$ have opposite senses.

An inequality that is satisfied by all real numbers is called an *absolute inequality.* Thus, $x^2 + 1 > 0$ is an absolute inequality. An inequality like $x - 3 > 0$ which is satisfied only by certain numbers is called a *conditional inequality.*

Properties of inequalities

The following fundamental properties are used in dealing with inequalities. The proof of only the first property is given; the other proofs are left as exercises.

I. The sense of an inequality is unchanged if the same number is added to or subtracted from both members.

Proof. Suppose $a > b$.
We wish to prove $a + c > b + c$ and $a - c > b - c$.
Now, since $a > b$ then $a - b$ is a positive number; call its value p; *i.e.*,

$$a - b = p$$

Now, $$(a + c) - (b + c) = p$$

and $$(a - c) - (b - c) = p$$

Hence, $$a + c > b + c$$

and $$a - c > b - c$$

For example, we know $15 > 7$. Adding 3 to both members gives $18 > 10$. Subtracting 10 from both members gives $5 > -3$.

II. The sense of an inequality is not changed if both members are multiplied by or both divided by the same *positive* number. For example,

Suppose $$4 > 2$$

Dividing by 2 $$2 > 1$$

or multiplying by 8 $$32 > 16$$

III. An inequality is changed in sense if both members are multiplied by or both divided by the same *negative* number.

For example, $$5 < 8$$

then multiplying both members by -2 gives

$$-10 > -16$$

Likewise $$14 > -7$$

then dividing both members by -7 gives

$$-2 < 1$$

IV. If both members of an inequality of positive quantities are raised to the same positive power or if the same *positive* root of each member is extracted, the sense of the inequality is unchanged. For example, $5 > 3$. Then squaring both sides gives $5^2 > 3^2$.

Likewise,
$$64 > 49$$
then taking the positive square root of both members gives
$$8 > 7$$

EXAMPLE 1. If a and b are positive numbers, prove that
$$\frac{a + b}{2} > \frac{2\,ab}{a + b} \text{ unless } a = b$$

Solution. Multiplying both members by $2(a + b)$ gives
$$(a + b)^2 > 4\,ab$$
or
$$a^2 + 2\,ab + b^2 > 4\,ab$$
Subtracting $4\,ab$ from both sides gives
$$a^2 - 2\,ab + b^2 > 0$$
or
$$(a - b)^2 > 0$$
This inequality is true unless $a = b$, for the square of any real number, except zero, is positive. By reversing the order of operations, it follows that the original inequality must be true.

EXAMPLE 2. If x and y are positive numbers, prove that
$$x^3 + y^3 > xy^2 + x^2y \text{ unless } x = y$$

Solution. Dividing each member by $x + y$ gives
$$x^2 - xy + y^2 > xy$$
Subtracting xy from both members gives
$$x^2 - 2\,xy + y^2 > 0$$
or
$$(x - y)^2 > 0$$

which is true unless $x = y$. By reversing the order of operations, it follows that the first inequality must be true.

EXERCISES

Prove the following inequalities, assuming that the letters represent positive real numbers:

1. $\frac{a^2 + 3b^2}{b} > 2a + 2b$ unless $a = b$
2. $\frac{x^2}{y} + \frac{y^2}{x} > x + y$ unless $x = y$
3. $a^3 + 1 > a^2 + a$ unless $a = \pm 1$
4. $\frac{a}{b} + \frac{b}{a} > 2$ unless $a = b$
5. $x + \frac{1}{x} > 2$ unless $x = 1$
6. $x^2 + y^2 + z^2 > xy + xz + yz$ unless $x = y = z$
7. $(x + y)(y + z)(z + x) > 8xyz$ unless $x = y = z$
8. $\sqrt{14} + \sqrt{6} > 2\sqrt{3} + \sqrt{7}$
9. $\sqrt{14} + \sqrt{5} > \sqrt{11} + \sqrt{7}$
10. $\sqrt{15} + \sqrt{3} < \sqrt{6} + \sqrt{10}$

Conditional linear inequalities

We know that if we solve the equation $3x - 5 = 0$, $x = \frac{5}{3}$. However, for certain values of x the function $3x - 5$ is positive, while for other values of x the function is negative. Let us now determine for what values of x the function is negative; *i.e.*,

$$3x - 5 < 0$$

Adding 5 to both members gives

$$3x < 5$$

Dividing both sides by 3 gives

$$x < \frac{5}{3}$$

We shall now interpret graphically the inequality $3x - 5 < 0$. To this end let $y = 3x - 5$ and draw the graph, Fig. 36, which is a straight line crossing the x axis at the point $(\frac{5}{3}, 0)$. When $x < \frac{5}{3}$, the graph is below the x axis; *i.e.*, the function $3x - 5$ is negative.

EXAMPLE. Find the values of x for which

$$x^2 - x - 12 > 0$$

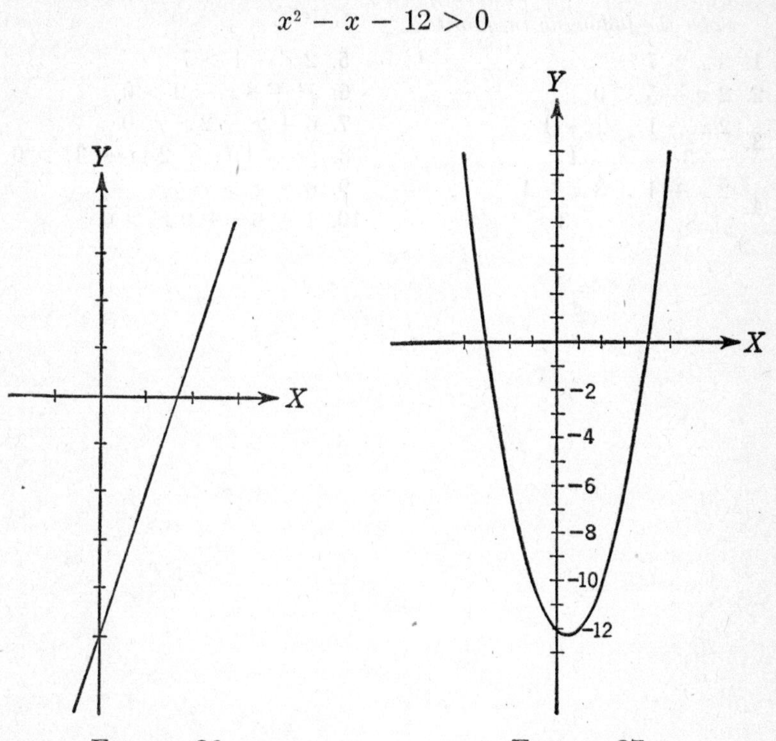

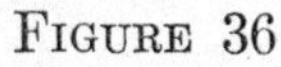
FIGURE 36

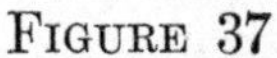
FIGURE 37

Solution. The graph of $y = x^2 - x - 12$, Fig. 37, cuts the x axis at $x = 4$ and $x = -3$. Graphically we see that the function $x^2 - x - 12$ is positive when $x > 4$ and when $x < -3$. Algebraically we can write

$$x^2 - x > 12$$
$$x^2 - x + \tfrac{1}{4} > 12 + \tfrac{1}{4}$$
$$(x - \tfrac{1}{2})^2 > \tfrac{49}{4}$$

Extracting the square root of both numbers gives,

$$x - \tfrac{1}{2} > \tfrac{7}{2} \text{ and } x - \tfrac{1}{2} < -\tfrac{7}{2} \qquad \text{Why?}$$
$$\therefore \quad x > 4, \qquad x < -3$$

EXERCISES

Solve the following inequalities:

1. $3x > 7$

2. $2x - 5 < 0$

3. $\frac{2x - 1}{3} > \frac{x + 1}{4}$

4. $\frac{2x + 1}{8} < \frac{3x - 4}{3}$

5. $2x - 1 > 7$

6. $x^2 + 8x - 9 > 0$

7. $6 + x - 2x^2 < 0$

8. $(x - 1)(x + 2)(x - 3) > 0$

9. $6 + x > x^2$

10. $1 + 6x + 9x^2 > 0$

CHAPTER XIV

Complex Numbers

Definition of complex numbers

If we should limit our number system to zero and the positive integers, could we solve such an equation as $5x - 3 = 0$? Obviously not. Hence it is necessary that we extend our number system to include rational fractions. Even though we can use zero, positive integers, and rational fractions, we still cannot solve an equation of the type $x + 4 = 0$, so we must include in our number system negative numbers. On the other hand, in order to solve an equation like $x^2 - 5 = 0$ it is necessary that we extend still further our number system so as to include the irrational numbers. Even with this extension, can we solve equations like $x^2 + 5 = 0$ and $x^2 - 7x + 21 = 0$? Obviously not. So we extend our number system still further so as to include numbers of the form $a + bi$, where a and b are real numbers and i * $= \sqrt{-1}$. Numbers of this type are called *complex*.

In the complex number $a + bi$, a is called the *real part* and bi the *imaginary part*. If $b = 0$, the complex number is real; thus $3 + 0i$ is a real number. If $a = 0$, $b \neq 0$, the complex number is a pure imaginary; thus $0 + 3i$ is a pure imaginary. Hence we see that complex numbers include real numbers and imaginary numbers as special cases.

Conjugate complex numbers are two complex numbers which

* Complex numbers are used extensively in the theory of electricity, and the square root of -1 is denoted by j, for i is used to denote current.

differ only in the sign of the imaginary part. Thus $4 + 3i$ and $4 - 3i$ are examples of conjugate complex numbers.

Graphic representation of complex numbers

The complex number $a + bi$ depends upon the two real numbers a and b and hence may be represented by a point in the plane. We represent the real numbers on the horizontal axis and the imaginary numbers on the vertical axis. Thus in Fig. 38 the points A, B, C, and D represent respectively the complex numbers, $3 + 2i$, $4 - 2i$, $-3 - 5i$, $-3 + 3i$.

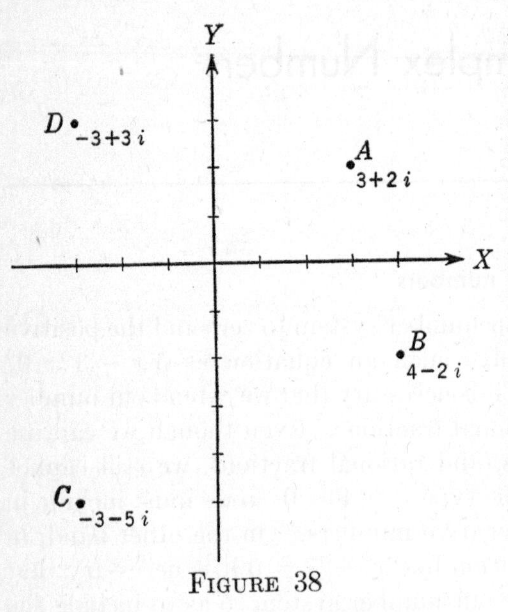

FIGURE 38

EXERCISES

Plot each of the following complex numbers:

1. $2 + 3i$
2. $4i$
3. $\frac{3}{5} - \frac{i}{2}$
4. $-i$
5. $-2 + 5i$
6. $3 + 0i$
7. $-\frac{2}{3} + \frac{i}{3}$
8. i
9. $-4 - 4i$
10. $-6i$
11. $-\frac{5}{3} - \frac{i}{3}$
12. $-.3 + .4i$
13. $2i - 7$

Assumption

It is assumed that complex numbers obey all the laws of algebra.

Addition and subtraction

Since complex numbers obey the laws of algebra, it follows that

$$a + bi \pm (c + di) = (a \pm c) + (b \pm d)i$$

That is, to add or subtract two complex numbers, add or subtract the real and imaginary parts separately.

EXAMPLE. Simplify $(3 + 2i) - (-7 + 4i) + (3 - 3i)$.

Solution. Removing the parentheses and combining terms gives

$$3 + 2i + 7 - 4i + 3 - 3i \text{ or } 13 - 5i$$

Graphic addition and subtraction of complex numbers

To add graphically the two complex numbers $a + bi$ and $c + di$, represent the numbers by points A and B respectively,

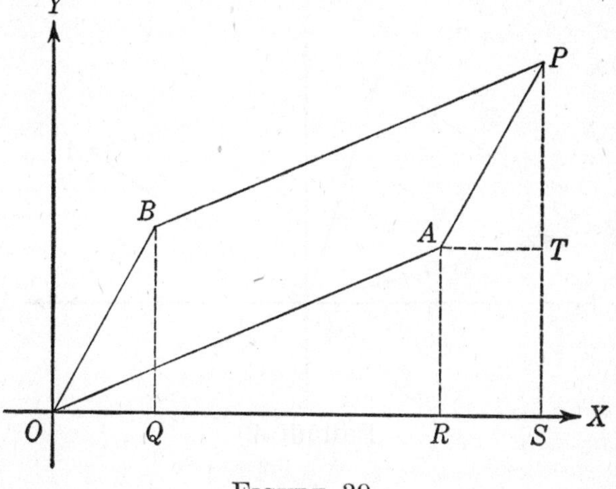

FIGURE 39

connect these points to the origin O, and then complete the parallelogram having OA and OB as adjacent sides. The point P represents the sum of the two complex numbers. To prove this statement, draw BQ, AR, PS perpendicular to the real axis and AT perpendicular to PS. Since A represents the complex number $a + bi$, $OR = a$, $RA = b$; since B represents the complex number $c + di$, $OQ = c$, $QB = d$. Moreover, $\triangle OBQ \cong \triangle APT$. Why? Therefore, $OQ = AT = RS = c$, and $QB = TP = d$. Now

$$OS = OR + RS = a + c,$$
$$SP = ST + TP = RA + TP = b + d$$

Therefore, P represents the complex number $(a + c) + (b + d)i$, which is the sum of the complex numbers $a + bi$ and $c + di$.

To subtract graphically one complex number from another, change the sign of the subtrahend and proceed as in addition.

EXAMPLE 1. Add graphically $3 + 2i$, $-4 + i$.

Solution. Point A represents $3 + 2i$, and point B represents $-4 + i$. Draw OA, OB and complete the parallelogram having

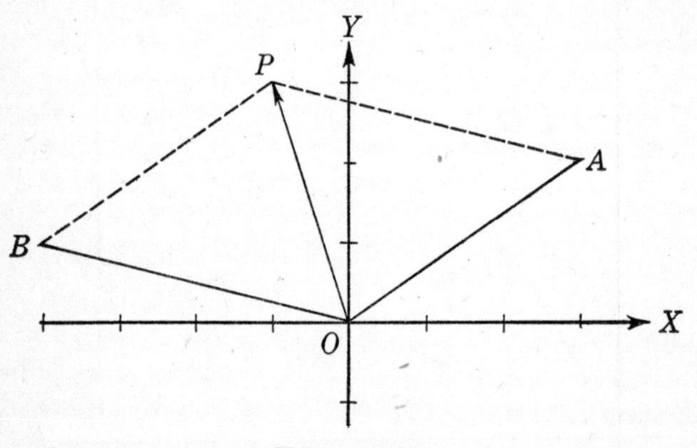

FIGURE 40

OA and OB as adjacent sides. Point P represents the sum of $3 + 2i$ and $-4 + i$. Graphically we see the sum is $-1 + 3i$. Check algebraically.

EXAMPLE 2. Find graphically $(3 + 2i) - (-2 + i)$.

Solution. This problem is equivalent to finding $(3 + 2i) + (2 - i)$. Let points A and B represent $(3 + 2i)$ and $(-2 + i)$ respectively. Extend BO to B' so that $OB' = OB$.

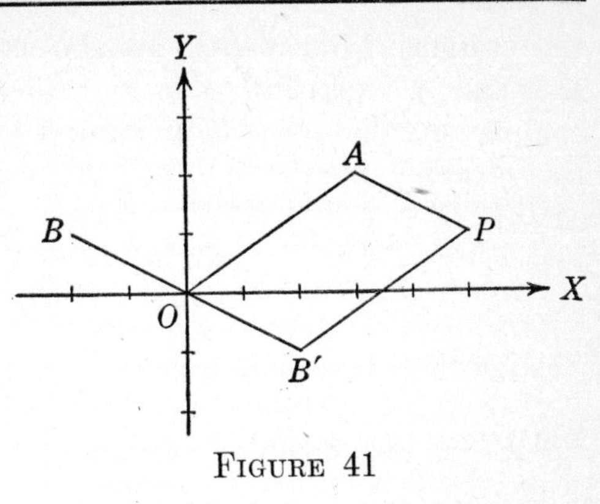

FIGURE 41

Then, proceeding as in example 1, we see that the complex number corresponding to point P is $5 + i$. Check algebraically.

EXERCISES

Perform algebraically and graphically each of the following operations:

1. $(2 + 3i) + (4 + i)$
2. $(3 + i) - (2 + i)$
3. $(4 + i) + (-2 - i)$
4. $(4 + i) - (-2 - i)$
5. $(-3 - 2i) + (4 + 3i)$
6. $(-3 - 2i) - (4 - 3i)$
7. $(-2 - i) - (i)$
8. $(4 + 3i) + (-2 + 3i)$
9. $(-2 - 3i) - (4 - 2i)$
10. $(-3 + i) + (4 + 3i)$
11. $(3 + 2i) + (4 + 3i) - (2 + i)$
12. $(3 - i) - (4 - 2i) + (4 + 3i)$

Equal complex numbers

Theorem. If $x \pm yi = 0$, then $x = 0$ and $y = 0$.

For if $x \pm yi = 0$, $x = \mp yi$, $x^2 = y^2(-1)$, or $x^2 + y^2 = 0$. We know that x and y stand for real numbers, and the only real numbers which satisfy $x^2 + y^2 = 0$ are $x = 0$, $y = 0$.

If $x_1 + y_1i = x_2 + y_2i$, then $x_1 = x_2$ and $y_1 = y_2$. For transposing terms gives $x_1 - x_2 + (y_1 - y_2)i = 0$. Hence $x_1 - x_2 = 0$, $y_1 - y_2 = 0$ or $x_1 = x_2$, $y_1 = y_2$.

Thus, two complex numbers are equal if and only if the real part of the first is equal to the real part of the second, and the imaginary part of the first is equal to the imaginary part of the second.

Geometrically two complex numbers are equal if and only if they represent the same point.

EXAMPLE. Find the real values of x and y which satisfy the equation

$$i + 2xi + 3y = 2yi - x + 5$$

Solution. It follows that

$$3y = -x + 5$$
$$1 + 2x = 2y$$

Solving these equations gives $x = \frac{7}{8}$, $y = \frac{11}{8}$.

Polar form of a complex number

Let the point P represent the complex number $x + yi$, Fig. 42, and connect P to the origin O. Let the length of OP be r, and let the angle which OP makes with OX be θ. Then

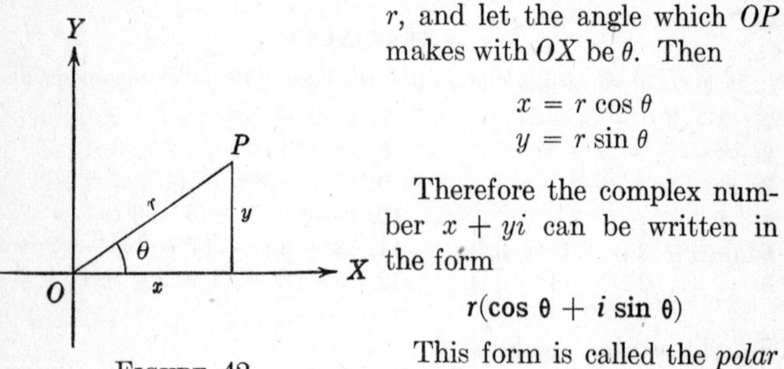

FIGURE 42

$$x = r\cos\theta$$
$$y = r\sin\theta$$

Therefore the complex number $x + yi$ can be written in the form

$$r(\cos\theta + i\sin\theta)$$

This form is called the *polar form* of a complex number. The angle θ is known as the *argument* or *amplitude*, and the length of r as the *modulus* or *absolute value*.

EXAMPLE. Find the polar form of $2 + 2\sqrt{3}\,i$. What is the argument? What is the modulus? Plot the complex number.

Solution. Now from Fig. 42

$$r = \sqrt{x^2 + y^2} = \sqrt{(2)^2 + (2\sqrt{3})^2} = \sqrt{4 + 12} = 4.$$

Moreover $\tan\theta = \dfrac{y}{x} = \dfrac{2\sqrt{3}}{2} = \sqrt{3}$; therefore $\theta = 60°$.

Hence, the modulus is 4 and the argument is 60°. Therefore the polar form is

$$4(\cos 60° + i\sin 60°)$$

EXERCISES

Find all the real values of x and y which satisfy each of the following equations:

1. $3x - 2yi = 4y - 3i + 6$
2. $x - y + xyi = 5 + 36i$
3. $5 + 4i - y = ixy + x$
4. $ix = 4i - iy + 5x$
5. $(3x + y + 1)i - x - 2y = 6$
6. $x + yi = 3x - 6 + i$

In each of the following examples find the argument, the modulus, and write the complex number in polar form:

7. $2i$
8. $4 + 4i$
9. $3 + 3\sqrt{3}\,i$
10. $2 - 2\sqrt{3}\,i$
11. $1 + \sqrt{3}\,i$
12. $-2 + 2i$

Change the following complex numbers to the form $x + yi$:

13. $2(\cos 30° + i \sin 30°)$
14. $7(\cos 60° + i \sin 60°)$
15. $8(\cos 90° + i \sin 90°)$
16. $\cos 330° + i \sin 330°$
17. $4(\cos 180° + i \sin 180°)$
18. $2\sqrt{2}(\cos 225° + i \sin 225°)$

Multiplication of complex numbers

Our assumption on page 236 makes it possible for us to multiply two complex numbers as follows:

$$(a + bi)(c + di) = ac + bci + adi + bdi^2$$
$$= (ac - bd) + (bc + ad)i$$

If the complex numbers are written in polar form, the multiplication may be performed as follows:

$$a + bi = r_1(\cos \theta_1 + i \sin \theta_1)$$
$$c + di = r_2(\cos \theta_2 + i \sin \theta_2)$$
$$(a + bi)(c + di) = r_1 r_2[\cos \theta_1 \cos \theta_2 + i(\sin \theta_1 \cos \theta_2 + \cos \theta_1 \sin \theta_2) - \sin \theta_1 \sin \theta_2]$$
$$= r_1 r_2[\cos(\theta_1 + \theta_2) + i \sin(\theta_1 + \theta_2)]$$

Therefore *the product of two complex numbers is a complex number whose modulus is equal to the product of the moduli, and whose argument is equal to the sum of the arguments of the two given complex numbers.*

EXAMPLE 1. Find the first four powers of i.

Solution.

$$\begin{aligned} i &= \sqrt{-1} \\ i^2 &= -1 \\ i^3 &= i^2 \cdot i = -i \\ i^4 &= i^2 \cdot i^2 = (-1)(-1) = 1 \end{aligned}$$

EXAMPLE 2. Evaluate $\sqrt{-16}\,\sqrt{-4}$.

Solution. By our fundamental assumption on page 68.

$$\sqrt{-a}\,\sqrt{-b} = -\sqrt{ab},\ a > 0,\ b > 0$$

Hence $\sqrt{-16} \cdot \sqrt{-4} = -\sqrt{64} = -8$

EXAMPLE 3. Simplify $(2 - i)^3$.

Solution.

$$\begin{aligned} (2 - i)^3 &= (2)^3 - 3(2)^2(i) + 3(2)(i)^2 - (i)^3 \\ &= 8 - 12\,i + 6\,i^2 - i^3 \\ &= 8 - 12\,i - 6 + i \\ &= 2 - 11\,i \end{aligned}$$

EXAMPLE 4. Evaluate $i^{73} + i^{103}$.

Solution.

$$\begin{aligned} i^{73} &= i^{72} \cdot i = (i^4)^{18} \cdot i = (1)^{18} \cdot i = i \\ i^{103} &= i^{100} \cdot i^3 = (i^4)^{25} \cdot i^3 = (1)^{25} i^3 = i^3 = -i \\ \therefore\quad i^{73} + i^{103} &= i - i = 0 \end{aligned}$$

EXAMPLE 5. Find graphically the product of $1 + \sqrt{3}\,i$ and $2 + 2\,i$.

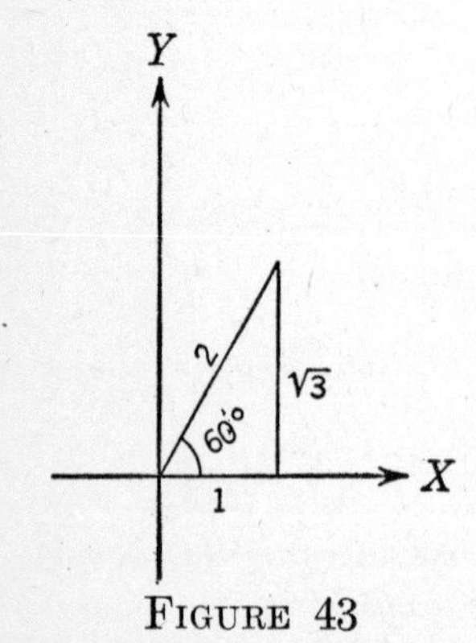

FIGURE 43

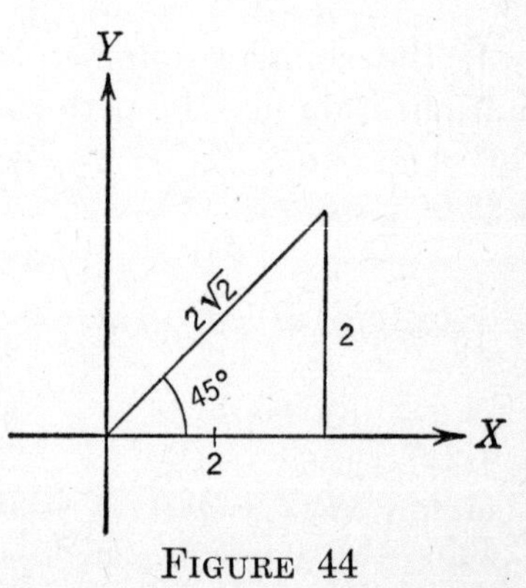

FIGURE 44

Solution. $1 + \sqrt{3}\, i$, Fig. 43, has a modulus of 2 and an argument of 60°. Why? $2 + 2\,i$, Fig. 44, has a modulus of $2\sqrt{2}$ and an argument of 45°. Why? $\therefore (1 + \sqrt{3}\ i)(2 + 2\,i)$, Fig. 45, has a modulus of $(2)(2\sqrt{2})$ or $4\sqrt{2}$ and an argument of $60° + 45°$ or 105°.

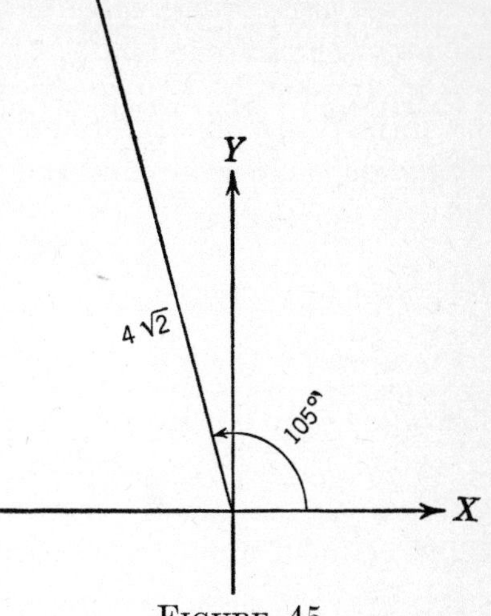

FIGURE 45

EXERCISES

Simplify:

1. $\sqrt{-3}\sqrt{-2}$
2. $\sqrt{-3}\sqrt{-3}$
3. $\sqrt{-12}\sqrt{-3}$
4. $\sqrt{3}\sqrt{-5}$
5. $(3\sqrt{-2})^2$
6. $(-2\sqrt{-5})^2$
7. $(3\sqrt{-2})^3$
8. $i^{12} - i^{40}$
9. $i^{30} + i^{31} + i^{32}$
10. $(2 - \sqrt{-3})^2$
11. $(2 + 3\,i)^3$
12. $(1 + \sqrt{-2})(2 + \sqrt{-3})$
13. $(3 + 2\,i)(3 - \sqrt{-4})$
14. $\sqrt{-6}\sqrt{-8}\sqrt{-12}$
15. $(\sqrt{-2\sqrt{-2}})^2$
16. $(3 - i)^2$
17. $(2 - i)^5$
18. $(1 - i)^6$
19. $(2 - i)^2(1 + i)^3$
20. $\sqrt{-4}\ \sqrt{-9}(-1 - i)^2$

Perform algebraically and graphically each of the following operations:

21. $(3 + 3\,i)(1 + i)$
22. $4(2\,i)$
23. $(1 + \sqrt{3}\,i)(2 + 2\,i)$
24. $(1 - i)(3 + 3\sqrt{3}\,i)$
25. $(-2 - 2\,i)(-1 + \sqrt{3}\,i)$
26. $(-1 + \sqrt{3}\,i)(-2 - 2\,i)(1 + i)$
27. Prove that $(\cos\theta + i\sin\theta)^3 = \cos 3\,\theta + i \sin 3\,\theta$

Division of complex numbers

The quotient of two complex numbers may be reduced to the form $a + bi$ if we rationalize the denominator by multiplying the numerator and denominator by the conjugate of the denominator.

EXAMPLE. Reduce $\frac{2+i}{3-i}$ to the form $a + bi$.

Solution.

$$\frac{2+i}{3-i} = \frac{2+i}{3-i} \cdot \frac{3+i}{3+i} = \frac{6+5i+i^2}{9-i^2}$$

$$= \frac{5+5i}{10} = \frac{1}{2} + \frac{1}{2}i$$

If two complex numbers are written in polar form, we have

$$\frac{r_1(\cos\theta_1 + i\sin\theta_1)}{r_2(\cos\theta_2 + i\sin\theta_2)} = \frac{r_1(\cos\theta_1 + i\sin\theta_1)(\cos\theta_2 - i\sin\theta_2)}{r_2(\cos\theta_2 + i\sin\theta_2)(\cos\theta_2 - i\sin\theta_2)}$$

$$= \frac{r_1[\cos(\theta_1 - \theta_2) + i\sin(\theta_1 - \theta_2)]}{r_2(\cos^2\theta_2 + \sin^2\theta_2)}$$

$$= \frac{r_1}{r_2}[\cos(\theta_1 - \theta_2) + i\sin(\theta_1 - \theta_2)]$$

Therefore, *the modulus of the quotient of two complex numbers is equal to the quotient of their moduli, and the argument of the quotient is equal to the argument of the numerator minus the argument of the denominator.*

EXAMPLE. Find graphically $\frac{1+\sqrt{3}\,i}{2+2i}$

Solution. $1 + \sqrt{3}$ has a modulus of 2 and an argument of

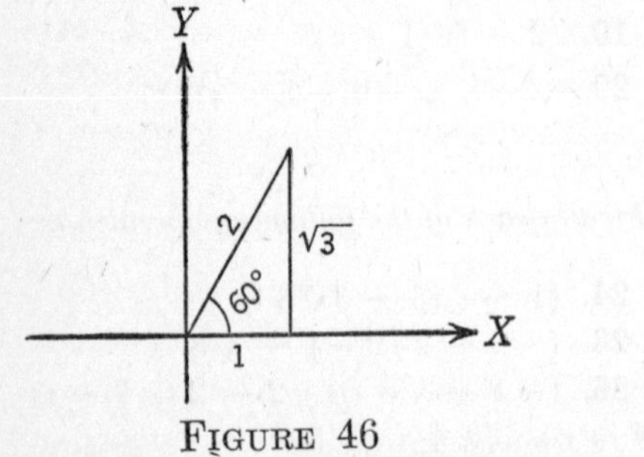

FIGURE 46

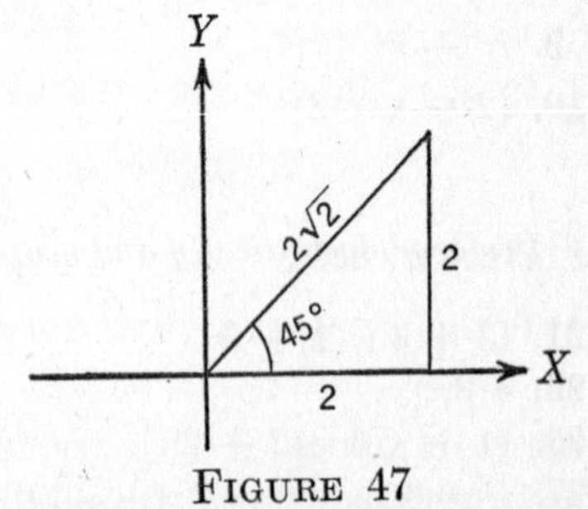

FIGURE 47

60°, Fig. 46, whereas $2 + 2i$ has a modulus of $2\sqrt{2}$ and an argument of 45°, Fig. 47. The modulus of $\frac{1 + \sqrt{3}\,i}{2 + 2i}$ is $\frac{2}{2\sqrt{2}} = \frac{\sqrt{2}}{2}$ and the argument is 60° − 45° or 15°, Fig. 48.

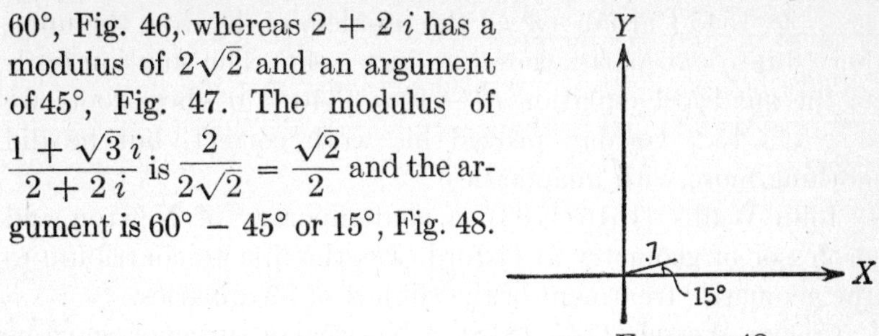

FIGURE 48

EXERCISES

Simplify each of the following expressions by writing it in the form $a + bi$:

1. $\frac{2}{i}$
2. $\frac{3 + i}{i}$
3. $\frac{2 + i}{1 - i}$
4. $\frac{5 + i}{3 - i}$
5. $\frac{1}{(1 + i)^2}$
6. $\frac{i}{(1 - i)^2}$
7. $\frac{i}{(1 - i)^3}$
8. $\frac{2 - 11i}{(2 - i)^3}$
9. $\frac{2 + i}{7 - 3i}$
10. $\left(\frac{1 + \sqrt{3}\,i}{2}\right)^2$
11. $\frac{4}{1 + i}$
12. $\left(\frac{1 + i}{\sqrt{2}}\right)^4$
13. $\frac{1 + 3i}{3 + 4i} - \frac{3 - 2i}{3 - 4i}$
14. $\frac{3}{(2 + i)^2} + \frac{5}{(2 - i)^2}$
15. $\frac{3 + 2i}{2 - 3i} + \frac{3 - 2i}{2 + 3i}$
16. $\frac{x + i\sqrt{a^2 - x^2}}{x - i\sqrt{a^2 - x^2}}$
17. $(2 + 2i)^3(-2 + 2i)^3$
18. $(1 - i)^2(1 + 2i)$

Historical note

When mathematicians began studying quadratic equations, they were immediately confronted with the problem of imaginary numbers. For centuries they paid no attention to them, assuming that an example involving imaginaries was meaningless. In 1545 Cardan solved the problem of dividing the number 10 into two parts whose product is 40. The solution leads to the quadratic equation $x^2 - 10x + 40 = 0$ whose roots are $5 \pm \sqrt{-15}$. Cardan proved his work correct, but he did nothing more with imaginaries.

John Wallis (1616–1703), a contemporary of Newton and professor of geometry at Oxford, was the first to contribute to the geometric treatment of the subject of imaginaries.

Caspar Wessel (1745–1818), a Norwegian surveyor, gave us the modern method of representing complex numbers. His work was published by the Royal Academy of Denmark in 1799.

De Moivre's theorem

If the complex number $r(\cos\theta + i\sin\theta)$ is multiplied by itself, we have

$$[r(\cos\theta + i\sin\theta)]^2 = r(\cos\theta + i\sin\theta)r(\cos\theta + i\sin\theta) = r^2(\cos 2\theta + i\sin 2\theta)$$

If we multiply both members by $r(\cos\theta + i\sin\theta)$, we have

$$[r(\cos\theta + i\sin\theta)]^3 = r^3(\cos 3\theta + i\sin 3\theta)$$

It is left as an exercise for the student to prove by mathematical induction that

$$[r(\cos\theta + i\sin\theta)]^n = r^n(\cos n\theta + i\sin n\theta)$$

where n is a positive integer.

For the special case $r = 1$, we have

$$(\cos\theta + i\sin\theta)^n = \cos n\theta + i\sin n\theta$$

This relation also holds if n is a negative integer.

For $$(\cos\theta + i\sin\theta)^{-1} = \frac{1}{\cos\theta + i\sin\theta} = \frac{\cos\theta - i\sin\theta}{\cos^2\theta + \sin^2\theta} = \cos(-\theta) + i\sin(-\theta)$$

Hence $$(\cos\theta + i\sin\theta)^{-n} = [\cos(-\theta) + i\sin(-\theta)]^n = \cos(-n\theta) + i\sin(-n\theta)$$

Moreover, if $n = \frac{1}{q}$ where q is a positive or negative integer, it follows, since

$$\left(\cos\frac{\theta}{q} + i\sin\frac{\theta}{q}\right)^q = \cos\theta + i\sin\theta \quad \text{that}$$

$$(\cos\theta + i\sin\theta)^{\frac{1}{q}} = \left[\left(\cos\frac{\theta}{q} + i\sin\frac{\theta}{q}\right)^q\right]^{\frac{1}{q}} = \cos\frac{\theta}{q} + i\sin\frac{\theta}{q}$$

and hence,

$$(\cos\theta + i\sin\theta)^{\frac{p}{q}} = \left(\cos\frac{\theta}{q} + i\sin\frac{\theta}{q}\right)^p = \cos\frac{p\theta}{q} + i\sin\frac{p\theta}{q}$$

Roots of a complex number

The nth root of the complex number $a + bi$ is

$$(a + bi)^{\frac{1}{n}} = \left[r(\cos\theta + i\sin\theta)\right]^{\frac{1}{n}} = r^{\frac{1}{n}}\left[\cos\frac{\theta}{n} + i\sin\frac{\theta}{n}\right]$$

But if k is any integer, we know that

$$\cos(\theta + k\,360°) = \cos\theta$$

$$\sin(\theta + k\,360°) = \sin\theta$$

Hence we can write

$$\begin{aligned}(a + bi)^{\frac{1}{n}} &= [r(\cos\theta + i\sin\theta)]^{\frac{1}{n}} \\ &= [r\{\cos(\theta + k\,360°) + i\sin(\theta + k\,360°)\}]^{\frac{1}{n}} \\ &= r^{\frac{1}{n}}\left(\cos\frac{\theta + k\,360°}{n} + i\sin\frac{\theta° + k\,360°}{n}\right)\end{aligned}$$

If we now assign to k the values $0, 1, 2, \cdots, n - 1$, we obtain n different quantities whose nth powers are $a + bi$. Hence:

Theorem. Any number except 0 has n distinct nth roots.

EXAMPLE 1. Find the value of $(2 + 2i)^5$.

Solution.

$2 + 2i$ written in polar form is $2\sqrt{2}(\cos 45° + i \sin 45°)$.

$$\begin{aligned} \therefore (2 + 2i)^5 &= [2\sqrt{2}(\cos 45° + i \sin 45°)]^5 \\ &= 128\sqrt{2}(\cos 225° + i \sin 225°) \\ &= 128\sqrt{2}\left[-\frac{1}{\sqrt{2}} - \frac{i}{\sqrt{2}}\right] \\ &= -128 - 128i \end{aligned}$$

EXAMPLE 2. Find the fifth roots of $2 + 2i$.

Solution. $2 + 2i$ written in polar form is

$$2\sqrt{2}(\cos 45° + i \sin 45°)$$

Hence, $[2\sqrt{2}(\cos 45° + i \sin 45°)]^{\frac{1}{5}}$

$$\begin{aligned} &= [2\sqrt{2}(\cos 45° + k\,360°) + i \sin (45° + k\,360°)]^{\frac{1}{5}} \\ &= (2\sqrt{2})^{\frac{1}{5}}[\cos (9° + k\,72°) + i \sin (9° + k\,72°)] \end{aligned}$$

For the values $k = 0, 1, 2, 3, 4$, we get

$$(2\sqrt{2})^{\frac{1}{5}}(\cos 9° + i \sin 9°)$$
$$(2\sqrt{2})^{\frac{1}{5}}(\cos 81° + i \sin 81°)$$
$$(2\sqrt{2})^{\frac{1}{5}}(\cos 153° + i \sin 153°)$$
$$(2\sqrt{2})^{\frac{1}{5}}(\cos 225° + i \sin 225°)$$
$$(2\sqrt{2})^{\frac{1}{5}}(\cos 297° + i \sin 297°)$$

Each of these five numbers is a fifth root of $2 + 2i$.

Query. Why is it not necessary to take k greater than 4?

EXERCISES

By using De Moivre's theorem, find the indicated powers, roots, and products:

1. $(1 + i)^6$
2. $(\cos 10° + i \sin 10°)^9$
3. $(4 + 4i)^4$
4. $(-2 + 2i)^5$
5. $[3(\cos 15° + i \sin 15°)]^{15}$
6. $(-1 - i\sqrt{3})^6$
7. $(3 - 3i)^5$
8. $(3 + i\sqrt{3})^8$

9. $\sqrt[3]{4 + 4i}$
10. $\sqrt{3 + i\sqrt{3}}$
11. $\sqrt[3]{-1 - i\sqrt{3}}$
12. $\sqrt[5]{\cos 45° + i \sin 45°}$
13. $\sqrt[5]{-4 + 4i}$
14. $\sqrt[10]{8(\cos 60° + i \sin 60°)}$
15. Find the cube roots of -8.
16. Find the fifth roots of 32.
17. Find the sixth roots of 729.
18. Find the cube roots of 27.

MASTERY TEST

Prove by mathematical induction:

1. $3 + 6 + 12 + \cdots + 3 \times 2^{n-1} = 3(2^n - 1)$
2. $1^2 + 3^2 + \cdots + (2n - 1)^2 = \dfrac{n(2n + 1)(2n - 1)}{3}$
3. $2 \times 4 + 4 \times 6 + \cdots + 2n(2n + 2) = \dfrac{n}{3}(2n + 2)(2n + 4)$

Simplify:

4. $\left(\dfrac{1 + \sqrt{3}\,i}{2}\right)^3$
5. $(1 + \sqrt{3}\,i)^4$
6. $(4 + 3i)^3 + (2 + i)^2 - (1 + i)^2$
7. $i^{78} + i^{75} + i^{200}$
8. $\dfrac{3 + i}{1 + 4i} - \dfrac{2 + 3i}{3 - 2i}$
9. $\dfrac{2 - i}{3 - i} + \dfrac{4 + i}{3 + i}$
10. $\dfrac{(2 - i)^2}{(1 - i)^2} - \dfrac{3}{(1 + i)} - \dfrac{4}{(i - 1)}$
11. $\dfrac{2}{i - 1} - \dfrac{3}{(1 + i)^2} - \dfrac{4}{(i - 1)^3}$
12. $\dfrac{1}{i^2} - \dfrac{1}{i^{37}} + \dfrac{1}{i^{75}} - \dfrac{1}{i^{783}}$

Represent graphically:

13. $(2 + 3i) + (-4 + i)$
14. $(-4 - i) - (3 - 2i)$
15. $(3 + 4i)(4 + 3i)$
16. $\dfrac{5 + 12i}{3 - 4i}$
17. Solve for x and y, $x + yi = 3 + 2i$.
18. Solve for x and y, $x^2 + y + yi = 5 + 2i$.
19. Show that one root of $x^4 - 6x^2 - 16x + 21 = 0$ is $-2 - i\sqrt{3}$.
20. Show that two roots of $x^4 - x^2 + 2x + 2 = 0$ are $1 + i$ and $1 - i$.
21. Find the square roots of $1 + i$.

22. Reduce to the form $a + bi$, $\dfrac{(2 - 3\,i)(5 + 2\,i)}{1 - i}$.

23. Find the cube roots of $-8\,i$.

24. Find the modulus and amplitude of $\dfrac{3 + i}{1 + 2\,i}$.

25. By De Moivre's theorem find the 6th power of

$$2(\cos 30^\circ + i \sin 30^\circ)$$

26. Find in trigonometric form the roots of the equation

$$x^8 = \sqrt{3} + i$$

27. Show that

$$x^3 + y^3 + z^3 - 3\,xyz = (x + y + z)(x + \omega y + \omega^2 z)(x + \omega^2 y + \omega z)$$

where ω is an imaginary cube root of 1.

28. Find the fifth roots of $16 + 16\sqrt{3}\,i$.

CHAPTER XV

Permutations Combinations Probability

Introduction

EXAMPLE. There are five trails leading to the top of Mt. Moosilauke, N. H. In how many ways can one go to the top of the mountain and return by a different trail?

Solution. How many ways can one reach the top? Having reached the top, how many ways can one descend? Obviously there are five ways to go to the top and having reached the top there are four ways one may descend. If we denote the trails by A, B, C, D, and E, the round trips can be represented schematically as follows:

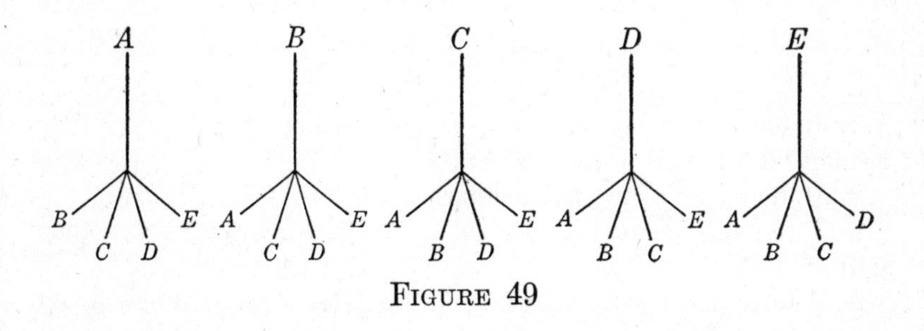

FIGURE 49

Therefore the total number of ways the round trip can be made is 5×4 or 20.

Fundamental principle

If an act can be performed in m different ways, and if, when it has been done, another act can be performed in p different ways, then both acts can be performed in the order stated in mp different ways. For, coupled to the first way of performing the first act, there are p ways of performing the second act; coupled to the second way of performing the first act, there are p ways of performing the second act; and so on for each of the m different ways of performing the first act. Therefore, the two acts can be performed in the order stated in mp ways. This fundamental principle can be extended to the form:

If one act can be performed in m ways, and if, when it has been done, a second act can be performed in p ways, and if when that has been done, a third can be performed in q ways, and so forth, then the number of ways in which they can all be performed in the order stated is $mpq \cdots$.

EXAMPLE. How many odd numbers of two unlike digits can be formed with the digits 1, 2, 3, 4, 5, 6, 7, 8, 9?

Solution. The units' digit can be either 1, 3, 5, 7, 9. That is, the units' digit can be chosen in 5 ways. Since the digits are unlike, the tens' digits can be chosen in 8 ways; for it can be any digit except the one used in the units' place. Therefore 5×8 or 40 odd numbers of two digits each can be formed with two unlike digits.

EXERCISES

1. In how many ways can one post 2 letters in 5 letter boxes, if they are not both posted in the same box?

2. In how many ways can one post 3 letters in 6 letter boxes?

3. Two coins are tossed on a table. In how many ways can they fall?

4. A town has 5 grocery stores and 3 butcher shops. In how many ways can a lady buy a sack of flour and a pound of steak?

5. An athletic field has 5 entrances. In how many ways can one enter and leave by a different entrance?

6. There are 6 different railroads between Chicago and Buffalo. In how many ways can one go from Chicago to Buffalo and return by a different route?

7. Four people enter a room in which there are 4 chairs. In how many ways can they be seated?

8. Four people enter a room in which there are 7 chairs. In how many ways can they be seated?

Permutation

A permutation is an arrangement of a certain number of things in a definite order. For example, the permutations of the letters a, b, c taken two at a time are

$$ab \quad ac \quad ba \quad ca \quad bc \quad cb$$

The permutations of the same letters taken three at a time are

$$abc \quad acb \quad bca \quad bac \quad cab \quad cba$$

The symbol ${}_nP_r$ is used to denote the number of permutations of n things taken r at a time. We have just seen that ${}_3P_2 = 6$ and ${}_3P_3 = 6$.

The number of permutations of n different things taken r at a time ($n \geqq r$)

The problem of finding the number of permutations of n different things taken r at a time is equivalent to finding the number of ways we can fill r places when we have n different things at our disposal.

We can fill the first place in n ways since we have n things at our disposal. The second place can be filled in $n - 1$ ways; hence the first two places can be filled in $n(n - 1)$ ways. Why? When the first two places are filled, the third place can be filled in $n - 2$ ways. Reasoning as before, we can fill the first three places in $n(n - 1)(n - 2)$ ways.

When $r - 1$ places have been filled, there are $n - (r - 1)$ or $n - r + 1$ things not in use. Hence the rth place can be filled in $n - r + 1$ ways. Therefore,

$$\mathbf{{}_nP_r = n(n - 1)(n - 2) \cdots (n - r + 1)}$$

If $r = n$,

$$_nP_n = n(n-1)(n-2) \cdots 3 \cdot 2 \cdot 1 = n!$$

EXERCISES

1. In how many ways can 5 boys be arranged in a column?

2. In how many ways can 4 persons sit on a bench?

3. If a bench holds 4 persons, in how many ways can it be filled from a group of 7 people?

4. A class of 10 enter a room in which there are 12 seats. In how many ways can the class be seated?

5. In how many ways can a baseball team be arranged if the pitcher and catcher play no other positions, and the remaining 7 men can play any position?

6. How many ways can the letters of the word *table* be arranged?

7. How many arrangements can be made by taking 4 letters of the word *compare?*

8. In how many ways can 9 boys stand in a line when:

a) A given boy is always at a given end?

b) A given boy is always at an end?

c) Two given boys are always together?

d) Two given boys are never together?

9. How many arrangements are there of the letters of the word *vowel*, when w is the middle letter?

10. How many numbers between 2000 and 3000 can be made with the digits 2, 3, 4, 7, 8, repetition of digits being allowed?

11. How many numbers between 2000 and 4000 can be formed with the digits 1, 2, 3, 7, 8, repetition of digits being allowed?

12. Find n when $_nP_3 = 210$.

13. Find n when $_nP_3 = 5\,{}_4P_2$.

14. Find n when $_nP_3 = \frac{2}{5}\,{}_{n-1}P_4$.

15. How many numbers of 7 digits, having 0 as the middle digit, can be made from the digits 0, 2, 4, 6, 1, 7, 9, repetition of digits not being allowed? How many of these numbers are odd?

16. In how many ways can 4 algebra books and 3 geometry books be arranged on a shelf so that the geometries are always together?

17. In how many ways can the letters of the word *capitol* be arranged if the vowels and the consonants retain their same relative positions?

18. In how many ways can the letters of the word *radium* be arranged? In how many of these arrangements will the vowels and consonants occupy alternate positions?

Permutation of n things not all different

The number of permutations N of n things taken all at a time, of which p are alike, q others are alike, r others are alike, and so on, is

$$N = \frac{n!}{p!\,q!\,r!\cdots}$$

Suppose the n things are letters and that p of them are a, q of them are b, r of them are c, and so on. If in any of the N permutations we replace the a's by p new letters different from each other and from the $n - p$ remaining letters, then by permuting these p letters among themselves without changing the position of any of the other letters, we will form $p!$ new permutations. By doing this in each of the N permutations, we would obtain $Np!$ new permutations. If we replace the b's by q new letters different from each other and from the $n - q$ remaining letters and so on, we obtain $N \cdot p! \cdot q! \cdot r! \cdots$ new permutations. Since the letters are now all different, they may be permuted in $n!$ ways. Therefore $N \cdot p!\,q!\,r! \cdots = n!$ or

$$N = \frac{n!}{p!q!r!\cdots}.$$

Example. How many permutations can be made using all of the letters of the word *Mississippi?*

Solution. There are 11 letters of which 4 are s, 2 are p, 4 are i. Therefore the number of permutations is

$$\frac{11!}{4!\,2!\,4!} = 34650$$

EXERCISES

1. Find the number of permutations that can be made from all the letters of the word:

a) *permutation.*
b) *assassination.*
c) *examination.*
d) *institutions.*
e) *combination.*

2. How many signals can be made by hoisting 4 white flags and 3 blue flags on a pole at the same time?

3. In how many ways can 4 cents, 3 nickels, 2 dimes, and 1 quarter be distributed among 10 children so that each child may receive one coin?

4. In how many ways can 3 dimes, 4 quarters, and 5 half dollars be arranged in a line?

5. How many different numbers of six digits each can be formed from the digits 1, 1, 2, 2, 2, 5?

Circular permutation

The number of ways n different things can be arranged in a circle is $(n - 1)!$.

The relative order of the objects is not changed by moving each object along the same number of places. Hence we must fix the position of one object and then arrange the remaining $(n - 1)$ objects in all possible ways. This can be done in $(n - 1)!$ ways.

Example. In how many ways can a party of 4 ladies and 4 gentlemen be seated at a table so that no 2 gentlemen are adjacent?

Solution. The ladies can be arranged in 3! ways. After they have been seated the gentlemen can be seated in 4! ways. Therefore there are $3! \times 4!$ or 144 ways of seating the party.

EXERCISES

1. How many ways can 4 keys be arranged on a ring?

2. How many ways can 6 people sit around a table?

3. In how many ways can 8 children form a ring?

4. In how many ways can 5 ladies and 5 gentlemen sit around a table so that no two ladies are adjacent?

5. In how many ways can 7 ladies and 7 gentlemen sit around a table so that there is a gentleman at the right of each lady?

Combination

Any finite group of things, irrespective of their order, is called a *combination*. Thus *abc*, *acb*, *bac*, *bca*, *cab*, *cba* are all different permutations but are the same combination. By the number of combinations of n things taken r at a time, we mean the number of sets or groups of r things which can be formed from the n things. We shall represent this number by the symbol ${}_nC_r$.

The number of combinations of n different things taken r at a time ($n \geqq r$)

Each combination consists of a group of r different things, and these can be arranged among themselves in $r!$ ways. Therefore, ${}_nC_r \times r!$ is equal to the total number of permutations of n things taken r at a time.

Hence
$$ {}_nC_r \times r! = {}_nP_r $$

and
$$ {}_nC_r = \frac{{}_nP_r}{r!} $$

or
$$ {}_nC_r = \frac{n(n-1)(n-2) \cdots (n-r+1)}{r!} \qquad (1) $$

Corollary I. The value of ${}_nC_r$ can be written

$$ {}_nC_r = \frac{n!}{r!(n-r)!} $$

Hint. Multiply the numerator and denominator of (1) by $(n-r)!$ and note that $[n(n-1) \cdots (n-r+1)](n-r)! = n!$

Corollary II. The number of combinations of n different things taken r at a time is equal to the number of combinations of n different things taken $(n-r)$ at a time. In symbols

$$ {}_nC_r = {}_nC_{n-r} $$

for
$$ {}_nC_{n-r} = \frac{n!}{(n-r)!\,[n-(n-r)]!} $$

$$ = \frac{n!}{(n-r)!\,r!} $$

$$ = {}_nC_r $$

EXAMPLE 1. In how many ways can a committee of 7 be chosen from 10 individuals?

Solution. The required number is

$$_{10}C_7 = {_{10}C_3} = \frac{10 \cdot 9 \cdot 8}{1 \cdot 2 \cdot 3} = 120 \text{ ways}$$

EXAMPLE 2. From 4 men and 4 women how many committees of 4 can be formed when the committee contains (1) exactly 3 women? (2) at least 3 women?

Solution. 1. The women can be chosen in $_4C_3$ ways, and the men in $_4C_1$ ways. The committee can, therefore, be formed in $_4C_3 \times {_4C_1}$ or 16 ways.

2. Since the committee is to contain at least 3 women, it can be formed as follows:

a) 3 women, 1 man.

b) 4 women.

Therefore, the number of possible committees is

$$_4C_3 \times {_4C_1} + {_4C_4} = 17$$

EXAMPLE 3. A man has in his pocket a penny, a nickel, a dime, a quarter, and a half dollar. In how many ways can he draw a sum of money from his pocket?

Solution. The number of ways is $_5C_1 + {_5C_2} + {_5C_3} + {_5C_4} + {_5C_5}$ or 31.

Total number of selections of some or all of n things

Each thing may be disposed of in two ways—namely, it may be chosen or it may be rejected. Since there are n things, they may be disposed of in $2 \times 2 \times 2 \cdots$ to n factors or 2^n ways. Among these 2^n ways is included the case in which all are rejected. Therefore, the number of ways of making the selection is $2^n - 1$.

EXAMPLE. If we employ $2^n - 1$ in the solution of example 3 above, we see that the total number of combinations or ways is $2^5 - 1$ or 31.

EXERCISES

1. How many straight lines can be drawn through 7 points in a plane, if no 3 points are in a straight line?

2. How many straight lines can be drawn through 4 points in a plane, if 3 of the points are in a straight line?

3. How many numbers of 3 digits each can be formed from the digits 1, 2, 3, 4, 5, 6, 7, 8:

a) If a repetition of digits is allowed?

b) If a repetition of digits is not allowed?

4. How many different numbers of 7 digits each can be formed with the digits 1, 1, 2, 2, 3, 3, 4, the second, fourth, and sixth digits being odd?

5. How many words containing 2 vowels and 3 consonants can be formed from 4 vowels and 15 consonants? (Any arrangement of the letters is considered a word.)

6. In how many ways can a pupil choose 9 questions out of 11 on an examination?

7. In how many ways can the letters of the word *different* be arranged? In how many of these arrangements do the *f*'s come together?

8. How many signals can be made with 6 flags of different colors which may be displayed singly or any number at a time in a vertical line?

9. From 8 Americans and 6 Englishmen a committee of 5 is to be chosen. In how many ways can the committee be chosen if it contains

a) exactly 4 Americans?

b) at least 4 Americans?

10. In how many different ways can 3 red beads, 3 blue beads, and 4 green beads be arranged in a row?

11. A crew contains 8 men; of these, 3 can row only on the port side, and 2 only on the starboard side. In how many ways can the crew be seated?

12. How many dominoes are there in a set numbered from double-blank to double-six?

13. How many handshakes may be exchanged among a party of 12 students if each student shakes hands with each other student once and only once?

14. In how many ways can a class of 18 students be divided into two groups of 6 and 12 respectively?

15. In how many ways can a class of 18 students be divided into three groups of 4, 6, 8 respectively?

16. Find n, when ${}_{n+2}C_4 = 11\ {}_nC_2$.

17. Find n, when ${}_nC_2 = {}_nC_3$.

18. Prove that ${}_nC_r + {}_nC_{r-1} = {}_{n+1}C_r$.

19. On a jury 3 voted for conviction and 9 for acquittal. In how many ways could this have been done?

20. How many different amounts can be weighed with 1, 2, 4, 8, and 16 gram weights?

21. A railway signal has 3 arms, and each arm can be placed in 2 positions besides the position of rest. How many signals can be given?

22. In how many ways can 999 men be chosen from 1001 men?

23. On a certain branch railway there are 158 stations. How many kinds of single trip local passenger tickets good either way are needed?

24. A set of 7 parallel lines meets a set of 9 parallel lines. How many parallelograms are formed?

25. In how many ways can 8 balls be placed in 3 boxes so that 4 balls are in the first box, 3 in the second, and 1 in the third?

26. How many diagonals can be drawn in an octagon?

27. How many diagonals can be drawn in an n-sided polygon?

28. If I have 10 friends, in how many ways can I invite one or more as guests to dinner?

29. How many arrangements can be made using all the letters of the word *isosceles* if all the arrangements—

a) end with *les*?
b) begin with *i*?
c) have the three *s*'s together.

30. How many different sums of money can be drawn from a bag containing a penny, a nickel, a dime, a quarter, a half dollar, and a dollar?

31. There are 10 points in a plane. If four of these points are in a straight line and no other three are in a straight line, how many straight lines are determined by these 10 points?

32. How many signals can be made by hoisting 7 flags together on a pole if 2 are white, 2 are black, and the rest are red?

33. How many of the signals in exercise 32 will have a red flag at each end?

34. In the Greek alphabet there are 24 letters. How many fraternity names of 3 letters each can be written, repetition of letters being allowed?

35. How many different sets of 4 hands of 13 cards can be dealt from a pack of 52 cards?

Probability

If a given event can happen in h ways and fail in f ways, and if each of the $h + f$ ways is equally likely to occur, the mathematical probability p of the event happening is

$$p = \frac{h}{h + f}$$

and the mathematical probability q of its failing is

$$q = \frac{f}{h + f}$$

Since $\frac{h}{h + f} + \frac{f}{h + f} = \frac{h + f}{h + f} = 1$, the probability of an event happening plus the probability of its failing is unity; *i.e.*, $p + q = 1$.

In place of saying that the probability of an event happening is $\frac{h}{h + f}$, we often say that the odds are h to f in favor of the event and f to h against the event.

Suppose we draw one card from an ordinary pack of 52 cards and wish to know what is the probability of drawing an ace. How many favorable cards are there? Obviously there are 4. The total number of cards which are favorable and unfavorable in the entire deck of 52 cards is 52. Hence $p = \frac{4}{52} = \frac{1}{13}$. What is the probability of *not* drawing an ace? Since $p + q = 1$, $q = 1 - \frac{1}{13} = \frac{12}{13}$.

Probability plays a very important part in all kinds of insurance. Naturally the probability of an event happening is reflected in the premium charged by an insurance company. The American Experience Table of Mortality shows that of 100,000 males living at age ten, 81,822 live to reach the age of 35. What is the probability of a person age 10 living to age 35? Is it .81822? What is the probability of a person age 10 not living to age 35?

EXAMPLE 1. Suppose a bag contains 4 red balls and 6 black balls. If one ball is drawn at random, what is the probability that it is (a) red? (b) black? (c) either red or black?

Solution. a) A red ball can obviously be drawn in 4 ways.

$$\therefore \quad h = 4$$

Since there are 10 balls in the bag, one ball can be drawn in 10 ways.

$$\therefore \quad h + f = 10$$

Hence $$p = \tfrac{4}{10} = \tfrac{2}{5}$$

b) A black ball can be drawn in 6 ways.

$$\therefore \quad h = 6$$

One ball can be drawn in 10 ways.

$$\therefore \quad h + f = 10$$

Hence $$p = \tfrac{6}{10} = \tfrac{3}{5}$$

c) The chance that the ball is either red or black is

$$\tfrac{2}{5} + \tfrac{3}{5} \text{ or } 1, \textit{i.e.}, \text{ certainty}$$

EXAMPLE 2. From a bag containing 4 black balls and 5 white balls, two balls are drawn. Find the probability that (a) both balls are black; (b) both balls are white; (c) one ball is white and one is black.

Solution. a) Two black balls can be drawn in ${}_4C_2$ ways.

$$\therefore \quad h = {}_4C_2 = 6$$

Two balls can be drawn in ${}_9C_2$ ways.

$$\therefore \quad h + f = {}_9C_2 = 36$$

Hence $$p = \tfrac{6}{36} = \tfrac{1}{6}$$

b) Two white balls can be drawn in ${}_5C_2$ ways.

$$\therefore \quad h = {}_5C_2 = 10$$

As in part (a) $$h + f = 36$$

Hence $$p = \tfrac{10}{36} = \tfrac{5}{18}$$

c) A white ball can be drawn in ${}_5C_1$ ways and a black ball in ${}_4C_1$ ways.

$$\therefore \quad h = {}_5C_1 \times {}_4C_1 = 20$$

As before, $h + f = 36$. Hence, $p = \frac{20}{36} = \frac{5}{9}$.
It should be noted that $\frac{1}{6} + \frac{5}{18} + \frac{5}{9} = 1$ or certainty.

EXAMPLE 3. There are 50 tickets in a lottery in which there is a first and a second prize. What is the probability of a man drawing a prize if he owns 5 tickets?

Solution. To win, he may draw 2 prizes and 3 blanks or 1 prize and 4 blanks.

$$\therefore \quad h = {}_2C_2 \times {}_{48}C_3 + {}_2C_1 \times {}_{48}C_4 = 17{,}296 + 389{,}160 = 406{,}456$$

The total number of ways five tickets can be drawn is ${}_{50}C_5$.

$$\therefore \quad h + f = {}_{50}C_5 = 2{,}118{,}760$$

Hence $$p = \frac{406{,}456}{2{,}118{,}760} = \frac{47}{245}$$

EXERCISES

1. Mr. Jones is one of 10 instructors each of whom has only one section in algebra. What is the probability of a student being assigned to Mr. Jones' class, if the assignments are made by lot?

2. If a coin is tossed, what is the probability that it will fall heads? tails?

3. What is the probability of drawing a heart in a single draw from an ordinary pack of 52 cards?

4. What is the probability of drawing a face card on a single draw from an ordinary pack of 52 cards?

5. From a bag containing 4 black balls and 5 white ones, a ball is drawn at random. What is the probability that it will be black? white?

6. One die is thrown. What is the probability of throwing (a) 3? (b) 5? (c) 6?

7. Two dice are thrown. What is the probability of throwing a total of (a) 2? (b) 3? (c) 4? (d) 5? (e) 6? (f) 7? (g) 8? (h) 9? (i) 10? (j) 11? (k) 12?

8. Three coins are tossed. What is the probability that there are exactly 2 heads and 1 tail?

9. From a pack of 52 cards, 4 cards are drawn. Find the probability that they are all face cards.

10. From a pack of 52 cards, 2 cards are drawn. What is the probability that—

a) both cards are red?
b) one card is red and one is black?
c) both cards are black?
d) both cards are hearts?
e) both cards are face cards?
f) one card is a face card and one is not?
g) both cards are aces?

11. From a bag containing balls numbered 1 to 12 respectively, four balls are drawn at random. What is the probability that—

a) the four numbers are even?
b) three are even and one is odd?
c) two are even and two are odd?
d) one is even and three are odd?
e) four are odd?

12. From the integers 1 to 50, one is chosen at random. Find the probability that the number chosen is exactly divisible by (a) 2; (b) 3; (c) 5; (d) 7.

13. A number of three digits is formed with the digits 1, 2, 3, 4, 5, 6. If repetition of digits is allowed, find the probability that the number is even; odd.

14. Three algebra and two geometry books are placed at random on a shelf. What is the probability that the geometries will be together?

15. From a bag containing 10 white balls and 8 black balls, 5 balls are drawn at random. What is the probability of drawing—

a) two white and three black balls?
b) four white balls and one black ball?
c) five white balls?
d) five black balls?
e) one white ball and four black balls?

Empirical probability

A probability in which the data depends upon experience is called *empirical*. For example, the probability that a certain house will burn within a year, the probability that a man aged 40 will have an accident within the next six months, etc., are examples of empirical probabilities.

The probability that a man may live a certain number of years or that he may die in a certain period, is also an empirical probability and is usually computed from the data given in the American Experience Table of Mortality. A copy of this table will be found on page 364. In this table l_x designates the number of people of the original group who are alive at age x. The symbol d_x designates the number of people of the original group who die between the ages x and $x + 1$. Hence,

$$d_x = l_x - l_{x+1}$$

The probability that a person age x will live for n years is denoted by the symbol ${}_np_x$, which is equal to $\frac{l_{x+n}}{l_x}$.

The probability that a person of age x will die in the next n years is denoted by the symbol ${}_nq_x$, which is equal to $\frac{l_x - l_{x+n}}{l_x}$.

EXAMPLE 1. Find the probability that a person age 27 will live to the age of 45.

Solution. From the table on page 364 we find $l_{27} = 87{,}596$ and $l_{45} = 74{,}173$.

Hence $${}_{18}p_{27} = \frac{74{,}173}{87{,}596} = .847$$

EXAMPLE 2. Find the probability that a person age 27 will die before reaching the age of 45.

Solution 1. Using the result of example 1, we have

$$\begin{aligned} {}_{18}q_{27} = 1 - {}_{18}p_{27} &= 1 - .847 \\ &= .153 \end{aligned}$$

Solution 2. $${}_{18}q_{27} = \frac{l_{27} - l_{45}}{l_{27}} = \frac{87{,}596 - 74{,}173}{87{,}596}$$

$$= \frac{13{,}423}{87{,}596} = .153$$

EXERCISES

1. Find the following probabilities:
   a) A person aged 20 will live 20 years.
   b) A person aged 35 will live 15 years.
   c) A person aged 27 will live to age 60.
   d) A person aged 45 will live to age 90.
2. Find the following probabilities:
   a) A person aged 27 will die within a year.
   b) A person aged 30 will die before reaching 40.
   c) A person aged 60 will not live to age 70.
   d) A person aged 75 will not live a year.
3. Find the following probabilities:
   a) A person aged 30 will live to age 40.
   b) A person aged 30 will live to age 60.
   c) A person aged 30 will live to age 90.
   d) A person aged 40 will not live to age 60.
   e) A person aged 80 will not live to age 90.
   f) A person aged 50 will live to age 80.
   g) A person aged 60 will live to age 90.

Expectation

Suppose the probability of an event happening in a single trial is p, then the expected number of successes in n trials is np. For example, suppose one makes 200 drawings from an ordinary pack of cards, replacing each card drawn before making the next draw, and that he wishes to know the expected number of spades he may draw. Since the probability of drawing a spade on a single draw is $\frac{13}{52}$ or $\frac{1}{4}$, the expected number of spades is $\frac{1}{4}(200)$ or 50.

If p is the probability that a person will win A dollars, then his expectation is defined at Ap. For example, suppose I win \$26 if I draw an ace from an ordinary pack of cards. The probability that I shall draw an ace is $\frac{4}{52}$ or $\frac{1}{13}$. Hence my expectation is $\frac{1}{13}(26)$ or \$2.00.

Mutually exclusive events

If two or more events are of such a nature that not more than one of them can happen in a given trial, the events are said to be mutually exclusive. For example, drawing the ace of spades and the deuce of clubs are mutually exclusive events. Would drawing an ace and a spade be mutually exclusive events?

Theorem. If $p_1, p_2, \cdots p_n$, are the separate probabilities of n exclusive events, then the probability p that some one of these events will occur on a particular trial is

$$p = p_1 + p_2 + \cdots + p_n$$

Proof. Let $E_1, E_2, E_3, \cdots E_n$ represent the events. Moreover, let us assume that any trial can occur in b ways, and that out of these b ways E_1 occurs a_1 ways, E_2 occurs a_2 ways, etc. Then $p_1 = \frac{a_1}{b}$, $p_2 = \frac{a_2}{b}, \cdots, p_n = \frac{a_n}{b}$. Since, by hypothesis, the events are mutually exclusive, $a_1, a_2, \cdots a_n$ are all different. Hence

$$p = \frac{a_1 + a_2 + \cdots + a_n}{b} = \frac{a_1}{b} + \frac{a_2}{b} + \cdots + \frac{a_n}{b}$$
$$= p_1 + p_2 + \cdots + p_n$$

Suppose we wished to find the probability of drawing an ace, a deuce, and a king from an ordinary pack of cards. Are these events mutually exclusive? What is the probability of drawing an ace? a deuce? a king? Since each of these probabilities is $\frac{1}{13}$, the required probability is $\frac{1}{13} + \frac{1}{13} + \frac{1}{13}$ or $\frac{3}{13}$. This result is readily checked as follows. The number of favorable cards is $4 + 4 + 4$ or 12. The number of favorable and unfavorable cards is 52. Hence the probability is $\frac{12}{52}$ or $\frac{3}{13}$.

Independent events

If two or more events occur without affecting one another, they are said to be *independent*.

Theorem. The probability of two independent events happening in a single trial in which both are possible, is the product of their separate probabilities of happening.

Proof. Suppose the first event can happen a ways out of b possible ways of happening or failing. Then the probability of its happening is $p_1 = \frac{a}{b}\cdot$ Suppose the second event can happen in c ways out of d possible ways of happening or failing. Then the probability of its happening is $p_2 = \frac{c}{d}\cdot$ By page 252, the total number of ways that two events can happen is ac; while the total number of ways they can happen and fail is bd. Hence, the probability that both events will happen is $\frac{ac}{bd} = \frac{a}{b}\cdot\frac{c}{d} = p_1p_2$. By similar reasoning, the rule can be extended to cover more than two events.

Example. If three coins are tossed, what is the probability that they will fall three heads?

Solution. Will the fall of one coin be independent of the fall of the others? How many ways can each coin fall? Obviously the probability of each coin falling heads is $\frac{1}{2}$. Hence the probability of three heads appearing is $\frac{1}{2}\cdot\frac{1}{2}\cdot\frac{1}{2}$ or $\frac{1}{8}$. This problem can also be solved as follows: Since each coin can fall two ways, the three coins can fall in $2 \times 2 \times 2$ or 8 ways. Only one way—namely, three heads—is favorable. Therefore the probability is $\frac{1}{8}$.

Dependent events

If the happening of one event influences the probability of the happening of a second event, the second event is said to be *dependent* on the first.

Theorem. If p_1 is the probability of an event happening; and if, after it has happened, the probability of a second event happening is p_2, then the probability that the two events will happen in the order named, is p_1p_2.

The proof of this statement is left as an exercise.

Example. From a pack of 52 cards a card is drawn at random and not replaced. A second card is then drawn. Find the probability that the first card is a spade and the second card is a heart.

Solution. The probability of drawing a spade on the first draw is $\frac{13}{52}$ or $\frac{1}{4}$. After a spade is drawn, the probability of drawing a heart is $\frac{13}{51}$. Hence, the probability of first drawing a spade and then a heart is $\frac{1}{4} \cdot \frac{13}{51} = \frac{13}{204}$.

Repeated trials

If p is the probability that an event will happen and q is the probability that it will fail in any trial, then the probability that it will happen exactly r times in n trials is

$$_nC_r \cdot p^r \cdot q^{n-r}$$

For example, let us find the probability of throwing exactly three aces in seven throws of a die. The probability of throwing an ace on any throw is $\frac{1}{6}$, while the probability of not throwing an ace is $\frac{5}{6}$. The probability that an ace will appear, let us say, on the first three throws and not on the last four, is

$$\tfrac{1}{6} \cdot \tfrac{1}{6} \cdot \tfrac{1}{6} \cdot \tfrac{5}{6} \cdot \tfrac{5}{6} \cdot \tfrac{5}{6} \cdot \tfrac{5}{6} \text{ or } (\tfrac{1}{6})^3(\tfrac{5}{6})^4$$

But the three aces may occur on any three of the seven throws, that is, they may occur in $_7C_3 = \dfrac{7 \cdot 6 \cdot 5}{1 \cdot 2 \cdot 3} = 35$ ways. Hence the total probability is $35(\frac{1}{6})^3(\frac{5}{6})^4$ or $\frac{21875}{279936}$.

It should be noted that

$$(q + p)^n = q^n + {_nC_1}q^{n-1}p + {_nC_2}q^{n-2}p^2 + \cdots + {_nC_r}q^{n-r}p^r + \cdots + p^n$$

and that the terms of this expansion give the respective probabilities of an event happening exactly $0, 1, 2, \cdots, r, \cdots, n$ times in n trials.

EXAMPLE 1. Find the probability of throwing at least 4 aces in 6 throws with a single die.

Solution. To throw *at least* 4 aces means that we must throw either 4, 5, or 6 aces. Hence the probability is

$$
\begin{aligned}
&{}_6C_4p^4q^2 + {}_6C_5p^5q + p^6 \\
&= \frac{6.5}{1.2}\left(\frac{1}{6}\right)^4\left(\frac{5}{6}\right)^2 + \frac{6}{1}\left(\frac{1}{6}\right)^5\left(\frac{5}{6}\right) + \left(\frac{1}{6}\right)^6 \\
&= \tfrac{375}{46656} + \tfrac{30}{46656} + \tfrac{1}{46656} \\
&= \tfrac{203}{23328}
\end{aligned}
$$

EXAMPLE 2. A die is thrown three times. What is the probability that a 5 is not thrown?

Solution. The probability of not throwing a 5 on any throw is $\frac{5}{6}$. Since the throws are unrelated, the probability of not throwing a 5 in three throws is $\frac{5}{6} \times \frac{5}{6} \times \frac{5}{6} = \frac{125}{216}$.

EXAMPLE 3. A die is thrown three times. What is the probability that at least one 5 is thrown?

Solution. The easiest way to solve the problem that something will occur *at least once* is to solve the contrary problem that it will not occur and then subtract this answer from unity, for $p + q = 1$. The probability that a 5 is not thrown (see example 2) is $\frac{125}{216}$. Hence the probability that at least one 5 is thrown is $1 - \frac{125}{216}$ or $\frac{91}{216}$.

EXERCISES

1. In a single throw with one die, what is the probability of throwing at least a 5?

2. From a class of 10 boys, two boys are selected. If in the class there are two brothers, what is the probability that they will be selected?

3. In a single throw of two dice, find the probability of throwing a total of at least (a) 3; (b) 5; (c) 7.

4. A bag contains 6 red balls, 5 green balls, 8 blue balls. Find the probability that if 6 balls are drawn they are (a) all red; (b) 3 red, 3 green; (c) 2 red, 2 green, 2 blue; (d) 6 blue.

5. Four coins are tossed. Find the probability that they will fall two heads and two tails.

6. What is the probability of throwing doublets in a single throw with two dice?

7. Nine boys stand in a line. Find the probability that—

a) A particular boy will stand at an end.

b) A particular boy will stand at a given end.
c) A particular boy will stand in the middle.
d) Two particular boys will be together.
e) Two particular boys will not be together.

8. From a panel of 20 men, 12 jurymen are drawn. What is the probability that a particular man will be drawn? What are the odds against his being drawn?

9. The odds against an event are 12 to 5. What is the probability of its happening?

10. The probability of an event happening is $\frac{3}{10}$. Find the odds against the event.

11. Two dice are thrown. What is the probability that two 5's will turn up?

12. Four cards are drawn from a pack of 52 cards. What is the probability that there will be one of each suit?

13. In tossing five coins, what is the probability that there will be exactly two heads?

14. In tossing three coins, what is the probability that at least two will fall heads?

15. Three cards are drawn from a pack. What is the probability that they will be an ace, king, and queen of the same suit?

16. In the alphabet there are 5 vowels. If 3 letters are selected, what is the chance they will be vowels?

17. In a set of dominoes which go up to double-six, a player draws a hand of 5 dominoes. What is the probability that he will draw at least 4 doubles?

18. Five ladies and 5 gentlemen take seats at random around a table. What is the probability that they will occupy alternate seats?

19. Four men agree to match coins for their dinner, the odd man paying the bill. Show that the probability of this happening on the first trial is $\frac{1}{2}$.

20. From a list of 12 friends, a lady selects 5 for a dinner party. What is the probability that two particular persons will be selected?

21. If a man holds 4 tickets in a lottery in which there are 120 tickets, what is his expectation if there is a single cash prize of $200?

22. Two cards are drawn from a pack of 52 cards. Find the probability that—

a) The first card is a deuce and the second card is a king.
b) The first card is a king and the second card is a deuce.
c) Either card is a king and the other a deuce.

23. Find the probability of throwing 2 aces in 5 throws of a die.

24. A tennis player's chance of winning a set is $\frac{1}{5}$. Find the probability that—

a) He will win the first two sets.

b) He will win three out of the first five sets.

25. If my chance of winning any single game of chess against my opponent is $\frac{3}{5}$, find the probability that I shall win at least four out of seven games.

Historical note

In the Middle Ages people believed in the mysticism of arrangements; hence there arose great interest in the study of permutations and combinations. The first book touching on the subject was Pacioli's *Suma* (1494) wherein is discussed the problem of how many ways a group of individuals can sit around a table. The first treatise on the subject, however, did not appear until 1713; it was Bernoulli's *Ars Conjectandi.*

Pascal (1623–1662) once raised the question: "Suppose two players of equal skill do not complete a game. If the stakes, the score of each person, and the necessary score to win, are known, how should the stakes be divided." He and Fermat (1608–1665) solved the problem independently of each other and arrived at the same solution. Their discussion aroused so much interest in the subject of probability that they are thought of as the founders of the subject although it had been touched on slightly by others before their time.

The binomial theorem for positive integral exponents

On page 226 we used mathematical induction to prove the binomial theorem for positive integral exponents. We shall now show how the theorem can be proved from the theory of combinations.

Consider the product

$$(x + y)(x + y)(x + y) \cdots (x + y) \qquad [n \text{ factors}]$$

where n is any positive integer. In the product, one term is x^n, and it is obtained by taking the letter x from each parenthesis. There will be n terms $x^{n-1}y$, for the letter y can be chosen from any of the n parentheses; and this can be done in ${}_nC_1$ or n ways. There will be ${}_nC_2$ terms $x^{n-2}y^2$, for the y's can be chosen from two of the n parentheses and the x from the remaining $n - 2$ parentheses. In general, there will be ${}_nC_r$ terms $x^{n-r}y^r$, for the y's can be chosen from any r of the n parentheses, and the x's from the remaining $n - r$ parentheses. Therefore,

$$(x + y)^n = x^n + {}_nC_1x^{n-1}y + {}_nC_2x^{n-2}y^2 + \cdots + {}_nC_rx^{n-r}y^r + \cdots + {}_nC_ny^n \quad (1)$$

This formula is called the binomial expansion of $(x + y)^n$. Since ${}_nC_r = {}_nC_{n-r}$, it follows that the coefficients of any two terms equally numbered from the beginning and the end are equal. If we replace y by $-y$, we have

$$(x - y)^n = x^n + {}_nC_1x^{n-1}(-y) + {}_nC_2x^{n-2}(-y)^2 + \cdots + (-y)^n$$

$$(x - y)^n = x^n - {}_nC_1x^{n-1}y + {}_nC_2x^{n-2}y^2 - \cdots + (-1)^ny^n$$

EXAMPLE 1. Expand $(2a - b)^5$.

Solution.

$$(2a - b)^5 = (2a)^5 - {}_5C_1(2a)^4(b) + {}_5C_2(2a)^3(b)^2 - {}_5C_3(2a)^2(b)^3 + {}_5C_4(2a)(b)^4 - b^5$$

$$= 32a^5 - 80a^4b + 80a^3b^2 - 40a^2b^3 + 10ab^4 - b^5$$

EXAMPLE 2. Find the sixth term of $(2a - 3b)^8$.

Solution. The sixth term is ${}_8C_5(2a)^3(-3b)^5$ or $-108{,}864a^3b^5$.

EXAMPLE 3. In the expansion of $\left(x^2 - \frac{1}{x}\right)^{10}$, find the coefficient of x^{11}.

Solution. We must first find what term contains x^{11}. Call it the kth term. Then

$${}_{10}C_{k-1}(x^2)^{11-k}\left(-\frac{1}{x}\right)^{k-1} \text{ is the term}$$

We wish the exponent of x in this term to be 11. Therefore, $22 - 2k - k + 1 = 11$ or $k = 4$. Hence the desired coefficient is $-{}_{10}C_3 = -120$.

EXERCISES

Expand and simplify each of the following expressions:

1. $(2a + 1)^3$
2. $(2a - 1)^5$
3. $(2x - y)^7$
4. $(2x + y)^8$
5. $\left(1 + \frac{1}{x}\right)^5$
6. $\left(1 - \frac{1}{x}\right)^8$
7. $\left(x - \frac{1}{x^2}\right)^6$
8. $\left(x + \frac{1}{x}\right)^7$

Find the numerical value of the following:

9. $(0.9)^5$ [*Hint.* $0.9 = (1 - 0.1)$]
10. $(0.9)^6$
11. $(0.99)^3$
12. $(0.99)^5$

Find and simplify—

13. The 5th term of $(2a - 1)^8$.
14. The 6th term of $(2x + 3y)^{10}$.
15. The 7th term of $\left(x + \frac{1}{x}\right)^{12}$.
16. The middle term of $(1 - a)^{14}$.
17. The middle term of $(2x - y)^{12}$.
18. The middle term of $\left(a - \frac{1}{a}\right)^{16}$.

Find the coefficient of—

19. x^8, in the expansion of $\left(x^2 - \frac{1}{x}\right)^{10}$.
20. x^{18}, in the expansion of $\left(x^2 + \frac{1}{2}\right)^{15}$.
21. x^{-17}, in the expansion of $\left(x^4 - \frac{k}{x^3}\right)^{15}$.
22. x^{25}, in the expansion of $\left(x^4 + \frac{a}{x^3}\right)^{15}$.
23. Prove that the total number of selections or combinations each containing some or all of n things is $2^n - 1$ (*i.e.*, ${}_nC_1 + {}_nC_2 \cdots + {}_nC_n = 2^n - 1$) by letting $x = y = 1$ in equation (1), page 273.

Historical note

Euclid, who wrote the first geometry text of importance (325 B.C.) proved that $(a + b)^2 = a^2 + 2ab + b^2$. About 1100 A.D. the Persian philosopher and poet Omar Khayyam discovered how to expand the binomial $(a + b)^n$ for $n = 3, 4, 5$, and 6. In 1742 Salvemini discovered the law for any positive integral value of n. Newton (1642–1727) stated the theorem when n is fractional or a negative integer. Abel (1802–1829) proved the theorem for general values of n including complex numbers.

MASTERY TEST

1. A contractor decides to hire 4 plumbers and 3 helpers. If 10 plumbers and 8 helpers apply for the job, in how many ways can a selection be made?

2. How many ways can 10 boys be divided into three groups of 5, 2, and 3 each?

3. If three dice are thrown, what is the probability of turning up a total of 7?

4. If six men and six women are seated at random in a row, what is the probability that the men and women will sit in alternate seats?

5. If the probability that I win a certain game is $\frac{2}{5}$, what is the probability that I shall win three consecutive games?

6. If I toss four coins, what is the probability that I shall have three heads and one tail?

7. Find and simplify the first four terms of $\left(\sqrt{x} - \dfrac{1}{\sqrt{x}}\right)^{10}$.

8. Find and simplify the sixth term of $\left(x^2 - \dfrac{1}{2x^3}\right)^{12}$.

9. Find the coefficient of x^{17} in $\left(x^3 - \dfrac{\sqrt{x}}{2}\right)^9$.

10. How many different permutations of the letters of the word *erroneous* will have vowels in the first five places?

11. If a set of twenty-five parallel lines intersects a set of sixteen parallel lines, how many parallelograms are formed?

12. A box contains 4 dimes, 5 nickels, and 3 quarters. If three coins are drawn at random, find the probability that they will be—

a) 3 dimes. d) 1 dime, 1 nickel, 1 quarter.
b) 3 nickels. e) 2 dimes, 1 nickel.
c) 3 quarters. f) 1 dime, 2 nickels.

13. Prove that ${}_{n-3}C_{r-2} + {}_{n-3}C_{r-3} = {}_{n-2}C_{r-2}$.

14. How many numbers greater than 10,000 can be formed with the digits 0, 1, 2, 3, 4, 5, repetition of digits being allowed?

15. How many sets of four hands of thirteen cards each can be dealt from a pack of 52 cards, the order of the hands and not the cards in the hands to be considered?

16. An automobile is made in six body styles, two choices of wheels, and five color schemes. How many cars are necessary in order to exhibit all possible models?

17. There are 100 tickets in a lottery. Three of the tickets are winners. If I buy two tickets what is the probability I will win something?

18. Six cards, four of which are black and two red, are shuffled and placed face down on a table. When the cards are turned over the player wins \$20 if the two red cards are next to each other. What is the player's expectation?

19. The probability that A can solve a certain problem is $\frac{5}{8}$, that B can solve it $\frac{3}{4}$, and that C can solve it $\frac{1}{3}$. Find the probability that the problem will be solved if all three men try.

20. In a home for the aged are three men age 72, 75, and 78 respectively. Find the probability that—

a) All will live one year.

b) At least one will die within a year.

c) All will die within a year.

CHAPTER XVI

Theory of Equations

An algebraic equation of degree n

On page 96 we learned that the function

$$f(x) = a_0x^n + a_1x^{n-1} + \cdot \cdot \cdot + a_n$$

where $a_0, a_1, \cdot \cdot \cdot, a_n$ are constants (real or imaginary) and $a_0 \neq 0$, is called a polynomial of degree n in x.

When such a polynomial is placed equal to zero, the resulting equation $f(x) = 0$ is called an *algebraic equation of degree n.*

In this chapter we shall study:

a) Properties of the polynomial $f(x)$.

b) Methods for finding exactly and approximately the roots of certain special numerical equations, $f(x) = 0$.

If $n = 2$, we have a quadratic equation. On page 134 we learned how to derive a general formula for finding the roots of a quadratic. It is possible to derive formulas for finding the roots of any third and fourth degree equations, but the results are complicated. Abel (see page 305) proved that it is impossible to derive a formula for the roots of a general algebraic equation of degree higher than four. However, it is possible to find to as high a degree of approximation as one desires, all the real roots of any algebraic equation with real numerical coefficients.

Fundamental theorem

Every equation $f(x) = 0$ has at least one root. In other words, there exists at least one number either real or complex that will satisfy $f(x) = 0$. The validity of the above theorem will be assumed as the proof is beyond the scope of this course.

If $f(x) = x^2 + 7x + 5$ is divided by $x - 1$, what is the remainder? What is the value of $f(1)$? Is the remainder equal to $f(1)$? If $f(x) = 2x^3 - 2x^2 + 3x - 5$ is divided by $x - 2$, is the remainder the same as $f(2)$?

Remainder theorem

If $f(x)$ is divided by $x - r$, the remainder is $f(r)$.

Proof. Let $f(x) = a_0x^n + a_1x^{n-1} + \cdots + a_{n-1}x + a_n$

Then $f(r) = a_0r^n + a_1r^{n-1} + \cdots + a_{n-1}r + a_n$

Subtracting and combining terms, we have

$$f(x) - f(r) = a_0(x^n - r^n) + a_1(x^{n-1} - r^{n-1}) + \cdots + a_{n-1}(x - r)$$

Now $x - r$ is a factor of each term in the right-hand member. If $x - r$ is factored out and the remaining factor is called $Q(x)$, we have

$$f(x) - f(r) = (x - r)Q(x)$$

or

$$f(x) = (x - r)Q(x) + f(r)$$

Dividing by $(x - r)$ gives

$$\frac{f(x)}{x - r} = Q(x) + \frac{f(r)}{x - r}$$

Therefore, when $f(x)$ is divided by $x - r$, the quotient is $Q(x)$ and the remainder is $f(r)$.

EXAMPLE 1. Find the remainder when $3x^3 - 5x^2 - 7x - 1$ is divided by $x + 2$.

Solution. Substituting for r the value -2, we have

$$f(r) = f(-2) = 3(-2)^3 - 5(-2)^2 - 7(-2) - 1 = -31$$

EXAMPLE 2. What is the remainder when $3x^4 - 5x^3 + 2x^2 - 7x + 7$ is divided by $x - 1$?

Solution. The remainder $= f(1) = 3 - 5 + 2 - 7 + 7 = 0$. Since the remainder is zero, is $x - 1$ a factor of $3x^4 - 5x^3 + 2x^2 - 7x + 7$?

Factor theorem

If r is a root of the equation $f(x) = 0$, then $x - r$ is a factor of $f(x)$.

Since r is a root of $f(x) = 0$, it satisfies the equation; *i.e.*, $f(r) = 0$. But $f(r)$ is the remainder when $f(x)$ is divided by $x - r$. Therefore, when $f(x)$ is divided by $x - r$, the remainder is 0; *i.e.*, $x - r$ is a factor of $f(x)$.

Converse of factor theorem

If $x - r$ is a factor of $f(x)$, then r is a root of the equation $f(x) = 0$.

Since $x - r$ is a factor of $f(x)$,

$$f(x) = (x - r)Q(x)$$

Substituting $x = r$, we have $f(r) = 0$.

$$\therefore \quad r \text{ is a root of the equation } f(x) = 0$$

EXAMPLE. Factor $2x^3 - 11x^2 + 17x - 6$ using the factor theorem.

Solution. Let $f(x) = 2x^3 - 11x^2 + 17x - 6$

Now $\quad f(2) = 2(8) - 11(4) + 17(2) - 6 = 0$

$\therefore$ $x - 2$ is a factor. Dividing $f(x)$ by $x - 2$ gives a quotient of $2x^2 - 7x + 3$, which factors into $(2x - 1)(x - 3)$.

Hence, $2x^3 - 11x^2 + 17x - 6 = (x - 2)(x - 3)(2x - 1)$.

Query. How does the degree of the given polynomial compare with the number of linear factors?

EXERCISES

Without dividing, find the remainder when:

1. $3x^3 + 3x^2 + 7x - 1$ is divided by $x - 1$.
2. $4x^3 + 2x^2 - 3x + 7$ is divided by $x - 2$.
3. $7x^4 - 2x^2 + 3x - 1$ is divided by $x + 1$.

4. $100\,x^{75} - 30\,x^{45} + 10\,x^{35} - x^{15} - 25$ is divided by $x - 1$.

5. $7(x + 2)^3 - 3(x + 3) - 7$ is divided by $x - 3$.

6. If the equation $f(x) = 0$ has only positive coefficients, prove that it cannot have a positive root.

7. Given $ax^3 + 3\,x^2 - 2\,ax + 1 = 0$. Find a:

a) When one root is 2.

b) When one factor of the left-hand member is $x + 1$.

8. When $ax^3 + 2\,x^2 - 2\,ax + 1$ is divided by $x - 2$ the remainder is 3. Find a.

9. If $f(a) \neq 0$, prove that $f(x)$ is not exactly divisible by $x - a$.

10. Show that $x^n + a^n$ is divisible by $x + a$ when n is odd, and not when n is even.

11. Find the polynomial of the second degree which vanishes when $x = 1$ and $x = 3$, and which assumes the value 12 when $x = 2$.

12. Find the polynomial of the third degree which vanishes when x equals -1, 0, and 3 and has the value 12 when $x = 1$.

13. Prove that $978\,x^{978} - 763\,x^{763} - 215$ is divisible by $x - 1$.

14. Prove that 3 is a root of the equation $3\,x^4 = 6\,x^3 + 2\,x^2 + 20\,x + 3$.

15. Is 6 a root of $x^3 - 3\,x^2 + 7\,x - 1 = 0$?

16. Prove that a is a root of $6\,x^{17} - 8\,a^7x^{10} - 4\,a^3x^{14} + 3\,a^8x^9 + 3\,a^{17} = 0$.

Synthetic division

We shall now explain a simple method of dividing a polynomial by a binomial of the form $x - k$; *i.e.*, by a binomial of the first degree in which the coefficient of x is unity.

Let us divide $3\,x^4 - 2\,x^3 + x^2 - 5\,x + 1$ by $x - 2$. Using long division we have

$$
\begin{array}{r|l|l}
x - 2 & 3\,x^4 - 2\,x^3 + x^2 - 5\,x + 1 & 3\,x^3 + 4\,x^2 + 9\,x + 13 \\
 & 3\,x^4 - 6\,x^3 & \\
\hline
 & \quad 4\,x^3 + x^2 & \\
 & \quad 4\,x^3 - 8\,x^2 & \\
\hline
 & \qquad 9\,x^2 - 5\,x & \\
 & \qquad 9\,x^2 - 18\,x & \\
\hline
 & \qquad\quad 13\,x + 1 & \\
 & \qquad\quad 13\,x - 26 & \\
\hline
 & \qquad\qquad 27 &
\end{array}
$$

This process can be abbreviated as follows. Note that the powers of x are omitted and only the coefficients of the terms are written.

$$
\begin{array}{r|rrrrr|l}
1-2 & 3 & -2 & 1 & -5 & 1 & 3+4+9+13 \\
 & & -6 & & & & \\
\cline{2-6}
 & & +4 & & & & \\
 & & & -8 & & & \\
\cline{3-6}
 & & & 9 & & & \\
 & & & & -18 & & \\
\cline{4-6}
 & & & & +13 & & \\
 & & & & & -26 & \\
\cline{5-6}
 & & & & & 27 &
\end{array}
$$

A still further abbreviation is as follows:

$$
\begin{array}{r|rrrrr}
+2 & 3 & -2 & 1 & -5 & 1 \\
 & & 6 & 8 & 18 & 26 \\
\hline
 & 3 & +4 & +9 & +13 & +27
\end{array}
$$

Note the 1 has been dropped from the divisor, the -2 has been changed to $+2$, allowing us to add rather than subtract.

The quotient is $3x^3 + 4x^2 + 9x + 13$ and the remainder is 27. The final abridged division is called *synthetic division.*

EXAMPLE 1. By synthetic division find the quotient and the remainder when $2x^4 - 3x^3 + x - 7$ is divided by $x + 2$.

Solution.
$$
\begin{array}{r|rrrrr}
-2 & 2 & -3 & 0 & 1 & -7 \\
 & & -4 & 14 & -28 & 54 \\
\hline
 & 2 & -7 & 14 & -27 & 47
\end{array}
$$

The quotient is $2x^3 - 7x^2 + 14x - 27$ and the remainder is 47.

EXAMPLE 2. If $f(x) = 2x^4 + 3x^3 + 7x^2 + 14x + 20$, find $f(-3)$.

Solution.
$$
\begin{array}{r|rrrrl}
-3 & 2 & 3 & 7 & 14 & 20 \\
 & & -6 & 9 & -48 & 102 \\
\hline
 & 2 & -3 & 16 & -34 & \underline{122 = f(-3)}
\end{array}
$$

EXERCISES

In the following exercises use synthetic division.

1. Find the remainder and quotient when $x^3 + 6x^2 - 3x + 7$ is divided by $x - 1$.

2. Find the remainder and quotient when $x^4 - 3x^3 - 2x - 3$ is divided by $x + 2$.

3. Show that 3 is a root of $x^3 - 4x^2 - 17x + 60 = 0$.

4. Is 3 a root of $x^4 - x^2 - x - 27 = 0$?

5. Find k so that 2 is a root of $x^4 - 3x^3 + 2x^2 - kx + 1 = 0$.

6. Find k so that $x + 2$ is a factor of $x^3 - 5x^2 + kx - 12$.

7. Find k so that $x + 3$ is a factor of $x^3 - 4x - 12k$.

Graphing a polynomial

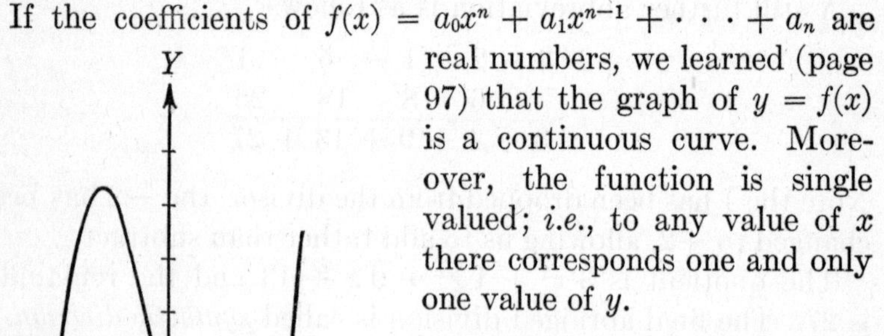

If the coefficients of $f(x) = a_0x^n + a_1x^{n-1} + \cdots + a_n$ are real numbers, we learned (page 97) that the graph of $y = f(x)$ is a continuous curve. Moreover, the function is single valued; *i.e.*, to any value of x there corresponds one and only one value of y.

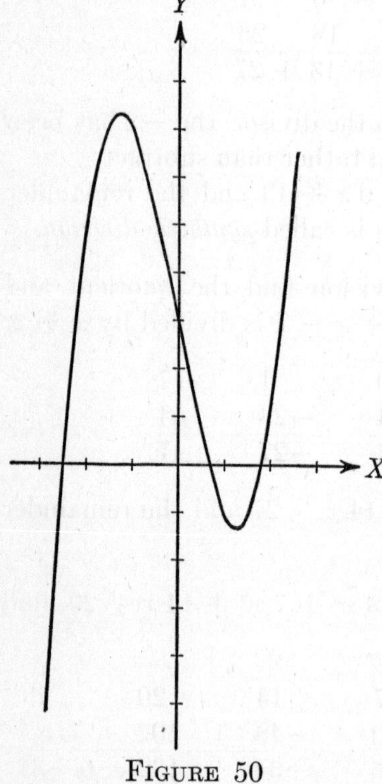

FIGURE 50

EXAMPLE. Construct the graph of $x^3 - 5x + 3$ and locate approximately the real zeros.

Solution. We learned on page 281 that synthetic division furnishes us with a convenient and easy method for evaluating $f(x)$ for any value of x. Thus $f(-3) = -9$ is obtained as follows:

$$\begin{array}{r|rrrr} -3 & 1 & 0 & -5 & 3 \\ & & -3 & 9 & -12 \\ \hline & 1 & -3 & 4 & \boxed{-9} \end{array}$$

In the same manner we obtain

$$\begin{aligned} f(-3) &= -9 \\ f(-2) &= 5 \\ f(-1) &= 7 \\ f(0) &= 3 \\ f(1) &= -1 \\ f(2) &= 1 \\ f(3) &= 15 \end{aligned}$$

Using these data we can construct the graph exhibited in Fig. 50. Since $f(-3)$ is negative and $f(-2)$ is positive, the curve crosses the x axis between $x = -3$ and $x = -2$. In other words, there is a zero of the function between these values of x. Now $f(-2.5) = -.125$ while $f(-2.4) = 1.176$. Hence the zero is between $x = -2.5$ and $x = -2.4$.

$$\begin{array}{r|rrrr} -2.5 & 1 & 0 & -5 & 3 \\ & & -2.5 & 6.25 & -3.125 \\ \hline & 1 & -2.5 & 1.25 & -.125 \end{array}$$

$$\begin{array}{r|rrrr} -2.4 & 1 & 0 & -5 & 3 \\ & & -2.4 & 5.76 & -1.824 \\ \hline & 1 & -2.4 & .76 & 1.176 \end{array}$$

Between what integral values of x do the positive zeros of the function lie? Between what values of x are the roots of $x^3 - 5x + 3 = 0$ situated?

EXERCISES

Draw the graphs of the following polynomials and locate approximately their real zeros between successive tenths.

1. $x^2 - 4x + 1$

2. $x^3 - 3x^2 + 1$

3. $x^3 - 2x + 5$

4. $6 - 11x + 6x^2 - x^3$

5. $x^3 + 2x^2 - 3x - 6$

6. $x^4 + x^3 - 7x^2 - x + 6$

7. $8x^4 - x^2 - 6x + 2$

8. $x^3 - 9x^2 - 385x + 375 = 0$

Depressed equations

If r is a root of the given equation $f(x) = 0$, then $f(x) = (x - r)Q(x)$. The equation $Q(x) = 0$ is called the depressed equation of $f(x)$, and the roots of $Q(x) = 0$ are the remaining roots of $f(x) = 0$. Why?

By means of the depressed equation we can solve an equation if all but two roots are known.

EXAMPLE. Solve $3x^4 - 16x^3 + 14x^2 + 24x - 9 = 0$ if two roots are 3 and -1.

Solution. Since 3 is a root, we shall divide the given equation by $x - 3$.

$$\begin{array}{r|rrrrr} 3 & 3 & -16 & 14 & 24 & -9 \\ & & 9 & -21 & -21 & 9 \\ \hline & 3 & -7 & -7 & 3 & 0 \end{array}$$

The depressed equation is $3x^3 - 7x^2 - 7x + 3 = 0$. Since -1 is a root of the given equation, it is also a root of $3x^3 - 7x^2 - 7x + 3 = 0$. Hence we shall divide by $x + 1$.

$$\begin{array}{r|rrrr} -1 & 3 & -7 & -7 & 3 \\ & & -3 & 10 & -3 \\ \hline & 3 & -10 & 3 & 0 \end{array}$$

The depressed equation is $3x^2 - 10x + 3 = 0$.

Now $\quad 3x^2 - 10x + 3 = (3x - 1)(x - 3) = 0$

$$\therefore \quad x = \tfrac{1}{3}, 3$$

The roots of the given equation are $3, -1, \frac{1}{3}, 3$.

Query. How does the number of roots compare with the degree of the given equation?

EXERCISES

Solve:

1. $x^3 - x^2 - x + 10 = 0$, one root being -2.
2. $x^4 - 2x^3 + 2x^2 - 2x + 1 = 0$, two roots being 1, 1.
3. $x^3 - 7x^2 + 15 + 7x = 0$, one root being 3.
4. $x^4 - 4x^3 + 6x^2 - 5x + 2 = 0$, two roots being 1, 2.
5. $2x^3 - 3x^2 - 29x - 30 = 0$, one root being 5.
6. $x^4 - 2x^3 - 3x^2 + 8x - 4 = 0$, two roots being 1, 2.
7. $3x^4 + 16x^3 + 14x^2 - 24x - 9 = 0$, two roots being 1, -3.

8. $6x^4 - 17x^3 + 7x^2 + 8x - 4 = 0$, two roots being $\frac{1}{2}$, $-\frac{2}{3}$.
9. $32x^3 + 32x^2 - 94x - 39 = 0$, one root being 1.5.
10. $2x^3 + x^2 + 2x - 12 = 0$, one root being 1.5.

Carl Friedrich Gauss (1777–1855)

For forty-five years Gauss was professor of astronomy at Göttingen. Not only was he a great mathematician, but he contributed to the fields of astronomy, electricity, magnetism, and geodesy. Gauss gave the first rigorous proof of the Fundamental Theorem.

Multiple roots

Suppose the roots of the equation $f(x) = 0$ are $r_1, r_2, r_3, \cdots, r_n$. It may happen that some of these numbers are equal. If $f(x)$ is exactly divisible by $x - r_1$, but not by $(x - r_1)^2$, then r_1 is called a simple root of $f(x) = 0$. If $f(x)$ is exactly divisible by $(x - r_1)^2$, but not by $(x - r_1)^3$, then r_1 is called a double root of $f(x) = 0$. If $f(x)$ is exactly divisible by $(x - r_1)^k$ and not by $(x - r_1)^{k+1}$, then r_1 is called a k-fold root, or a root of order k.

What are the orders of the roots of the equation

$$(x - 1)(x + 2)^3(x - 4)^5 = 0?$$

Theorem. Every equation $f(x) = 0$ of the nth degree has n roots and no more if each root of order k is counted as k roots.

By the fundamental theorem, $f(x) = 0$ has a root r_1. By the factor theorem $f(x) = (x - r_1)Q_{n-1}(x)$, where $Q_{n-1}(x)$ is a polynomial of degree $n - 1$. By the fundamental theorem $Q_{n-1}(x) = 0$ has a root r_2. Hence,

$$Q_{n-1}(x) = (x - r_2)Q_{n-2}(x)$$
$$\therefore \quad f(x) = (x - r_1)(x - r_2)Q_{n-2}(x)$$

Continuing this process, we find

$$f(x) = (x - r_1)(x - r_2) \cdots (x - r_n)Q_n(x)$$

where $Q_n(x)$ is the constant a_0 if $f(x) = a_0x_n + a_1x_{n-1} + \cdots + a_n$. Hence $f(x) = a_0(x - r_1)(x - r_2) \cdots (x - r_n)$, where $r_1, r_2, r_3, \cdots, r_n$ are roots of the equation $f(x) = 0$.

No other number can be a root. For example, suppose s were a root, different from $r_1, r_2, \cdots, r_n$. Then we would have

$$f(s) = a_0(s - r_1)(s - r_2) \cdots (s - r_n)$$

Since s is different from all the r's, no factor of the right-hand member is zero; hence $f(s)$ is not zero. Therefore s is not a root.

If some of the numbers $r_1, r_2, \cdots, r_n$ are equal, we have multiple roots.

How many roots has the equation

$$(x - 1)(x - 3)^4(x - 2)^3 = 0?$$

What are the roots?

Corollary. If two polynomials in one and the same variable of degrees not greater than n are equal to each other for more than n different values of the variable, then the coefficients of like powers of the variable in the two polynomials are equal.

If $a_0x^n + a_1x^{n-1} + \cdots + a_n = b_0x^n + b_1x^{n-1} + \cdots + b_n$ (1)

for more than n values of x, then the relation

$$(a_0 - b_0)x^n + (a_1 - b_1)x^{n-1} + \cdots + (a_n - b_n) = 0 \quad (2)$$

is satisfied by more than n values of x.

If any of the coefficients in equation (2) except the last one, are different from zero, then equation (2) is of degree equal to or less than n. By our hypothesis equation (2) is satisfied by more than n values of the variable; *i.e.*, the equation has more than n roots. But by the original theorem this is impossible and hence all of the coefficients of equation (2) are zero. That is,

$$a_0 - b_0 = 0, a_1 - b_1 = 0, \cdots, a_n - b_n = 0$$

or

$$a_0 = b_0, a_1 = b_1, \cdots, a_n = b_n$$

Therefore the given polynomials are identical.

EXAMPLE. Find the relation among p, q, and r so that $x^3 + px^2 + qx + r$ may be a perfect cube.

Solution. Assume

$$x^3 + px^2 + qx + r = (x + a)^3$$
$$= x^3 + 3x^2a + 3xa^2 + a^3$$

Equating coefficients gives
$$r = a^3$$
$$q = 3a^2$$
$$p = 3a$$

From these expressions we derive the relations $p^3 = 27r$, and $p^2 = 3q$, which are the necessary and sufficient conditions that $x^3 + px^2 + qx + r$ be a perfect cube.

Query. If the relation $p^3 = 27r$ alone is satisfied, will the given cubic be a perfect cube? Does $x^3 + 3x^2 + 9x + 1$ satisfy this relation? Is the given expression a perfect cube?

EXERCISES

1. How many roots has the equation $x^5 + 2x^3 + 7x + 5 = 0$? How many of the roots are positive?

2. How many roots has the equation $x^5 - 3x^4 + 2x^3 - 3x^2 + 2x - 5 = 0$? How many of these roots are negative?

3. If $a_0x^n + a_1x^{n-1} + \cdots + a_n = 0$ is satisfied by more than n distinct values of x, prove that $a_0 = a_1 = \cdots = a_n = 0$.

4. Find under what conditions $x^3 + px^2 + qx + r$ is divisible by $x^2 + ax + b$.

5. If $ax^3 + bx^2 + cx + d$ is divisible by $x^2 + h$, prove that $ad = bc$.

The graph of $y = f(x) = a_0(x - r_1)(x - r_2) \cdots (x - r_n)$

Suppose that all of the coefficients of $f(x)$ are real numbers and that the function $f(x)$ is expressed as the product of n distinct real linear factors. Let us assume $a_0 > 0$ and that $r_1 > r_2 > r_3 \cdots > r_{n-1} > r_n$. Hence if $x > r_1$, all the factors are positive and the graph is above the x axis. When x lies between r_1 and r_2, that is when $r_1 > x > r_2$, then one factor is negative, and the graph is below the x axis. When $r_2 > x > r_3$, two factors are negative, their product is positive, and the graph is above the x axis.

Continuing this process, we see that the graph cuts the x axis at points where $x = r_1, r_2, r_3 \cdots$ and resembles the graph in Fig. 51.

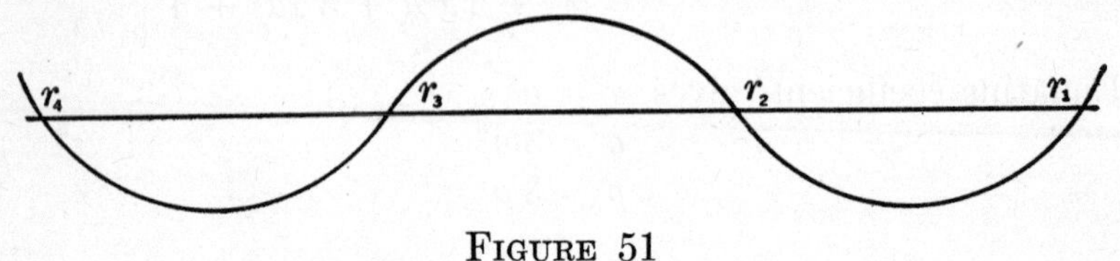

FIGURE 51

If r_1 is a real number and x increases from a value less than r_1 to a value greater than r_1, $(x - r_1)^k$ changes from a negative to a positive value when k is odd; but it is always positive or zero when k is even. From these facts, together with some from the calculus, the truth of the following statement can be verified. If the polynomial $f(x)$ contains the factor $(x - r_1)^k$, the graph of $y = f(x)$ crosses the x axis sharply at $x = r_1$ when $k = 1$; it is tangent to the x axis on each side when k is odd and greater than one; when k is even, the curve is tangent to the x axis but does not cross it.

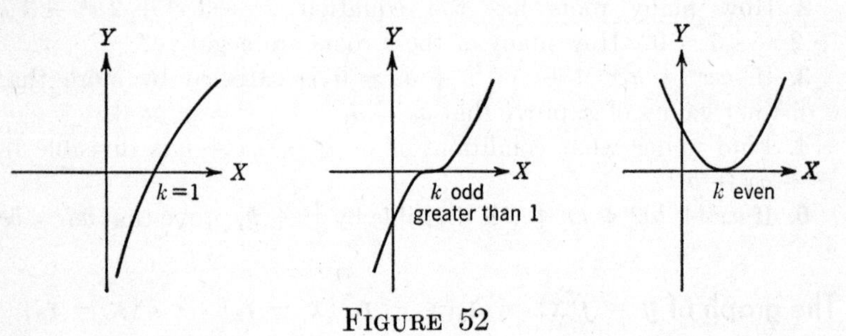

FIGURE 52

EXAMPLE 1. Sketch $y = 3(x + 1)(x - 2)(x - 4)$.

Solution. The following points are readily obtained.

x	-2	-1	0	1	2	3	4	5
y	-72	0	24	18	0	-12	0	54

If we let one horizontal space represent one unit and one vertical space nine units, we have the graph in Fig. 53.

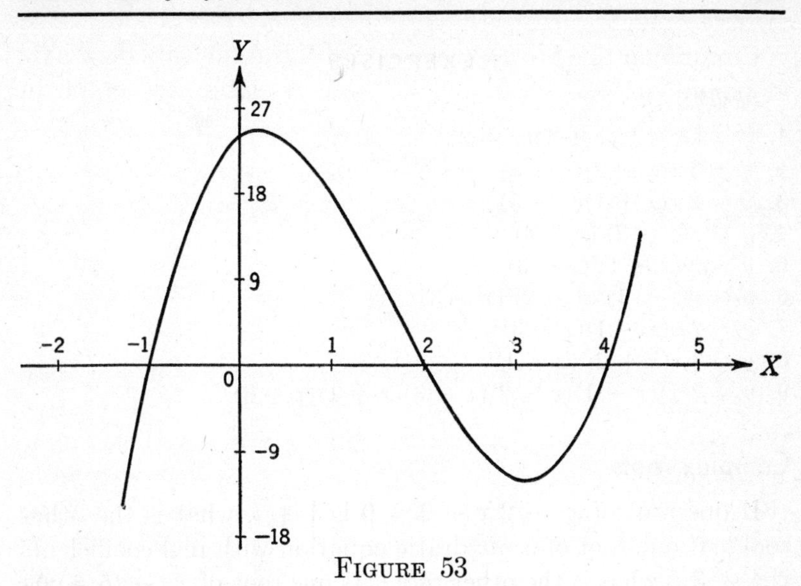

FIGURE 53

EXAMPLE 2. Sketch $y = x(x - 2)^2(x - 3)^3$.

Solution. The zeros of the function are 0, 2, and 3. Since $(x - 2)^2$ is always positive when x has any value different from 2, the curve touches the x axis at $x = 2$ and does not cross it.

Moreover, since $(x - 3)^3$ is positive when $x > 3$ and negative when $x < 3$, the curve crosses the axis at $x = 3$.

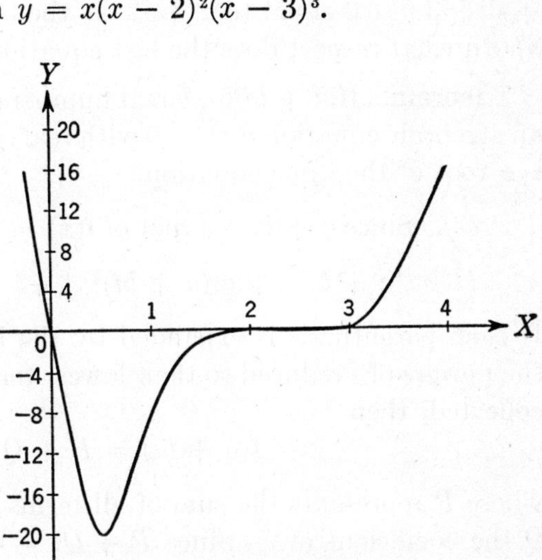

FIGURE 54

From the following table we can construct the graph.

x	-1	0	1	2	2.5	3	4
y	576	0	-8	0	$-.08$	0	16

EXERCISES

Sketch:

1. $y = (x - 1)(x + 1)(x - 3)$
2. $y = 3x(x - 2)(x - 3)$
3. $y = 2x(x + 1)(x - 3)$
4. $y = x(x - 2)^2(x - 3)$
5. $y = x^2(x - 1)^2(x - 3)$
6. $y = x(x - 1)^2(x - 2)^3(x - 3)^4$
7. $y = 2x(x - 1)(x - 3)^5$
8. $y = 3x(x + 2)^5(x + 1)^7$
9. $y = 2(x)(x - 1)(x - 2)(x - 3)(x + 1)(x + 3)$

Complex roots

If one root of $x^2 - 2x + 2 = 0$ is $1 + i$, what is the other root? If one root of a quadratic equation with real coefficients is $4 + 3i$, what is the other root? Is one root of $x^2 - (5 + i)x + 6 + 3i = 0$ equal to $2 + i$? Is the other root $2 - i$? Is it 3? In what respect does the last equation differ from the first?

Theorem. If $a + bi$ (a, b real numbers, $i^2 = -1$) is a root of an algebraic equation $f(x) = 0$ with real coefficients, then $a - bi$ is a root of the same equation.

Proof. Since $a + bi$ is a root of $f(x) = 0$, then

$$a_0(a + bi)^n + a_1(a + bi)^{n-1} + \cdots + a_n = 0$$

If each parenthesis is expanded by the binomial theorem and the powers of i reduced to their lowest terms, and like terms are collected, then

$$f(a + bi) = P + Qi$$

where P represents the sum of all terms independent of i, and Q the coefficient of i. Since $P + Qi = 0$ by hypothesis, then by page 239 $P = 0$ and $Q = 0$.

We wish to prove that $f(a - bi) = 0$; *i.e.*, we wish to show that $a - bi$ is a root of $f(x) = 0$. Now $f(a - bi)$ can be obtained from $f(a + bi)$ by replacing i by $-i$.

$$\therefore \quad f(a - bi) = P - Qi$$

where P and Q represent the *same* quantities as before. But we have just proved that $P = 0$ and $Q = 0$. Therefore, $f(a - bi) = 0$, or $a - bi$ is a root of $f(x) = 0$.

EXAMPLE. Solve $x^4 + 4x^3 + 5x^2 + 2x - 2 = 0$, one root being $-1 + i$.

Solution. If one root is $-1 + i$, a second root is $-1 - i$.

To form the equation with roots $-1 + i$ and $-1 - i$, we proceed as on page 144. The sum of the roots is -2 and their product is 2. Therefore the equation is $x^2 + 2x + 2 = 0$. Dividing $x^4 + 4x^3 + 5x^2 + 2x - 2$ by $x^2 + 2x + 2$ gives $x^2 + 2x - 1$. Therefore

$$x^4 + 4x^3 + 5x^2 + 2x - 2 = (x^2 + 2x + 2)(x^2 + 2x - 1) = 0$$

Hence $\quad x^2 + 2x - 1 = 0, \quad$ and $\quad x = -1 \pm \sqrt{2}$

The roots are $-1 + i, -1 - i, -1 + \sqrt{2}, -1 - \sqrt{2}$

EXERCISES

1. Solve $x^4 + 4x^3 + 6x^2 + 4x + 5 = 0$, one root being i.
2. Solve $x^4 - 2x^3 + 5x^2 - 2x + 4 = 0$, one root being $1 - i\sqrt{3}$.
3. Solve $x^4 - 4x^3 + 5x^2 + 8x - 14 = 0$, one root being $2 + i\sqrt{3}$.
4. Solve $x^5 - 2x^4 - x^3 + 2x^2 + 10x = 0$, one root being $2 + i$.
5. Solve $4x^4 - 7x^3 + 13x^2 + 136 = -4x$, one root being $2 + 2i$.

Surd roots

The expressions $a + \sqrt{b}$ and $a - \sqrt{b}$ where a and b are real, and b is a positive number, not a perfect square, are called *conjugate surds*.

Theorem. If the surd $a + \sqrt{b}$ ($b > 0$, b not a perfect square) is a root of an algebraic equation $f(x) = 0$ with rational coefficients, then $a - \sqrt{b}$ is also a root of the same equation.

The proof of this theorem is similar to the proof of the theorem for complex roots given on page 290 and is left as an exercise.

EXERCISES

Solve each of the following equations:

1. $2x^3 - 5x^2 - 10x + 3 = 0$ given one root to be $2 + \sqrt{3}$.

2. $3x^3 - 8x^2 - 2x + 4 = 0$ given one root to be $1 - \sqrt{3}$.

3. $2x^3 - 13x^2 + 14x - 4 = 0$ given one root to be $3 - \sqrt{5}$.

4. $2x^4 - 23x^3 + 45x^2 - 31x + 7 = 0$ given one root to be $5 - 3\sqrt{2}$.

5. Form the quartic equation with real coefficients two of whose roots are $3 + \sqrt{3}$, $3 + i\sqrt{3}$.

Graphing a function which contains some imaginary factors

It follows from page 290 that when the coefficients of $f(x)$ are real, imaginary factors occur in conjugate pairs. Thus, if $x - a - bi$ is a factor, then $x - a + bi$ is also a factor. Hence, $(x - a - bi)(x - a + bi)$ or $(x - a)^2 + b^2$ is a factor. Now $(x - a)^2 + b^2$ can never be zero. Why? Hence, corresponding to the factors of the quadratic function, there are no intersections of the graph with the x axis.

EXAMPLE. Sketch $y = (x^2 - 1)(x^2 - 8x + 17)$.

Solution. From the following table

x	-2	-1	0	1	2	3	4	5
y	111	0	-17	0	15	16	15	48

the graph in Fig. 55 is readily constructed.

Note that the curve crosses the x axis but twice. What are the real zeros?

EXERCISES

Sketch the following curves. Locate approximately the real zeros of the functions.

1. $y = x^3 - 8x^2 + 17x$

2. $y = x^4 - 8x^3 + 13x^2 + 32x - 68$

3. $y = x^4 + 4x^2 + 3$

4. $y = x^4 + x^3 + 6x^2 + 4x + 5$

5. $y = x^5 - 2x^4 - x^3 + 2x^2 + 10x$

6. $y = 4x^4 - 7x^3 + 13x^2 + 4x - 8$

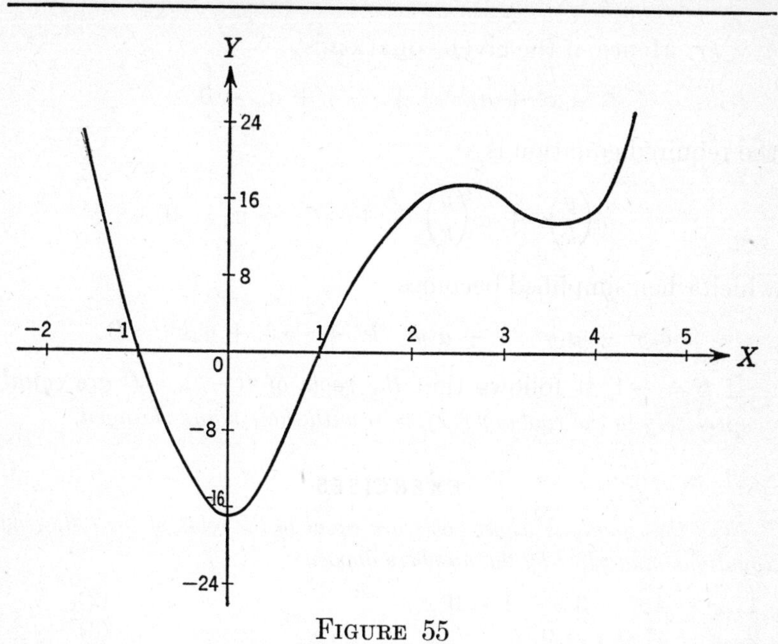

FIGURE 55

Transforming equations

How do the roots of the equations $(x - 1)(x - 2)(x - 3) = 0$ and $(x - 2)(x - 4)(x - 6) = 0$ compare? Are the roots of the second equation twice those of the first equation? The first equation can be written as $x^3 - 6x^2 + 11x - 6 = 0$ and the second as $x^3 - 12x^2 + 44x - 48 = 0$. Can you see how to find the terms of the second equation from the corresponding terms of the first equation?

Theorem. To transform a given equation $f(x) = 0$ into another whose roots are those of $f(x) = 0$ each multiplied by some constant k, multiply the second term of $f(x)$ by k, the third by k^2, and so on, taking account of missing terms if there are any.

Proof. The desired equation is $f\left(\frac{y}{k}\right) = 0$. For, if $f(x)$ is satisfied by $x = r$, then the equation $f\left(\frac{y}{k}\right) = 0$ is satisfied by

$y = kr$. Hence, if the given equation is

$$a_0x^n + a_1x^{n-1} + \cdots + a_n = 0$$

the required equation is

$$a_0\left(\frac{y}{k}\right)^n + a_1\left(\frac{y}{k}\right)^{n-1} + \cdots + a_n = 0$$

which when simplified becomes

$$a_0y^n + a_1y^{n-1}k + a_2y^{n-2}k^2 + \cdots + a_nk^n = 0$$

If $k = -1$, it follows that *the roots of* $f(-x) = 0$ *are equal respectively to the roots of* $f(x) = 0$ *with their signs changed.*

EXERCISES

Find the equations whose roots are equal to the roots of the following equations multiplied by the numbers opposite:

1. $x^3 - 4x^2 + 3x - 1 = 0$ (2)
2. $x^4 - x^2 - 1 = 0$ (3)
3. $x^5 - 3x^3 + x^2 - 1 = 0$ (−1)
4. $2x^3 - 3x^2 + 3x - 5 = 0$ (−2)
5. $1 - 2x - 3x^2 - x^3 = 0$ (3)
6. $3 - 2x - x^3 - x^5 = 0$ (−2)

Obtain equations whose roots are equal to the roots of the following equations with opposite signs:

7. $x^3 - 2x + 1 = 0$
8. $x^{15} - 1 = 0$
9. $x^8 - x^6 + 2x^4 - x - 1 = 0$
10. $1 - x + x^2 - x^3 + x^4 - x^5 = 0$

Problem. To transform an equation into another whose roots are those of the given equation, diminished by a constant k. Let the given equation be

$$a_0x^n + a_1x^{n-1} + \cdots + a_n = 0 \qquad (1)$$

Our problem is to transform this equation into another whose roots are k less than the corresponding roots of equation (1). If x is a root of (1), then $y = x - k$ would be a corresponding root of the desired equation. If $y = x - k$, then $x = y + k$; equation (1) is transformed into

$$a_0(y + k)^n + a_1(y + k)^{n-1} + \cdots + a_n = 0 \quad (2)$$

which is the desired equation. If equation (2) is simplified, it takes the form

$$A_0y^n + A_1y^{n-1} + \cdots + A_n = 0 \quad (3)$$

However, in most cases the labor involved in simplifying (2) is great; hence we shall employ another method.

If in equation (2) we substitute for y the value $x - k$, the result is equation (1). Since equation (3) is equivalent to equation (2), equation (3) will reduce to equation (1) when for y we substitute $x - k$. Hence,

$$a_0x^n + a_1x^{n-1} + \cdots + a_n \equiv A_0(x - k)^n + A_1(x - k)^{n-1} + \cdots + A_n$$

$$\equiv [A_0(x - k)^{n-1} + A_1(x - k)^{n-2} + \cdots + A_{n-1}](x - k) + A_n$$

It is now obvious that if the left-hand member of equation (1) is divided by $(x - k)$, the remainder is A_n. In the same manner we can show that if the quotient is divided by $(x - k)$, the remainder is A_{n-1}; if the second quotient is divided by $x - k$, the remainder is A_{n-2}; and so on.

We therefore have the following rule:

To form the equation whose roots are those of the equation $f(x) = 0$ diminished by k, divide $f(x)$ and each successive resulting quotient by $x - k$, until a constant quotient is obtained. The first remainder is the constant term, and each successive remainder is the coefficient of the next higher power of x in the desired equation, where the last quotient is the coefficient of the highest power of x.

Transforming an equation into one whose roots are those of the given equation increased by k, may be effected by the same process as diminishing the roots by k, for increasing the roots by k is the same as diminishing them by $-k$.

EXAMPLE. Transform the equation $3x^4 - 2x^3 + x - 1 = 0$ into an equation, each of whose roots are those of the given equation diminished by 2.

Solution. 2

3	−2	0	1	−1
	6	8	16	34
3	4	8	17	[33]
	6	20	56	
3	10	28	[73]	
	6	32		
3	16	[60]		
	6			
3	[22]			

The desired equation is

$$3x^4 + 22x^3 + 60x^2 + 73x + 33 = 0$$

EXERCISES

Transform the following equations into equations whose roots are those of the given equations diminished by h:

1. $3x^4 - 2x^3 + 5x^2 - x - 1 = 0$ $\qquad h = 1$
2. $4x^4 - 3x^3 + 2x^2 + x + 1 = 0$ $\qquad h = 2$
3. $x^3 - 2x - 1 = 0$ $\qquad h = 3$
4. $x^5 - x - 1 = 0$ $\qquad h = 5$
5. $x^3 + 2x^2 - x + 1 = 0$ $\qquad h = .5$
6. $2x^3 - 3x^2 - x + 1 = 0$ $\qquad h = 1.5$
7. $3x^3 - x^2 - 2x + 1 = 0$ $\qquad h = 2.5$
8. $x^6 - 1 = 0$ $\qquad h = 2$

Transform the following equations into equations whose roots are those of the given equations increased by h:

9. $x^3 + 3x^2 - x - 1 = 0$ $\qquad h = 1$
10. $2x^3 - x^2 + 4x + 1 = 0$ $\qquad h = 2$
11. $4x^4 - 3x - 1 = 0$ $\qquad h = 3$
12. $x^4 - x^2 - x + 1 = 0$ $\qquad h = .5$
13. $2x^4 + x^3 - 2x^2 + x - 1 = 0$ $\qquad h = 1.5$

Variations in sign

A change or variation of sign in $f(x)$ occurs whenever a term follows one of opposite sign. Thus, in $7x^6 - 3x^4 + 4x^2 - 7x - 1 = 0$, the signs are $+ - + - -$, and the variations are three.

Theorem. If $f(x)$ has real coefficients and is exactly divisible by $x - r$, where r is a positive number, then the number of variations of sign in the quotient $Q(x)$ is at least one less than the number of variations of sign in $f(x)$.

If $f(x) = a_0x^n + \cdot \cdot \cdot + a_n$, $a_0 > 0$, and $r > 0$ by hypothesis, then it follows from the nature of synthetic division that the coefficients in $Q(x)$ must be positive until a negative coefficient is reached in $f(x)$. Then, or perhaps not until later, does a coefficient of $Q(x)$ become negative or zero, and then these coefficients will remain negative at least until a positive coefficient is reached in $f(x)$. That is, $Q(x)$ has no variations except as occur in the corresponding or earlier terms of $f(x)$. By hypothesis $f(x)$ is exactly divisible by $x - r$; hence the sign of the last term in $Q(x)$ must be opposite to that in $f(x)$. Hence the number of variations of sign in $Q(x)$ must be *at least* one less than the number of variations of sign in $f(x)$.

Descartes' rule of signs

Theorem. If the equation $f(x) = 0$ has real coefficients, it can have no more positive roots than there are variations of sign in $f(x)$; and it can have no more negative roots than there are variations of sign in $f(-x)$.

Suppose the equation $f(x) = 0$ has the positive roots r_1, $r_2, \cdot \cdot \cdot, r_p$ $(p \leqq n)$. If we divide $f(x)$ by $x - r_1$, the quotient by $x - r_2$, and so on, the final quotient $Q(x)$ will, from the last theorem, contain at least p fewer variations of sign than $f(x)$. But the least number of variations of sign $Q(x)$ can have is zero. Hence, $f(x)$ must have at least p variations, or at least as many variations of sign as $f(x) = 0$ has positive roots.

But we know that the negative roots of $f(x) = 0$ are the positive roots of $f(-x) = 0$. Therefore, from the above it follows that the number of negative roots cannot exceed the number of variations of sign in $f(-x)$.

It should be noted that Descartes' rule does not tell how many positive and how many negative roots an equation has. It says merely that an equation cannot have *more than* a certain number of positive roots and not *more than* a certain number of negative roots.

EXAMPLE. Discuss the number of positive, negative, zero, and imaginary roots of $f(x) = 4x^6 + 2x^4 - x^3 + x^2 = 0$.

Solution. The signs of $f(x)$ are $+ + - +$. Since there are two variations there can be at most two positive roots. The signs of $f(-x)$ are $+ + + +$. Since there are no variations there are no negative roots. Moreover, since x^2 is a factor of $f(x)$, zero is a double root. There are in all six roots. Hence there are either (a) two positive roots, no negative roots, two zero roots, two imaginary roots, or (b) no positive or negative roots, two zero roots, four imaginary roots.

EXERCISES

Using Descartes' rule of signs, what conclusions can be drawn regarding the roots of the following equations?

1. $x^3 - 2x + 1 = 0$
2. $x^5 - 3x^4 + x - 3 = 0$
3. $x^5 - 3x^4 + 2x^3 - 5x^2 + x - 3 = 0$
4. $x^{24} - x^{23} - 1 = 0$
5. $x^n - 1 = 0$ (n even).
6. $x^n - 1 = 0$ (n odd).
7. Prove that the equation $x^6 - 7x^2 - x + 3 = 0$ has at least two imaginary roots. How many imaginary roots may it have?
8. Show that $x^4 + x^2 + x - 1 = 0$ has two and only two imaginary roots.
9. Show that $x^8 + 5x^3 + 3x - 9 = 0$ has six and only six imaginary roots. Find one root.
10. What information does Descartes' rule give about the roots of $x^5 - 4x^4 + x^3 = 0$?

Rational roots

Theorem. A rational root, not zero, of the equation $f(x) = 0$ in which the coefficient of the highest power of x is unity and the other coefficients are integers, is an integer and an exact divisor of the constant term.

Proof. We must first show that the equation cannot have a rational fraction for a root. Suppose the rational fraction $\frac{a}{b}$ (a and b are integers and $b > 1$) reduced to its lowest terms is a root of $f(x) = 0$. Then

$$\left(\frac{a}{b}\right)^n + p_1\left(\frac{a}{b}\right)^{n-1} + \cdot \cdot \cdot + p_{n-1}\left(\frac{a}{b}\right) + p_n = 0$$

If we multiply both members by b^{n-1}, we have

$$\frac{a^n}{b} + p_1a^{n-1} + p_2a^{n-2}b + \cdot \cdot \cdot + p_nb^{n-1} = 0$$

or $$\frac{a^n}{b} = -(p_1a^{n-1} + p_2a^{n-2}b + \cdot \cdot \cdot + p_nb^{n-1})$$

All the terms in the right-hand member are integers. Hence the left-hand member must be an integer. Since a and b have by hypothesis no common factor other than 1, $\frac{a^n}{b}$ can only be an integer if $b = 1$, which means that $\frac{a}{b}$ must be an integer which in turn contradicts our hypothesis.

Now suppose $x = r$ is an integral root.

Then, $$r^n + p_1r^{n-1} + p_2r^{n-2} + \cdot \cdot \cdot + p_n = 0$$

Transposing p_n and dividing by r gives

$$r^{n-1} + p_1r^{n-2} + p_2r^{n-3} + \cdot \cdot \cdot + p_{n-1} = \frac{-p_n}{r}$$

Now each term of the left-hand member is an integer; hence $\frac{p_n}{r}$ must be an integer, which means p_n must be exactly divisible by r.

To find the rational roots of an equation with rational coefficients

First reduce the equation so that the coefficient of the highest power of x is unity and the coefficients of the other powers of x are integers. Then proceed as in the following examples:

EXAMPLE 1. Solve the equation $x^3 - 4x^2 + x + 6 = 0$.

Solution. From Descartes' rule of signs we know the equation may have two positive roots and one negative root. If the equation has rational roots they must be factors of 6 (page 299). Hence we need try only 1, -1, 2, -2, 3, -3, 6, -6. By synthetic division we have

$$\begin{array}{r|rrrr} 2 & 1 & -4 & 1 & 6 \\ & & 2 & -4 & -6 \\ \hline & 1 & -2 & -3 & 0 \end{array}$$

Hence 2 is a root, and the depressed equation is $x^2 - 2x - 3 = 0$. The roots of this equation are -1 and 3. Hence the roots of the given equation are 2, -1, 3.

EXAMPLE 2. Solve the equation $2x^3 + x^2 + 2x + 1 = 0$.

Solution. First write the equation so that the coefficient of the highest power of x is unity;

$$x^3 + \tfrac{1}{2}x^2 + x + \tfrac{1}{2} = 0$$

Since the equation must be reduced to one with integral coefficients, we shall now multiply the roots by k and then determine k so that the coefficients will be integers.

$$x^3 + \tfrac{1}{2}kx^2 + k^2x + \tfrac{1}{2}k^3 = 0$$

Obviously, $k = 2$ makes all the coefficients integers.

Thus, $$x^3 + x^2 + 4x + 4 = 0 \qquad (1)$$

From Descartes' rule of signs we see that this equation has no positive roots. The negative rational roots must be negative integral factors of -4, namely -1, -2, -4. By synthetic division

$$\begin{array}{r|rrrr} -1 & 1 & 1 & 4 & 4 \\ & & -1 & 0 & -4 \\ \hline & 1 & 0 & 4 & 0 \end{array}$$

The depressed equation is $x^2 + 4 = 0$; its roots are $\pm 2\,i$. Therefore the roots of (1) are $-1, 2\,i, -2\,i$, and the roots of the given equation are $-\frac{1}{2}, i, -i$.

EXERCISES

Solve the following equations:

1. $x^3 + x^2 + x + 1 = 0$
2. $x^3 + 5\,x^2 + 15\,x + 18 = 0$
3. $x^3 + x^2 - 4\,x - 4 = 0$
4. $x^3 + 6\,x^2 + 11\,x + 6 = 0$
5. $x^3 - 7\,x - 6 = 0$
6. $x^4 - 2\,x^3 - 7\,x^2 + 8\,x + 12 = 0$
7. $6\,x^3 + 7\,x^2 - 9\,x + 2 = 0$
8. $2\,x^4 + 3\,x^3 - 10\,x^2 - 12\,x + 8 = 0$
9. $2\,x^3 - 5\,x^2 + 10\,x - 7 = 0$
10. $6\,x^4 - 5\,x^3 - 30\,x^2 + 20\,x + 24 = 0$
11. $x^3 - 5\,x^2 + 11\,x - 10 = 0$
12. $2\,x^3 + x^2 - 5\,x - 3 = 0$
13. $4\,x^4 - 4\,x^3 - x^2 - 5\,x + 3 = 0$
14. $2\,x^4 + x^3 - 15\,x^2 - 9\,x - 27 = 0$
15. $8\,x^4 + 2\,x^3 - 41\,x^2 + 34\,x - 6 = 0$

Cardan (1501–1576) and Ferrari (1522–1560)

Cardan's *Ars Magna* (1545), the first important algebra to appear in print, was devoted mostly to the solution of algebraic equations of the third and fourth degree. Cardan is believed to be the first mathematician to use complex numbers. In his *Ars Magna* appears a solution of the general cubic $x^3 + px + q = 0$. Today it is thought that the solution is the work of Niccolo Tartaglia, a contemporary Italian mathematician.

Ferrari was born of humble parentage. At the age of fifteen he became a servant in the home of Cardan, who recognized his ability and trained him to be a teacher of mathematics. He was very successful as a teacher and rose to a professorship at the University of Bologna. Cardan was unable to solve the equation $x^4 + 6x^2 + 36 = 60x$, so he gave it to his pupil Ferrari who found the solution. Cardan then published the solution in his *Ars Magna* with due credit to Ferrari.

Roots and coefficients

If r_1 and r_2 are the roots of a quadratic, the equation is

$$(x - r_1)(x - r_2) = 0$$

or

$$x^2 - (r_1 + r_2)x + r_1r_2 = 0$$

If r_1, r_2, and r_3 are the roots of a cubic equation, the equation is

$$(x - r_1)(x - r_2)(x - r_3) = 0$$

or $x^3 - (r_1 + r_2 + r_3)x^2 + (r_1r_2 + r_1r_3 + r_2r_3)x - r_1r_2r_3 = 0$

If r_1, r_2, r_3, and r_4 are the roots of a quartic equation, the equation is

$$(x - r_1)(x - r_2)(x - r_3)(x - r_4) = 0$$

or

$$x^4 - (r_1 + r_2 + r_3 + r_4)x^3 + (r_1r_2 + r_1r_3 + r_1r_4 + r_2r_3 + r_2r_4 + r_3r_4)x^2 - (r_1r_2r_3 + r_1r_2r_4 + r_1r_3r_4 + r_2r_3r_4)x + r_1r_2r_3r_4 = 0$$

From the above results it appears probable that in an equation in which the first coefficient is 1:

1. The coefficient of the second term, with its sign changed, is the sum of the roots.
2. The coefficient of the third term is the sum of the products of the roots, taken two at a time.
3. The coefficient of the fourth term, with its sign changed, is the sum of the products of the roots taken three at a time. And so on.

To prove that these relations hold for any equation we employ mathematical induction.

Outline of proof. Assume the above relations hold for an equation of the kth degree; *i.e.*, assume

$$x^k + S_1x^{k-1} + S_2x^{k-2} + \cdots + S_k = 0$$

where $S_i = (-1)^i$ (sum of the products of roots taken i at a time). Multiply this equation by $x - r_{k+1}$ and then show that the above relations are true for an equation of degree $k + 1$. Now, since the relations are true for an equation of the 3rd degree, they are true for an equation of the 4th degree; since they are true for an equation of the 4th degree, they are true for an equation of the 5th degree; and so on. Hence, in the equation

$$x^n + p_1x^{n-1} + p_2x^{n-2} + \cdots + p_n = 0$$

$p_1 =$ *minus* the sum of the roots.
$p_2 =$ the sum of the products of the roots taken two at a time.
$p_3 =$ *minus* the sum of the products of the roots taken three at a time.

. . . .

$p_n = (-1)^n$ times the product of all the roots.

For example, if the roots of $2x^3 - 5x^2 + 7x - 3 = 0$ are r_1, r_2, and r_3, then

$$\begin{aligned} r_1 + r_2 + r_3 &= \tfrac{5}{2} \\ r_1r_2 + r_1r_3 + r_2r_3 &= \tfrac{7}{2} \\ r_1r_2r_3 &= \tfrac{3}{2} \end{aligned}$$

Example. Solve the equation $2x^3 - x^2 - 8x + 4 = 0$ if two of the roots are numerically equal but opposite in sign.

Solution. Let the roots be a, $-a$, b. Then

$$\begin{aligned} a - a + b &= \tfrac{1}{2} \\ -a^2 + ab - ab &= -4 \\ -a^2b &= -2 \end{aligned}$$

Hence $b = \frac{1}{2}$, $a = \pm 2$. The roots are 2, -2, $\frac{1}{2}$.

EXERCISES

1. Solve $x^3 + x^2 - 4x - 4 = 0$, given that two of the roots are numerically equal but opposite in sign.

2. Solve $x^4 - 6x^3 - 9x^2 + 54x = 0$, given that the roots are in arithmetic progression.

3. Solve $x^3 - 7x^2 + 14x - 8 = 0$, given that the roots are in geometric progression.

4. Solve $4x^3 - 20x^2 - 23x - 6 = 0$, knowing that two of the roots are equal.

5. Solve $x^3 - 9x^2 + 11x + 21 = 0$, knowing that the roots form an arithmetic progression.

6. Solve $4x^3 + 16x^2 - 9x - 36 = 0$, given that the sum of two roots is zero.

7. Solve $12x^3 + 43x^2 - 22x - 8 = 0$, given that one root is the reciprocal of another.

8. Solve $4x^3 - 12x^2 + 11x - 3 = 0$, given that the roots are in arithmetic progression.

9. Solve $x^3 + 7x^2 + 14x + 8 = 0$, given that the roots are in geometric progression.

10. Solve $x^3 - x^2 - 10x - 8 = 0$, given that one root is twice another.

11. Solve $4x^3 + 32x^2 - x - 8 = 0$, if the sum of two roots is zero.

12. Solve $x^4 - 4x^3 + 3x^2 + 4x - 4 = 0$, given that two of the roots are equal.

13. Form the equations whose roots are:

a) 1, 2, 3
b) 3, −1, 2
c) 2, 4, 8

14. Given the equation $x^3 - 7x^2 + 14x + k = 0$; find k so that one root is twice another.

The roots of $x^3 + px^2 + qx + r = 0$ are a, b, and c. Find in terms of the coefficients:

15. $a + b + c$

16. $a^2 + b^2 + c^2$

17. $a^3 + b^3 + c^3$

18. $a^2b^2 + a^2c^2 + b^2c^2$

19. $\frac{ab}{c} + \frac{bc}{a} + \frac{ac}{b}$

20. $\frac{1}{a^2} + \frac{1}{b^2} + \frac{1}{c^2}$

Form the equation whose roots are:

21. $2 \pm \sqrt{3}, 3 \pm \sqrt{2}$

22. $3 \pm 2i, 2 \pm 3i$

23. Using the relation between roots and coefficients, determine whether 1 and 3 are roots of $x^3 - 6x^2 + 11x - 6 = 0$.

24. Solve $x^3 - 3x^2 - 10x + 24 = 0$, if one root is twice another.

25. Given $x^3 - 6x^2 + 11x + k = 0$; find k, if the sum of two of the roots is equal to the third.

26. Solve $8x^3 - 22x^2 - 43x + 12 = 0$, if one root is the reciprocal of another.

27. Given $x^4 - 6x^3 + k_1x^2 + k_2x + 24 = 0$; find k_1 and k_2 if the sum of two roots is 4 and the product of the other two is 6.

28. Solve $x^3 + 11x = 6x^2 + 6$, given that the roots are in arithmetic progression.

29. Solve $x^4 - 15x^3 + 70x^2 - 120x + 64 = 0$, given that the roots form a geometric progression.

30. Given $x^3 + 5x^2 - 4x + k = 0$; find k, so that two of the roots are numerically equal but opposite in sign.

Niels Henrik Abel (1802–1829)

Abel, a Norwegian mathematician, possessed one of the most brilliant mathematical minds of the nineteenth century. After Cardan, Tartaglia, and Ferrari showed how to solve any third or fourth degree equation, many mathematicians tried to solve an equation of the fifth degree. Abel showed that the roots of the general equation of the fifth degree, as well as of higher degrees, cannot be expressed in terms of its coefficients by means of radicals. He also proved the binomial theorem for general values of the exponent including complex numbers.

Irrational roots

On page 300 we learned how to find all the rational roots of an equation with integral coefficients. The question now arises how to find the irrational roots. There are several methods of determining such a root to as high a degree of approximation as one may wish. We shall now explain Horner's method.

Horner (1786–1837) and his method

Horner was not a university graduate; neither was he a well-known mathematician. However, he discovered a method, which now bears his name, of approximating the values of the roots of equations of the third or higher degrees.

EXAMPLE. Find the positive roots of

$$x^4 - 2\,x^3 + 3\,x^2 - 29\,x + 46 = 0$$

Solution. By Descartes' rule we see that there may be four positive roots and that there are no negative roots.

Before trying to find the irrational roots, it is advisable that we find all the rational roots by the method of page 300. By trial we find that $x = 2$ is a root.

$$\begin{array}{r|rrrrr} 2 & 1 & -2 & 3 & -29 & 46 \\ & 2 & 0 & & 6 & -46 \\ \hline & 1 & 0 & 3 & -23 & 0 \end{array}$$

The depressed equation is

$$x^3 + 3\,x - 23 = 0 \qquad (1)$$

To locate the positive roots of this equation we note from the following table

x	0	1	2	3
y	-23	-19	-9	13

that the graph of $y = x^3 + 3\,x - 23$ crosses the x axis between $x = 2$ and $x = 3$. Hence there is a root between 2 and 3.

The curve does not cross the axis again for any positive value of x. Why? We also know that there are no negative roots. Therefore the other two roots are imaginary.

Since equation (1) has a root between 2 and 3, if we diminish the roots of (1) by 2, the new equation will have a root between 0 and 1. Geometrically this is equivalent to moving the y axis in Fig. 56 two units to the right.

We shall now transform equation (1) into one whose roots are 2 less than those of the original equation.

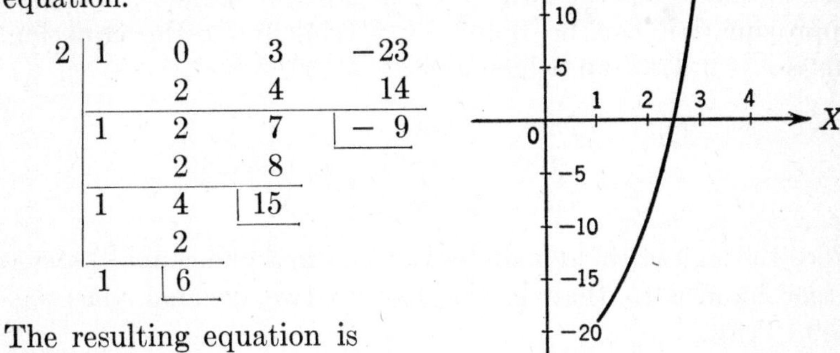

2	1	0	3	−23
		2	4	14
	1	2	7	− 9
		2	8	
	1	4	15	
		2		
	1	6		

The resulting equation is

$$x^3 + 6x^2 + 15x - 9 = 0$$

FIGURE 56

From our graph we estimate the root to be near .5. It is now necessary for us to verify this estimate.

.5	1	6	15	−9
		.5	3.25	9.125
	1	6.5	18.25	.125 = $f(.5)$

Since the remainder is positive, we know that for $x = .5$ the curve is above the x axis; *i.e.*, $x = .5$ is to the right of the point of intersection of the curve and the x axis. We must find the largest tenth for which the remainder is negative. We shall now try .4. It is left as an exercise for you to show that $f(.4) = -1.976$. Since $f(.4)$ is negative and $f(.5)$ is positive, if we diminish the roots by .4, the new equation will have a root between 0 and .1

.4	1	6	15	−9
		.4	2.56	7.024
	1	6.4	17.56	−1.976
		.4	2.72	
	1	6.8	20.28	
		.4		
	1	7.2		

The new equation $x^3 + 7.2x^2 + 20.28x - 1.976 = 0$ has roots which are 2.4 less than the roots of the given equation.

We must now diminish the roots of the last equation by the largest hundredth that will give a negative remainder. A rough approximation can be found by solving for x the equation $20.28x - 1.976 = 0$, which gives $x = .09$.

$$\begin{array}{r|rrrr} .09 & 1 & 7.2 & 20.28 & -1.976 \\ & & .09 & .6561 & 1.884249 \\ \hline & 1 & 7.29 & 20.9361 & - \end{array}$$

Since the sign of the remainder is minus and one cannot have a larger hundredth than 9, the root to two decimal places is 2.49. Why?

Horner's rule for positive roots

1. Apply Descartes' rule.
2. Plot the curve corresponding to the equation so as to locate the integers between which the roots lie.
3. To find a particular root transform the equation into one whose roots are those of the given equation diminished by the smaller of the two numbers which bound the location interval.
4. Estimate the nearest tenth to which the root lies. Determine by synthetic division the exact tenths between which the root lies.
5. Transform the last equation into one whose roots are diminished by the lesser of the two numbers which bound the tenths interval.
6. Proceed similarly to determine the root to as many decimal places as desired.

Note 1. If the given equation has rational roots, depress the equation and proceed with the depressed equation.

Note 2. To find a negative root, transform the equation into one whose roots are opposite in sign. The negative root of the original equation is a positive root in the transformed equation, and its numerical value can be found by the method for positive roots.

EXERCISES

In the following equations compute to two decimal places the root which lies between the indicated limits:

1. $x^3 + x - 3 = 0$ root between 1 and 2.
2. $x^3 + 3x^2 - 2x - 5 = 0$ root between 1 and 2.
3. $x^3 - 6x^2 + 10x + 23 = 0$ root between -1 and -2.
4. $x^3 + 3x - 70 = 0$ root between 3 and 4.
5. $x^3 - 2x^2 + x + 10 = 0$ root between -1 and -2.
6. $x^3 - 2x^2 + 2x - 100 = 0$ root between 5 and 6.
7. An open box is made from a rectangular piece of tin 24 inches long and 18 inches wide by cutting equal squares from each corner and turning up the sides. What should be the length of the side of the squares if the box contains 300 cu. inches?

MASTERY TEST

1. Without dividing, find the remainder when $3x^5 - 2x^3 + x - 1$ is divided by $x - 2$.
2. Find k, if $x^4 - 3x^3 + kx - 1$ is divided by $x - 1$ and the remainder is -3.
3. Solve $x^4 - 6x^3 + 17x^2 = 28x - 20$, given that 2 is a double root.
4. Find the rational roots of $x^3 + x^2 = 20 - 5x$.
5. Graph $y = x^3 - 6x + 2$.
6. By Horner's method solve $x^3 - 3 = 0$, thus finding the value of $\sqrt[3]{3}$ correct to three decimal places.
7. Solve the equation $2x^4 + 2x^2 = x^3 + 4x + 24$ if one root is $2i$.
8. Find the equation whose roots are 2 less than the roots of $3x^4 - 2x^2 + x - 1 = 0$.
9. Using Descartes' rule of signs determine the number of positive and negative roots of $3x^7 - 2x^5 + x^4 = 2x - 7$.
10. Form the equation of lowest degree with rational coefficients having $2 + 3i$ and -4 as two roots.
11. Find to the nearest hundredth all of the roots of $x^3 + 6x^2 + 9x + 3 = 0$.
12. If 1 is a double root of $x^4 + 2x^3 + 4 - 4x = 3x^2$, find all the roots of the given equation.
13. In the equation $x^3 - 7x = 6$, one root is twice another. Find the roots.
14. Solve $x^2 + x + 5i + 1 = 2ix$ for x.

15. If $\log_{10} 2 = .30$, find x from the equation $5^x = 2^{2x-3}$

16. Show graphically that the sum of the roots of the equation $x^3 - 1 = 0$ is zero.

17. Solve for x, $\sqrt{x - \sqrt{1 - x}} = 1 - \sqrt{x}$.

18. Solve for x and y:

$$x^2 - 6 = y$$
$$y^2 - 6 = x$$

19. Show that the roots of the equation $x^3 - 1 = 0$ form a geometric progression.

CHAPTER XVII

Partial Fractions

Partial fractions

One of the important problems of elementary algebra is to combine two or more fractions into a single fraction. Thus,

$$\frac{4}{x} - \frac{1}{x-1} = \frac{3x-4}{x^2-x}$$

In certain mathematical problems, especially in the calculus, it is often necessary to perform the reverse process, that is to say, to find what fractions added together produce a given fraction. This process is called decomposing the given fraction into partial fractions. For example, $\frac{-2}{x^2-1}$ can be decomposed into

$$\frac{1}{x+1} - \frac{1}{x-1}, \text{ for } \frac{1}{x+1} - \frac{1}{x-1} = \frac{(x-1)-(x+1)}{x^2-1}$$

$$= \frac{-2}{x^2-1}.$$

We shall only consider proper fractions; *i.e.*, fractions whose numerators are of *lower* degree than their denominators. If the given fraction is not a proper fraction, we shall, by division, reduce it to a mixed expression; that is, to an integral part plus a proper fraction. Thus,

$$\frac{x^3+4}{x^2-1} = x + \frac{x+4}{x^2-1}$$

Moreover, we shall assume that the numerator and the denominator of the given fraction are prime to each other and that the partial fractions shall be of the following types:

$$\frac{A}{ax+k} \qquad \frac{B}{(ax+k)^m} \qquad \frac{Cx+D}{ax^2+bx+c} \qquad \frac{Ex+F}{(ax^2+bx+c)^n}$$

We shall further assume that A, B, C, D, E, and F are constants, that m and n are positive integers, that $a \neq 0$, and that $ax^2 + bx + c$ cannot be factored into real linear factors. The methods of resolving rational fractions into partial fractions will be given without proof. Those interested in the proofs of the methods should consult Chrystal's *Algebra*. Four cases will be considered and illustrated by means of examples.

Case 1. The denominator can be resolved into factors of the first degree, all of which are real and distinct.

Example. Resolve into partial fractions

$$\frac{6\,x^2+5\,x-2}{2\,x^3-x^2-x}$$

Solution. The sum of the three fractions $\frac{A}{x}, \frac{B}{x-1}, \frac{C}{2\,x+1}$ will be a fraction with the denominator $2\,x^3 - x^2 - x$. We must therefore find A, B, and C so that

$$\frac{6\,x^2+5\,x-2}{2\,x^3-x^2-x} \equiv \frac{A}{x} + \frac{B}{x-1} + \frac{C}{2\,x+1} \qquad (1)$$

If we assume x does not equal 0, 1 or $-\frac{1}{2}$, we can clear (1) of fractions, which gives us the identity

$$6\,x^2+5\,x-2 \equiv A(x-1)(2\,x+1) + Bx(2\,x+1) + Cx(x-1) \qquad (2)$$

or $$6\,x^2+5\,x-2 \equiv 2\,Ax^2 - Ax - A + 2\,Bx^2 + Bx + Cx^2 - Cx$$

From page 286 we know that the coefficients of like powers of x are equal. Hence

$$\begin{aligned} -2 &= -A \\ 5 &= -A + B - C \\ 6 &= 2A + 2B + C \end{aligned}$$

Solving these equations gives $A = 2$, $B = 3$, and $C = -4$.

Hence $$\frac{6x^2 + 5x - 2}{2x^3 - x^2 - x} = \frac{2}{x} + \frac{3}{x-1} - \frac{4}{2x+1}$$

Check. $$\frac{2}{x} + \frac{3}{x-1} - \frac{4}{2x+1}$$
$$= \frac{2(x-1)(2x+1) + 3x(2x+1) - 4x(x-1)}{x(x-1)(2x+1)}$$
$$= \frac{6x^2 + 5x - 2}{2x^3 - x^2 - x}$$

Note. Instead of equating the coefficients of the like powers of x, we may find the values of A, B, and C as follows: Identity (1) is true for all values of x except 0, 1, and $-\frac{1}{2}$, but identity (2) is true for all values of x. Substituting $x = 0$, gives $A = 2$; substituting $x = 1$, gives $B = 3$; substituting $x = -\frac{1}{2}$, gives $C = -4$.

EXERCISES

Resolve each of the following fractions into partial fractions and check your answer:

1. $\dfrac{2x}{(x-1)(x+1)}$
2. $\dfrac{3x+1}{x(x-1)(x+1)}$
3. $\dfrac{4x+2}{(x-4)(x+1)}$
4. $\dfrac{2x-1}{(x-1)(x+2)}$
5. $\dfrac{3x+2}{x^3-4x}$
6. $\dfrac{6x^2+2x-1}{x(x+1)(x-1)}$
7. $\dfrac{7-2x}{4x^2-1}$
8. $\dfrac{2x^2-x-1}{x^3-9x}$
9. $\dfrac{x^2+4}{x^3-25x}$
10. $\dfrac{21+x}{2x^2-7x-15}$

11. $\dfrac{4x+1}{(x-1)(x+1)(x+3)}$

12. $\dfrac{x^3+3}{x^2-1}$ *Hint.* First reduce to a mixed expression.

13. $\dfrac{x^3-2}{x^3-x}$

14. $\dfrac{x^4-x^2+1}{x^3-x}$

15. $\dfrac{20x+19}{2x^2-7x-15}$

16. $\dfrac{x^3+x}{6x^2+x-2}$

Case 2. When the denominator can be resolved into real linear factors, some of which are repeated.

EXAMPLE. Resolve into partial fractions $\dfrac{4x^3-5x^2-3x+2}{x^2(x-1)^2}$.

Solution. The sum of the fractions $\dfrac{A}{x}, \dfrac{B}{x^2}, \dfrac{C}{x-1}, \dfrac{D}{(x-1)^2}$ will have a denominator of $x^2(x-1)^2$. Therefore, we shall determine A, B, C, and D so that

$$\frac{4x^3-5x^2-3x+2}{x^2(x-1)^2} \equiv \frac{A}{x}+\frac{B}{x^2}+\frac{C}{x-1}+\frac{D}{(x-1)^2}.$$

If we assume x is not equal to 0 or 1, we have, clearing of fractions,

$$4x^3-5x^2-3x+2 \equiv Ax(x-1)^2+B(x-1)^2 + Cx^2(x-1)+Dx^2$$

$$\therefore \quad 4x^3-5x^2-3x+2 \equiv Ax^3-2Ax^2+Ax+Bx^2-2Bx + B+Cx^3-Cx^2+Dx^2.$$

But we know that the coefficients of like powers of x are equal. Hence

$$\begin{aligned} 2 &= B \\ -3 &= A-2B \\ -5 &= -2A+B-C+D \\ 4 &= A+C \end{aligned}$$

which solved gives $A = 1$, $B = 2$, $C = 3$, $D = -2$.

Hence $\dfrac{4x^3-5x^2-3x+2}{x^2(x-1)^2} = \dfrac{1}{x}+\dfrac{2}{x^2}+\dfrac{3}{(x-1)}-\dfrac{2}{(x-1)^2}$

The check is left as an exercise for the student.

EXERCISES

Resolve each of the following fractions into partial fractions and check your answer:

1. $\dfrac{2x^2 - x + 2}{x(x-1)^2}$
2. $\dfrac{3x + 1}{x^2(x-1)}$
3. $\dfrac{4x^2 + 1}{x^2(3x+2)}$
4. $\dfrac{2x + 5}{x(x-1)^2}$
5. $\dfrac{x^2 - x + 1}{x(x+1)^3}$
6. $\dfrac{9x^2}{(9x^2-1)^2}$
7. $\dfrac{4x^2 - x + 1}{x^2(x-1)^2}$
8. $\dfrac{2x^2 - 1}{(x+1)^2(x-1)^2}$
9. $\dfrac{3x^2 - 2x + 1}{x^2(x+2)^2}$
10. $\dfrac{x^2 - 2x + 3}{x^2(x-1)}$
11. $\dfrac{x^2 + 3x - 1}{x^2(2x-1)^2}$
12. $\dfrac{x^3 + 4x + 1}{(x-1)^3}$

Case 3. When the denominator contains a quadratic factor which is not repeated and which cannot be factored into real linear factors.

EXAMPLE. Resolve into partial fractions

$$\frac{-2x^3 - x^2 - 2x + 3}{(x^2+1)(x^2+3)}$$

Solution. Since $x^2 + 1$ and $x^2 + 3$ cannot be factored into real linear factors, and since the required fractions are to be proper, the numerators must be of the form $Ax + B$. Hence, we shall assume that

$$\frac{-2x^3 - x^2 - 2x + 3}{(x^2+1)(x^2+3)} \equiv \frac{Ax + B}{x^2 + 1} + \frac{Cx + D}{x^2 + 3}$$

Clearing of fractions gives

$$-2x^3 - x^2 - 2x + 3 \equiv (Ax + B)(x^2 + 3) + (Cx + D)(x^2 + 1)$$

or

$$-2x^3 - x^2 - 2x + 3 \equiv Ax^3 + Bx^2 + 3Ax + 3B + Cx^3 + Dx^2 + Cx + D$$

Equating coefficients gives

$$\begin{aligned} 3 &= 3B + D \\ -2 &= 3A + C \\ -1 &= B + D \\ -2 &= A + C \end{aligned}$$

Solving gives $A = 0$, $B = 2$, $C = -2$, $D = -3$.

Therefore

$$\frac{-2x^3 - x^2 - 2x + 3}{(x^2+1)(x^2+3)} = \frac{2}{x^2+1} - \frac{2x+3}{x^2+3}$$

The check is left as an exercise.

EXERCISES

Resolve each of the following fractions into partial fractions and check your answer:

1. $\dfrac{2x+1}{x(x^2+1)}$
2. $\dfrac{5x^2+4x+3}{(x+1)(x^2+1)}$
3. $\dfrac{2x^2-1}{3x^3+3x}$
4. $\dfrac{2x+1}{(x^2+2)(2x-1)}$
5. $\dfrac{4x^3+x^2}{x^4+x^2+1}$
6. $\dfrac{2x^2-3x+5}{x^3-8}$
7. $\dfrac{2x+1}{(3x^2+1)(x-1)}$
8. $\dfrac{3+3x+2x^2}{(x^2+1)(x^2+3)}$
9. $\dfrac{6}{(3x-1)(x^2+2)}$
10. $\dfrac{33x-3x^2-44}{(x^2-3x-4)(x^2-3x+4)}$
11. $\dfrac{x^5+x^4-1}{x^4+x^2}$
12. $\dfrac{13x^3+4x^2+12x+1}{6x^4+13x^2+6}$

Case 4. When the denominator contains quadratic factors which are repeated but which cannot be factored in linear factors.

EXAMPLE. Resolve into partial fractions

$$\frac{2 + x + 8x^2 + x^3 + 3x^4}{x(x^2+1)^2}$$

Solution. The sum of the fractions $\dfrac{A}{x}$, $\dfrac{Bx+C}{x^2+1}$, $\dfrac{Dx+E}{(x^2+1)^2}$

will have a denominator of $x(x^2+1)^2$. Therefore we shall assume

$$\frac{2+x+8x^2+x^3+3x^4}{x(x^2+1)^2} \equiv \frac{A}{x} + \frac{Bx+C}{x^2+1} + \frac{Dx+E}{(x^2+1)^2}$$

Clearing of fractions gives

$$2+x+8x^2+x^3+3x^4 \equiv A(x^2+1)^2 + (Bx+C)(x^2+1)x + (Dx+E)x.$$

It is left as an exercise to show by two methods that $A=2$, $B=1$, $C=1$, $D=3$, $E=0$. Hence,

$$\frac{2+x+8x^2+x^3+3x^4}{x(x^2+1)^2} = \frac{2}{x} + \frac{x+1}{x^2+1} + \frac{3x}{(x^2+1)^2}$$

The check is left as an exercise.

EXERCISES

Resolve each of the following fractions into partial fractions and check your answer:

1. $\dfrac{x^4+x^3+3x+1}{x(x^2+1)^2}$
2. $\dfrac{3x+1}{(x^2+1)^2x^2}$
3. $\dfrac{x^3+3}{(x-1)(x^2-x+1)^2}$
4. $\dfrac{10}{x^2(2x^2+1)^2}$
5. $\dfrac{4}{(x^2+3)(x^2+5)^2}$
6. $\dfrac{4x^2+6x+10}{(3x^2+2x+7)(x+3)}$

REVIEW EXERCISES

Resolve each of the following fractions into partial fractions and check your answer:

1. $\dfrac{2x+3}{x^2-3x+2}$
2. $\dfrac{2x-10}{(x-1)(x+4)}$
3. $\dfrac{1}{4x^3-x}$
4. $\dfrac{2x+4}{(x+1)(3x-2)}$
5. $\dfrac{3x-2}{(x+1)(x-1)}$
6. $\dfrac{2x+4}{(2x^2+1)^2(x-1)}$
7. $\dfrac{3x+5}{(x-1)^2x^2}$
8. $\dfrac{x+4}{3x^3+x}$
9. $\dfrac{x^3-8x^2+6x+7}{(x-2)(x-3)(x^2+1)}$
10. $\dfrac{x^3+x^2+x+7}{x^2(x+7)(x^2+x+1)}$
11. $\dfrac{x+169}{(2x^2+2x+1)^2(x-2)}$
12. $\dfrac{17x^2+5x-7}{(10x^2+11x-6)(x-1)}$

CHAPTER XVIII

Determinants

Determinants of the second order

In many mathematical computations there arise expressions of the form $a_1b_2 - a_2b_1$. This expression is often written in the form

$$\begin{vmatrix} a_1 & b_1 \\ a_2 & b_2 \end{vmatrix} \tag{1}$$

which is called a *determinant of the second order*. The numbers a_1, a_2, b_1, b_2 are called the *elements* of the determinant. The elements a_1, b_2 form what is called the *principal diagonal.*

To evaluate a second-order determinant—*i.e.*, to determine what number it represents—subtract from the product of the terms in the principal diagonal the product of the other two terms.

EXAMPLE. Evaluate $\begin{vmatrix} 3 & -2 \\ 7 & 4 \end{vmatrix}$

Solution. $\begin{vmatrix} 3 & -2 \\ 7 & 4 \end{vmatrix} = (3)(4) - (7)(-2) = 26.$

Simultaneous equations in two unknowns

If we solve the equations:

$$a_1x + b_1y = c_1$$
$$a_2x + b_2y = c_2$$

by the usual method of elimination, we obtain

$$x = \frac{c_1b_2 - c_2b_1}{a_1b_2 - a_2b_1} \qquad y = \frac{a_1c_2 - a_2c_1}{a_1b_2 - a_2b_1} \tag{2}$$

provided $a_1b_2 - a_2b_1 \neq 0$. It is obvious that these values can be written in the form

$$x = \frac{\begin{vmatrix} c_1 & b_1 \\ c_2 & b_2 \end{vmatrix}}{\begin{vmatrix} a_1 & b_1 \\ a_2 & b_2 \end{vmatrix}} \qquad y = \frac{\begin{vmatrix} a_1 & c_1 \\ a_2 & c_2 \end{vmatrix}}{\begin{vmatrix} a_1 & b_1 \\ a_2 & b_2 \end{vmatrix}} \tag{3}$$

provided, of course, that $\begin{vmatrix} a_1 & b_1 \\ a_2 & b_2 \end{vmatrix} \neq 0$.

It should be noted:

1. That the determinants in the denominators are the same and that they are formed from the coefficients of x and y in the original equations.
2. That each determinant in the numerator is formed from the determinant in the denominator by replacing the coefficients of the unknown whose value is sought, by the constant terms.

Example. Solve by determinants the equations

$$3x + 4y = 5$$
$$2x - 3y = -1$$

Solution.

$$x = \frac{\begin{vmatrix} 5 & 4 \\ -1 & -3 \end{vmatrix}}{\begin{vmatrix} 3 & 4 \\ 2 & -3 \end{vmatrix}} = \frac{-15 + 4}{-9 - 8} = \frac{11}{17}$$

$$y = \frac{\begin{vmatrix} 3 & 5 \\ 2 & -1 \end{vmatrix}}{\begin{vmatrix} 3 & 4 \\ 2 & -3 \end{vmatrix}} = \frac{-3 - 10}{-9 - 8} = \frac{13}{17}$$

Check.

$$3(\tfrac{11}{17}) + 4(\tfrac{13}{17}) = \tfrac{85}{17} = 5 \quad 2(\tfrac{11}{17}) - 3(\tfrac{13}{17}) = -\tfrac{17}{17} = -1$$

EXERCISES

Evaluate each of the following determinants:

1. $\begin{vmatrix} 4 & 5 \\ 3 & -2 \end{vmatrix}$

2. $\begin{vmatrix} 7 & 8 \\ -1 & 4 \end{vmatrix}$

3. $\begin{vmatrix} 112 & 467 \\ 891 & 231 \end{vmatrix}$

4. $\begin{vmatrix} a & b \\ 2a & b \end{vmatrix}$

5. $\begin{vmatrix} 4a - b & 3a - 2b \\ a - b & 2a + b \end{vmatrix}$

6. $\begin{vmatrix} x_1 & y_1 \\ x_1 & y_1 \end{vmatrix}$

7. $\begin{vmatrix} -\sin\theta & -\cos\theta \\ \cos\theta & \sin\theta \end{vmatrix}$

8. $\begin{vmatrix} \sin\alpha & \cos\alpha \\ \sin\beta & \cos\beta \end{vmatrix}$

9. $\begin{vmatrix} \tan\alpha & \sec\alpha \\ \sec\alpha & \tan\alpha \end{vmatrix}$

Solve by determinants the following pairs of equations:

10. $4x + 3y = 7$
    $2x - y = 1$

11. $3x - 2y = 5$
    $4x + y = -2$

12. $7x + 8y = 11$
    $-2x + 3y = 5$

13. $23x - 4y = 8$
    $17x + y = -3$

14. $\dfrac{2x - 3y}{5} = 3$
    $\dfrac{3x}{5} = y - 2$

15. $2x + y = 7$
    $\dfrac{y}{5} - 3x = \dfrac{5}{7}$

16. $x\sin\theta + y\cos\theta = \sin\theta$
    $x\cos\theta + y\sin\theta = \cos\theta$

17. $x + y\tan^2\theta = \sec^2\theta$
    $x\sec^2\theta + y = \sec^2\theta + 1$

18. Prove that $\begin{vmatrix} a_1 & b_1 \\ a_2 & b_2 \end{vmatrix} = \begin{vmatrix} a_1 & a_2 \\ b_1 & b_2 \end{vmatrix}$
    State in words what you have proved.

19. Prove that:
    $$\begin{vmatrix} m\,a_1 & b_1 \\ m\,a_2 & b_2 \end{vmatrix} = m\begin{vmatrix} a_1 & b_1 \\ a_2 & b_2 \end{vmatrix}$$
    State in words what you have proved.

20. Prove that:
    $$\begin{vmatrix} a_1 & b_1 \\ a_2 & b_2 \end{vmatrix} = -\begin{vmatrix} b_1 & a_1 \\ b_2 & a_2 \end{vmatrix}$$
    State in words what you have proved.

Determinants of the third order

To the square array

$$\begin{vmatrix} a_1 & b_1 & c_1 \\ a_2 & b_2 & c_2 \\ a_3 & b_3 & c_3 \end{vmatrix} \qquad (4)$$

which we call a determinant of the third order, we assign the value

$$a_1b_2c_3 + a_2b_3c_1 + a_3b_1c_2 - a_1b_3c_2 - a_2b_1c_3 - a_3b_2c_1 \qquad (5)$$

The expression (5) is called the expansion or development of the determinant; the numbers a_1, b_1, c_1, etc., are called the elements, and the elements $a_1b_2c_3$ form the principal diagonal.

One should note that each term of (5) consists of the product of three elements, one and only one from each row, and one and only one from each column.

A simple method of obtaining the expansion (5) from the determinant (4) is as follows:

> Form the product of each element of the first column by the second-order determinant formed by cutting out the row and the column to which the element belongs; change the sign of the second product and take the algebraic sum of the three products.

EXAMPLE 1. Evaluate $\begin{vmatrix} a_1 & b_1 & c_1 \\ a_2 & b_2 & c_2 \\ a_3 & b_3 & c_3 \end{vmatrix}$

Solution.

$$\begin{vmatrix} a_1 & b_1 & c_1 \\ a_2 & b_2 & c_2 \\ a_3 & b_3 & c_3 \end{vmatrix} = a_1 \begin{vmatrix} b_2 & c_2 \\ b_3 & c_3 \end{vmatrix} - a_2 \begin{vmatrix} b_1 & c_1 \\ b_3 & c_3 \end{vmatrix} + a_3 \begin{vmatrix} b_1 & c_1 \\ b_2 & c_2 \end{vmatrix}$$

$$= a_1(b_2c_3 - b_3c_2) - a_2(b_1c_3 - b_3c_1) + a_3(b_1c_2 - b_2c_1)$$
$$= a_1b_2c_3 - a_1b_3c_2 - a_2b_1c_3 + a_2b_3c_1 + a_3b_1c_2 - a_3b_2c_1$$

EXAMPLE 2. Evaluate $\begin{vmatrix} 5 & 2 & 1 \\ -3 & 2 & -2 \\ 4 & -1 & 1 \end{vmatrix}$

Solution.

$$\begin{vmatrix} 5 & 2 & 1 \\ -3 & 2 & -2 \\ 4 & -1 & 1 \end{vmatrix} = 5 \begin{vmatrix} 2 & -2 \\ -1 & 1 \end{vmatrix}$$

$$+ 3 \begin{vmatrix} 2 & 1 \\ -1 & 1 \end{vmatrix} + 4 \begin{vmatrix} 2 & 1 \\ 2 & -2 \end{vmatrix}$$

$$= 5(2 - 2) + 3(2 + 1) + 4(-4 - 2)$$
$$= 0 + 9 - 24 = -15$$

EXERCISES

Evaluate each of the following determinants:

1. $\begin{vmatrix} 1 & 1 & 1 \\ 1 & 1 & 1 \\ 1 & 1 & 1 \end{vmatrix}$

2. $\begin{vmatrix} 2 & 1 & 1 \\ 1 & 2 & 1 \\ 1 & 1 & 2 \end{vmatrix}$

3. $\begin{vmatrix} 2 & 1 & 3 \\ 1 & -1 & 1 \\ 1 & 2 & -1 \end{vmatrix}$

4. $\begin{vmatrix} a & b & c \\ b & c & a \\ c & a & b \end{vmatrix}$

5. $\begin{vmatrix} 0 & 0 & 1 \\ 1 & 1 & 1 \\ 5 & 6 & 1 \end{vmatrix}$

6. $\begin{vmatrix} a & b & c \\ b & a & c \\ c & a & b \end{vmatrix}$

7. $\begin{vmatrix} 3 & 2 & a \\ a & -1 & 1 \\ 1 & a & a \end{vmatrix}$

8. $\begin{vmatrix} 10 & 8 & 7 \\ 3 & 2 & 1 \\ 4 & -1 & 3 \end{vmatrix}$

Second method of evaluating a third-order determinant

A very convenient rule for evaluating a third-order determinant is as follows:

Rewrite the first two columns at the right of the determinant.

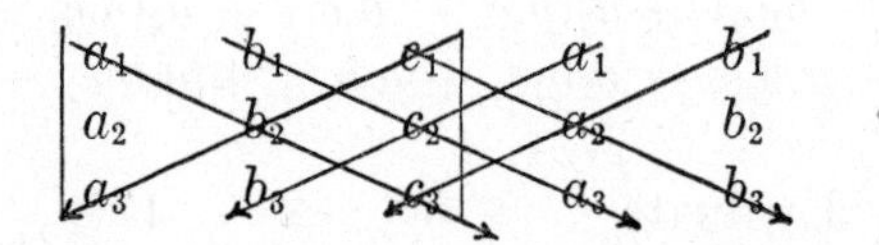

Form all possible products by multiplying diagonally to the right; form all possible products by multiplying diagonally to the left; from the sum of the first products, subtract the sum of the second products.

This method does not apply to determinants of any other order.

EXAMPLE. Evaluate: $\begin{vmatrix} 3 & 4 & 2 \\ 2 & -5 & 1 \\ 1 & 3 & 4 \end{vmatrix}$

Solution.

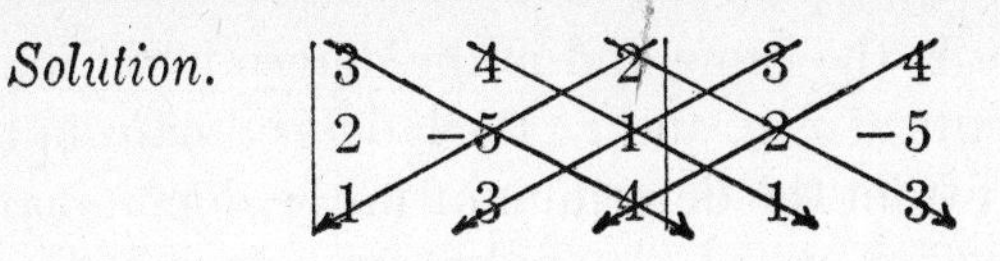

$$(3)(-5)(4) + (4)(1)(1) + (2)(2)(3) - (2)(-5)(1) - (3)(1)(3) - (4)(2)(4) = -60 + 4 + 12 + 10 - 9 - 32 = -75$$

EXERCISES

Evaluate by the above method, ex. 1–8 on page 322.

Solution of a set of three simultaneous equations

If we were to solve the system of equations

$$\begin{aligned} a_1x + b_1y + c_1z &= d_1 \\ a_2x + b_2y + c_2z &= d_2 \\ a_3x + b_3y + c_3z &= d_3 \end{aligned}$$

by the usual method of elimination, we should find that

$$x = \frac{d_1b_2c_3 + d_3b_1c_2 + d_2b_3c_1 - d_1b_3c_2 - d_2b_1c_3 - d_3b_2c_1}{a_1b_2c_3 + a_3b_1c_2 + a_2b_3c_1 - a_1b_3c_2 - a_2b_1c_3 - a_3b_2c_1}$$

$$y = \frac{a_1d_2c_3 + a_3d_1c_2 + a_2d_3c_1 - a_1d_3c_2 - a_2d_1c_3 - a_3d_2c_1}{a_1b_2c_3 + a_3b_1c_2 + a_2b_3c_1 - a_1b_3c_2 - a_2b_1c_3 - a_3b_2c_1}$$

$$z = \frac{a_1b_2d_3 + a_3b_1d_2 + a_2b_3d_1 - a_1b_3d_2 - a_2b_1d_3 - a_3b_2d_1}{a_1b_2c_3 + a_3b_1c_2 + a_2b_3c_1 - a_1b_3c_2 - a_2b_1c_3 - a_3b_2c_1}$$

provided the common denominator is not zero. These results may be written in the form

$$x = \frac{\begin{vmatrix} d_1b_1c_1 \\ d_2b_2c_2 \\ d_3b_3c_3 \end{vmatrix}}{\begin{vmatrix} a_1b_1c_1 \\ a_2b_2c_2 \\ a_3b_3c_3 \end{vmatrix}} \qquad y = \frac{\begin{vmatrix} a_1d_1c_1 \\ a_2d_2c_2 \\ a_3d_3c_3 \end{vmatrix}}{\begin{vmatrix} a_1b_1c_1 \\ a_2b_2c_2 \\ a_3b_3c_3 \end{vmatrix}} \qquad z = \frac{\begin{vmatrix} a_1b_1d_1 \\ a_2b_2d_2 \\ a_3b_3d_3 \end{vmatrix}}{\begin{vmatrix} a_1b_1c_1 \\ a_2b_2c_2 \\ a_3b_3c_3 \end{vmatrix}}$$

provided $\begin{vmatrix} a_1b_1c_1 \\ a_2b_2c_2 \\ a_3b_3c_3 \end{vmatrix} \neq 0$

Each denominator is the same and is the determinant made up from the coefficients of x, y, and z. Each determinant in the numerator is formed from the determinant in the denominator by replacing the coefficients of the unknown whose value is sought, by the constant terms.

EXAMPLE. Solve by determinants:

$$\begin{aligned} 2x - y - z &= -3 \\ x + y + z &= 6 \\ x - 2y + 3z &= 6 \end{aligned}$$

Solution.

$$x = \frac{\begin{vmatrix} -3 & -1 & -1 \\ 6 & 1 & 1 \\ 6 & -2 & 3 \end{vmatrix}}{\begin{vmatrix} 2 & -1 & -1 \\ 1 & 1 & 1 \\ 1 & -2 & 3 \end{vmatrix}} \qquad y = \frac{\begin{vmatrix} 2 & -3 & -1 \\ 1 & 6 & 1 \\ 1 & 6 & 3 \end{vmatrix}}{\begin{vmatrix} 2 & -1 & -1 \\ 1 & 1 & 1 \\ 1 & -2 & 3 \end{vmatrix}} \qquad z = \frac{\begin{vmatrix} 2 & -1 & -3 \\ 1 & 1 & 6 \\ 1 & -2 & 6 \end{vmatrix}}{\begin{vmatrix} 2 & -1 & -1 \\ 1 & 1 & 1 \\ 1 & -2 & 3 \end{vmatrix}}$$

It is left as an exercise for the student to evaluate these determinants and to show that $x = 1$, $y = 2$, $z = 3$. Check these results.

EXERCISES

Solve by determinants the following sets of equations:

1. $5x + 2y - 4z = -3$
   $4x + 5y + 2z = 20$
   $3x - 3y + 5z = 12$
2. $3x + 6y + 2z = 3$
   $x + 3y - z = 5$
   $2x - 3y - 3z = 6$
3. $3x + 4y + 5z = 26$
   $2x + 3y + 4z = 20$
   $3x + 5y + 6z = 31$
4. $3x + y - z = 3$
   $2x + 4y + z = 12$
   $x + y + z = 7$
5. $8x - 3y + 5z = 42$
   $3x - 5y - 7z = 3$
   $2x + 4y + 5z = 19$
6. $x + y = 2$
   $3x - z = 2$
   $2y + z = 3$

7. $2x - 5y = -19$
$3y - 4z = -7$
$5x = 2z - 2$

8. $\frac{1}{x} + \frac{1}{y} = 6$
$\frac{1}{y} + \frac{1}{z} = 10$
$\frac{1}{z} + \frac{1}{x} = 8$

9. $x + y + z = 1$
$ax + by + cz = d$
$a^2x + b^2y + c^2z = d^2$

10. $ax + y - z = a^2 + a - 1$
$-x + ay + z = a^2 - a + 1$
$x - y + az = a$

Inversion

In order to understand the development of a determinant containing more than three rows and three columns, it is necessary that we understand the idea of an inversion. If in a series of different positive integers a greater integer precedes a smaller, we say there is an inversion. For example, in 1, 2, 4, 3 we say there is one inversion since 4 precedes 3. In 4, 3, 1, 2 we say there are 5 inversions since 4 precedes 3, 1, and 2, and 3 precedes 1 and 2. How many inversions are there in 635214?

Determinants of the *n*th order

The square array

$$\begin{vmatrix} a_1 & b_1 \cdot \cdot \cdot q_1 \\ a_2 & b_2 \cdot \cdot \cdot q_2 \\ \cdot & \cdot \cdot \cdot \cdot \cdot \\ \cdot & \cdot \cdot \cdot \cdot \cdot \\ \cdot & \cdot \cdot \cdot \cdot \cdot \\ a_n & b_n \cdot \cdot \cdot q_n \end{vmatrix}$$

of n^2 elements is called a *determinant of the nth order* and will be denoted by the Greek letter delta (Δ). This determinant stands for the algebraic sum of all the different products of n factors each that can be formed by taking one, and only one, element from each row, and one, and only one, element from each column, and giving to each such product a plus or minus sign according as the number of inversions of the subscripts is even or odd (normal order being $1, 2, \cdot \cdot \cdot n$) when the letters have the same order they have in the principal diagonal.

For example, suppose we had a fifth-order determinant and

the order of the letters in the principal diagonal is $a\ b\ c\ d\ e$; what is the sign of the term $a_1\ e_2\ b_3\ d_4\ c_5$? Arranging the letters in the order $a\ b\ c\ d\ e$, gives $a_1\ b_3\ c_5\ d_4\ e_2$. We note that there are 4 inversions among the subscripts and hence the sign of the term is plus.

Theorem A. If in a given permutation two objects are interchanged, the number of inversions with respect to the normal order is increased or decreased by an odd number.

Let us consider the permutations $XrsY$ and $XsrY$, where X and Y denote the groups of objects which precede and follow the interchanged objects r and s. Any inversion in X and Y, and any inversion due to the fact that X, r, s precede Y, are common to $XrsY$ and $XsrY$. Therefore, the number of inversions in $XrsY$ is equal to the number in $XsrY$ increased or decreased by 1 (according as rs is or is not in the normal order).

Now let us consider two objects such as r and s separated by i objects. If the objects r and s are interchanged, the number of inversions is still changed by an odd number. For by $i + 1$ interchanges of adjacent pairs the object r can be brought into the position immediately following s, and by i further interchanges of adjacent pairs, s may be brought to occupy the position formerly held by r. Each of these $(i + 1) + i = 2\,i + 1$ interchanges of adjacent pairs has increased or decreased the number of inversions by 1. Hence the net result of these $2\,i + 1$ interchanges has increased or decreased the number of inversions by an odd number.

Theorem B. If in any term of the expansion of a determinant two adjacent elements are interchanged, the combined number of inversions among the subscripts and letters is either zero or it is increased or diminished by two.

Proof. From Theorem A it follows that the number of inversions among the subscripts is either increased or diminished by one. Likewise, from Theorem A, it follows that the number of inversions among the letters is either increased or diminished by one. Hence the combined number of inversions for the subscripts and letters is either zero, two more, or two less.

Theorem C. If in any term of the expansion of a determinant the elements are rearranged in any order, the combined number of inversions among the subscripts and letters is either zero or is changed by an even number.

Proof. Any arrangement can be formed from the original order by interchanging adjacent elements. Applying Theorem B to each such change, either leaves the combined number of inversions zero, two more, or two less. Hence, for the sum of all the interchanges, the total number of inversions is either zero or a multiple of two; *i.e.*, it is even.

Theorem D. If in any term of the expansion of a determinant the number of inversions among the subscripts is even (or odd) when the letters are in their normal order, the number of inversions among the letters will be even (or odd) when the subscripts are arranged in their normal order.

Proof. Suppose the subscripts are brought in their normal order. To do this, let us assume that the number of necessary inversions is even (or odd). Since the combined number of inversions of subscripts and letters is even, it then follows that the number of inversions among the letters must be even (or odd).

Theorem E. Each term of the expansion of a determinant has a plus or minus sign according as the number of inversions in the letters is even or odd, the subscripts being in normal order.

The proof is left as an exercise. Apply Theorems B and D.

Properties of Determinants

Theorem I. *The expansion of a determinant of order n contains $n!$ terms.*

The number of terms is equal to the number of permutations of the subscripts $1, 2, \cdots n$. This number is $n!$ (See page 225.)

Theorem II. *If each element in any row or column of a determinant is multiplied by m, the value of the determinant is multiplied by m.*

By the definition of a determinant, each term of the expansion contains one, and only one, element from each row and each column. Therefore, the factor m will appear once, and only once, in each term of the expansion. If m is factored out, the remaining factor is the expansion of the original determinant.

For example, the determinant $\begin{vmatrix} 204 & 98 \\ 102 & 147 \end{vmatrix}$ can be written

$$(102)(49)\begin{vmatrix} 2 & 2 \\ 1 & 3 \end{vmatrix} = (102)(49)(4) = 19{,}992$$

Theorem III. *The value of a determinant is not changed if rows and columns are interchanged, the first row becoming the first column, the second row the second column, etc.*

That is
$$\begin{vmatrix} a_1 & b_1 \cdots q_1 \\ a_2 & b_2 \cdots q_2 \\ \cdot & \cdots\cdots \\ \cdot & \cdots\cdots \\ \cdot & \cdots\cdots \\ a_n & b_n \cdots q_n \end{vmatrix} = \begin{vmatrix} a_1 & a_2 \cdots a_n \\ b_1 & b_2 \cdots b_n \\ \cdot & \cdots\cdots \\ \cdot & \cdots\cdots \\ \cdot & \cdots\cdots \\ q_1 & q_2 \cdots q_n \end{vmatrix}$$

The proof is left as an exercise for the student. *Hint.* Note that the principal diagonals are the same. Use Theorem D.

Theorem IV. *If two rows or two columns of a determinant are interchanged, the sign of the determinant is changed.*

From Theorem III we know that if the rows and the columns are interchanged the value of the determinant is not changed; therefore it will be sufficient for us to consider only the interchange of two rows.

Case I. Suppose two adjacent rows are interchanged. In this case the order of the letters in the principal diagonal, and in each term of the expansion is left unchanged. However, two adjacent subscripts in each term of the expansion are interchanged; hence there will be either one more or one less inversion in each term, and the sign of each term and of the determinant is changed.

Case II. Suppose the two rows we wish to interchange are separated by k rows. By k interchanges of adjacent rows the lower row can be brought adjacent to and just below the upper one. Now the upper row can be brought into the position originally occupied by the lower row by $k + 1$ further interchanges of adjacent rows. Hence interchanging the two rows is equivalent to $2k + 1$ interchanges of adjacent rows. Since $2k + 1$ is an odd number, the process changes the sign of the determinant.

Theorem V. *If two rows or two columns of a determinant are identical, the value of the determinant is zero.* Let the value of the determinant be Δ. If we interchange two rows or two columns, then the value of the determinant is $-\Delta$. Since the rows or columns which are interchanged are identical, the value of the determinant is unchanged. Therefore $\Delta = -\Delta$, or $2\Delta = 0$, and $\Delta = 0$.

Corollary. If one row or column of a determinant is a multiple of another row or column, the value of the determinant is zero.

Minors. If in a determinant the row and the column in which any given element appears is cut out, the determinant formed by the remaining elements is called the *minor* of that element.

For example, in the determinant $\begin{vmatrix} a_1 & b_1 & c_1 \\ a_2 & b_2 & c_2 \\ a_3 & b_3 & c_3 \end{vmatrix}$

the minor of a_1 is $\begin{vmatrix} b_2 & c_2 \\ b_3 & c_3 \end{vmatrix}$, of b_2, $\begin{vmatrix} a_1 & c_1 \\ a_3 & c_3 \end{vmatrix}$, of c_2, $\begin{vmatrix} a_1 & b_1 \\ a_3 & b_3 \end{vmatrix}$

The minor of a_1 is denoted by A_1, of b_2 by B_2, etc.

EXERCISES

Without expanding prove that:

1. $\begin{vmatrix} 3 & 6 & 1 \\ 1 & 2 & 1 \\ 2 & 4 & 1 \end{vmatrix} = 0$

2. $\begin{vmatrix} 1 & 2 & 3 \\ 3 & 2 & 1 \\ 6 & 4 & 2 \end{vmatrix} = 0$

3. $\begin{vmatrix} 3 & 4 & 5 \\ 6 & 7 & 8 \\ 1 & 2 & 3 \end{vmatrix} = \begin{vmatrix} 3 & 6 & 1 \\ 4 & 7 & 2 \\ 5 & 8 & 3 \end{vmatrix}$

4. $\begin{vmatrix} 7 & 3 & 6 \\ 2 & 4 & 8 \\ 2 & 5 & 1 \end{vmatrix} = -\begin{vmatrix} 3 & 7 & 6 \\ 4 & 2 & 8 \\ 5 & 2 & 1 \end{vmatrix}$

5. $\begin{vmatrix} 6 & 15 & 1 \\ 8 & 20 & 8 \\ 10 & 10 & 2 \end{vmatrix} = 40\begin{vmatrix} 3 & 3 & 1 \\ 1 & 1 & 2 \\ 5 & 2 & 2 \end{vmatrix}$

6. $\begin{vmatrix} 7 & 1 & 7 & 6 & -1 & -2 \\ 8 & 2 & 8 & 7 & 2 & -4 \\ 1 & -3 & 2 & 1 & 3 & 6 \\ 2 & 4 & 3 & 2 & 4 & -8 \\ 3 & 5 & 4 & -1 & 5 & -10 \\ 4 & 6 & 5 & 3 & 6 & -12 \end{vmatrix} = 0$

7. In the following determinant find the value of the minors of 3, 5, and 9:

$$\begin{vmatrix} 3 & 1 & 8 \\ 2 & 2 & 9 \\ 7 & 5 & 11 \end{vmatrix}$$

8. Find the minors of b_2, c_3, d_1, and a_4 in the following determinant:

$$\begin{vmatrix} a_1 & b_1 & c_1 & d_1 \\ a_2 & b_2 & c_2 & d_2 \\ a_3 & b_3 & c_3 & d_3 \\ a_4 & b_4 & c_4 & d_4 \end{vmatrix}$$

Laplace's expansion

The value of a determinant is the algebraic sum of the products of each element in any row or column by its corresponding minor, the sign of each product being positive or negative according as the sum of the number of the row and the number of the column containing the element is even or odd.

First, it is obvious that in the expansion, A_1 is the coefficient of a_1, for A_1 is a determinant of order $n - 1$ in terms of the elements $a_2, a_3, \cdots a_n$ and its expansion contains a term for each permutation of the numbers $2, 3, \cdots, n$. Since the number of inversions is not changed by prefixing a_1, the signs of the terms are correct.

Second, consider the element e situated in the ith row and jth column. The element e can be brought to the position originally occupied by a_1 (*i.e.* first row and the first column) by $i - 1$ transpositions of rows and $j - 1$ transpositions of columns; that is to say, by a total of $i + j - 2$ transpositions.

Hence, if $i + j$ is even, the sign of the determinant is left unchanged; while if $i + j$ is odd, the sign of the determinant is changed. Now that element e occupies the first row and first column, we know from the first paragraph that its coefficient is its minor. Moreover, the relative positions of the elements not in the ith row and jth column are not affected by these transpositions; hence the minor of the element in the original position is the same as the minor of the element when it occupies the position originally occupied by a_1. Therefore, the coefficient of e, which is situated in the ith row and jth column is $(-1)^{i+j}E$, where E is the minor of the element e.

Illustrations:

$$\begin{vmatrix} a_1 & b_1 & c_1 & d_1 \\ a_2 & b_2 & c_2 & d_2 \\ a_3 & b_3 & c_3 & d_3 \\ a_4 & b_4 & c_4 & d_4 \end{vmatrix} = \begin{cases} a_1A_1 - a_2A_2 + a_3A_3 - a_4A_4, & \text{or} \\ -b_1B_1 + b_2B_2 - b_3B_3 + b_4B_4, & \text{or} \\ c_1C_1 - c_2C_2 + c_3C_3 - c_4C_4, & \text{or} \\ -d_1D_1 + d_2D_2 - d_3D_3 + d_4D_4. \end{cases}$$

If in the expansion of a determinant by minors with respect to a certain column or row, the elements of this column or row are replaced by corresponding elements of some other column or row, the resulting expression vanishes. For example,

$$b_1A_1 - b_2A_2 + b_3A_3 - b_4A_4 = 0$$

for we have replaced the column of a's by the column of b's; therefore the determinant has two columns identical. The same proof applies to a determinant of any order n. Hence, *if a determinant vanishes when for any element a we substitute another element b, then $a - b$ is a factor of the expansion of the determinant.* This follows immediately from the factor theorem. Since the expansion of the determinant is a polynomial in a, say $f(a)$, and this polynomial has the property that $f(b) = 0$, then by page 279 $a - b$ is a factor of $f(a)$. For example, if

$$\Delta = \begin{vmatrix} x^2 & x & 1 \\ 1 & 1 & 1 \\ 4 & 2 & 1 \end{vmatrix}$$

we see that when $x = 1$ the first two rows are identical. Hence $x - 1$ is a factor of the expansion. Likewise, when $x = 2$, the first and third rows are identical and $x - 2$ is also a factor. Moreover, it is clear that Δ is of second degree in x. The coefficient of x^2 is

$$\begin{vmatrix} 1 & 1 \\ 2 & 1 \end{vmatrix} \text{ or } -1.$$

Hence,
$$\Delta = \begin{vmatrix} x^2 & x & 1 \\ 1 & 1 & 1 \\ 4 & 2 & 1 \end{vmatrix} = -(x - 1)(x - 2)$$

Theorem VI. *If each of the elements of any row or any column of a determinant consists of the sum of two members, the determinant may be expressed as the sum of two determinants.*

Let the given determinant be

$$\begin{vmatrix} (a_1 + a_1') & b_1 \cdots q_1 \\ (a_2 + a_2') & b_2 \cdots q_2 \\ \vdots & \vdots \\ (a_n + a_n') & b_n \cdots q_n \end{vmatrix}$$

If we expand in terms of the first column, we have

$$(a_1 + a_1')A_1 - (a_2 + a_2')A_2 + \cdots + (-1)^{n-1}(a_n + a_n')A_n =$$

$$[a_1A_1 - a_2A_2 + \cdots + (-1)^{n-1}a_nA_n] + [a_1'A_1 - a_2'A_2 + \cdots + (-1)^{n-1}a_n'A_n]$$

or
$$\begin{vmatrix} a_1 & b_1 \cdots q_1 \\ a_2 & b_2 \cdots q_2 \\ \vdots & \vdots \\ a_n & b_n \cdots q_n \end{vmatrix} + \begin{vmatrix} a_1 & b_1 \cdots q_1 \\ a_2 & b_2 \cdots q_2 \\ \vdots & \vdots \\ a_n & b_n \cdots q_n \end{vmatrix}$$

Corollary. If to the elements in any row or column there be added the corresponding elements in any other row or column, each multiplied by a given number k, the value of the determinant is unchanged. The proof is left to the student as an exercise.

Evaluating determinants of any order

The theorems just proved enable us to evaluate a determinant of any order. The following examples will demonstrate the methods.

EXAMPLE 1. Evaluate:

$$\begin{vmatrix} 15 & 16 & 17 \\ 16 & 17 & 18 \\ 17 & 18 & 19 \end{vmatrix}$$

Multiply the first column by -1 and add the result to the second and third columns. This gives

$$\begin{vmatrix} 15 & 1 & 2 \\ 16 & 1 & 2 \\ 17 & 1 & 2 \end{vmatrix}$$

Hence by Corollary I, Theorem V, the value of the determinant is 0.

EXAMPLE 2. Evaluate:

$$\begin{vmatrix} 3 & -1 & 2 & 4 \\ 1 & 2 & 1 & 2 \\ 2 & -3 & 6 & 3 \\ 3 & 4 & 7 & 1 \end{vmatrix}$$

We shall try to transform the determinant in such a way that all the elements but one in some row or column are 0. If we expand in terms of this row or column, the determinant will immediately reduce to one of the third order.

Suppose we add 2 times the first row to the second row, then add -3 times the first row to the third row, and then add 4 times the first row to the fourth row. These operations give

$$\begin{vmatrix} 3 & -1 & 2 & 4 \\ 7 & 0 & 5 & 10 \\ -7 & 0 & 0 & -9 \\ 15 & 0 & 15 & 17 \end{vmatrix}$$

Expanding in terms of the second column gives

$$-(-1)\begin{vmatrix} 7 & 5 & 10 \\ -7 & 0 & -9 \\ 15 & 15 & 17 \end{vmatrix} = \begin{vmatrix} 7 & 5 & 10 \\ -7 & 0 & -9 \\ 15 & 15 & 17 \end{vmatrix}$$

If we multiply the first row by -3 and add it to the last row, we have

$$\begin{vmatrix} 7 & 5 & 10 \\ -7 & 0 & -9 \\ -6 & 0 & -13 \end{vmatrix}$$

Expanding in terms of the second column gives

$$-5\begin{vmatrix} -7 & -9 \\ -6 & -13 \end{vmatrix} = -5(91 - 54) = -185$$

EXERCISES

Evaluate the following determinants:

1. $\begin{vmatrix} 35 & 36 & 37 \\ 36 & 37 & 38 \\ 37 & 38 & 39 \end{vmatrix}$

2. $\begin{vmatrix} 3 & 4 & 1 & 2 \\ 1 & 2 & 4 & -1 \\ 2 & 7 & 6 & 5 \\ 5 & 4 & 3 & 1 \end{vmatrix}$

3. $\begin{vmatrix} 6 & 1 & 2 & 2 \\ 1 & 2 & 1 & 1 \\ 0 & 1 & 2 & 1 \\ 3 & 2 & 1 & 0 \end{vmatrix}$

4. $\begin{vmatrix} 4 & 8 & 2 & 7 \\ 3 & 2 & 2 & 2 \\ 4 & 2 & 4 & 5 \\ 5 & 6 & 3 & 3 \end{vmatrix}$

5. $\begin{vmatrix} 47 & 36 & 25 \\ 43 & 23 & 13 \\ 35 & 28 & 33 \end{vmatrix}$

6. $\begin{vmatrix} 34 & 23 & 14 \\ 23 & 34 & 35 \\ 12 & 21 & 26 \end{vmatrix}$

7. $\begin{vmatrix} 2 & 2 & 1 & 0 \\ -2 & -2 & -1 & 2 \\ 1 & 1 & 4 & 1 \\ 1 & -1 & 2 & -1 \end{vmatrix}$

8. $\begin{vmatrix} a & c & b & d \\ b & 0 & x & 0 \\ c & y & 0 & 0 \\ d & 0 & 0 & z \end{vmatrix}$

9. $\begin{vmatrix} 32 & 12 & 23 & 3 \\ 33 & 13 & 24 & 3 \\ 34 & 14 & 25 & 3 \\ 35 & 15 & 26 & 3 \end{vmatrix}$

10. $\begin{vmatrix} 1 & -1 & 1 & -1 \\ -1 & 1 & -1 & 1 \\ 1 & -1 & 1 & -1 \\ -1 & 1 & -1 & 1 \end{vmatrix}$

11. $\begin{vmatrix} 1 & 2 & 3 & 4 \\ 5 & 6 & 7 & 8 \\ 9 & 10 & 11 & 12 \\ 13 & 14 & 15 & 16 \end{vmatrix}$

12. $\begin{vmatrix} 2 & 4 & 6 & 8 \\ 8 & 6 & 4 & 2 \\ -1 & 3 & -5 & 7 \\ 7 & -5 & 3 & -1 \end{vmatrix}$

13. $\begin{vmatrix} a+1 & 1 & 1 & 1 \\ 1 & b+1 & 1 & 1 \\ 1 & 1 & c+1 & 1 \\ 1 & 1 & 1 & d+1 \end{vmatrix}$

14. $\begin{vmatrix} a & 0 & b & 0 & c \\ 0 & a & 0 & b & 0 \\ c & 0 & a & 0 & b \\ 0 & c & 0 & a & 0 \\ b & 0 & c & 0 & a \end{vmatrix}$

15. $\begin{vmatrix} 30 & 18 & 9 & 24 \\ 40 & 28 & 17 & 37 \\ 54 & 33 & 13 & 46 \\ 12 & 8 & 4 & 11 \end{vmatrix}$

16. $\begin{vmatrix} 1 & 0 & 0 & 1 & 0 \\ 1 & 1 & 1 & 1 & 1 \\ 2 & 3 & 1 & 2 & -1 \\ 1 & 1 & 1 & -1 & 1 \\ -1 & 1 & 1 & 1 & -1 \end{vmatrix}$

Resolve into factors:

17. $\begin{vmatrix} x & y & 1 \\ y & y & 1 \\ z & z & 1 \end{vmatrix}$

18. $\begin{vmatrix} 1 & 1 & 1 \\ a & b & c \\ a^3 & b^3 & c^3 \end{vmatrix}$

19. $\begin{vmatrix} x & x^2 & yz \\ y & y^2 & xz \\ z & z^2 & xy \end{vmatrix}$

20. $\begin{vmatrix} 1 & a & a^2 & a^3 \\ 1 & b & b^2 & b^3 \\ 1 & c & c^2 & c^3 \\ 1 & d & d^2 & d^3 \end{vmatrix}$

Cramer's rule for solving simultaneous linear equations

Suppose we are given n linear equations in n unknowns and wish their solution. Let the equations be

$$\begin{aligned} a_1x_1 + b_1x_2 + c_1x_3 + \cdots + p_1x_n &= q_1 \\ a_2x_1 + b_2x_2 + c_2x_3 + \cdots + p_2x_n &= q_2 \\ \cdots\cdots\cdots\cdots\cdots\cdots\cdots\cdots \\ a_nx_1 + b_nx_2 + c_nx_3 + \cdots + p_nx_n &= q_n \end{aligned}$$

The determinant Δ formed by the coefficients of the unknowns is called *the determinant of the system.* Thus

$$\Delta = \begin{vmatrix} a_1 & b_1 & \cdots & p_1 \\ a_2 & b_2 & \cdots & p_2 \\ \vdots & \vdots & & \vdots \\ a_n & b_n & \cdots & p_n \end{vmatrix}$$

If we multiply the equations by A_1, $-A_2$, A_3, $-A_4$, etc., respectively, and add the results, we have

$$x_1(a_1A_1 - a_2A_2 + \cdots) + x_2(b_1A_1 - b_2A_2 + \cdots) + \cdots$$
$$+ x_n(p_1A_1 - p_2A_2 + \cdots) = q_1A_1 - q_2A_2 + \cdots$$

From page 331 it follows that the coefficient of x_1 is Δ and the coefficients of the other unknowns are zero. The right-hand member is the determinant formed by replacing the column of a's in Δ by the column of q's. We shall denote this determinant by Δ_{aq}. Therefore

$$\Delta x_1 = \Delta_{aq}$$

and

$$x_1 = \frac{\Delta_{aq}}{\Delta}, \quad \text{provided } \Delta \neq 0$$

Similarly

$$x_2 = \frac{\Delta_{bq}}{\Delta}, \cdots, x_n = \frac{\Delta_{pq}}{\Delta} \quad \text{provided } \Delta \neq 0$$

Or, stated in words, the value of any unknown is equal to a fraction whose denominator is the determinant of the system and whose numerator is the determinant obtained from the latter determinant by replacing the coefficients of the unknown sought by the column of constant terms.

We have proved that *if* the equations have roots they are the values just found. It is left as an exercise for the student to prove that the values found satisfy the given equations.

EXERCISES

Solve each of the following systems of equations by determinants:

1. $2x - y - z = 0$
$2x + 3w = 5$
$3x + y + z = 5$
$2x - 3y - w = -2$

2. $x - 2y - z = 4$
$x + w = 1$
$x + z = 12$
$x + y + z + w = 5$

3. $x + y + z + w = 4$
$x - z = 0$
$y + z - w = 3$
$2x - z - 3w = 1$

4. $3x + 2y - z = 5$
$x - y - w = 0$
$3x - 2y - z - w = 4$
$y - w = 1$

5. $x + y + z + w = 4$
$ax + by - az - bw = 0$
$cx - dw = c - d$
$my - 2nz - 3nw = m - 5n$

6. $\frac{1}{x} + \frac{1}{y} - \frac{1}{z} = \frac{7}{12}$
$\frac{2}{x} - \frac{3}{y} + \frac{1}{z} = \frac{1}{4}$
$\frac{4}{x} - \frac{2}{y} - \frac{3}{z} = \frac{7}{12}$

When the denominator equals zero

From the preceding discussion we know that

$$\Delta x_1 = \Delta_{aq},\ \Delta x_2 = \Delta_{bq},\ \cdots,\ \Delta x_n = \Delta_{pq}$$

If $\Delta = 0$, we might naturally conclude that

$$\Delta_{aq} = 0,\ \Delta_{bq} = 0,\ \cdots\ \Delta_{pq} = 0$$

However, it is possible to write a system of equations in which $\Delta = 0$ and in which one or more of the determinants Δ_{aq}, Δ_{bq}, $\cdots$ are not zero. For example, the system

$$2x_1 + x_2 = 1,\ 2x_1 + x_2 = 3 \text{ has } \Delta = \begin{vmatrix} 2 & 1 \\ 2 & 1 \end{vmatrix} = 0,$$

$$\Delta_{aq} = \begin{vmatrix} 1 & 1 \\ 3 & 1 \end{vmatrix} = -2,\ \Delta_{bq} = \begin{vmatrix} 2 & 1 \\ 2 & 3 \end{vmatrix} = 4$$

The given equations are inconsistent. If $\Delta_{aq} = \Delta_{bq} = \cdots = \Delta_{pq} = 0$, the system is *consistent*, but the values of the unknowns are not completely determined. For example, $3x_1 + x_2 = 1$, $6x_1 + 2x_2 = 2$, has $\Delta = 0$, $\Delta_{aq} = 0$, $\Delta_{bq} = 0$. The equations are consistent, but the values of x_1 and x_2 cannot be uniquely determined.[1]

Consistent equations

When a system of equations has a common solution, the equations are called *consistent*. Consider the three equations

$$a_1x + b_1y + c_1 = 0$$
$$a_2x + b_2y + c_2 = 0$$
$$a_3x + b_3y + c_3 = 0$$

[1] A complete discussion of the case $\Delta = 0$ is beyond the scope of this text. For such a discussion the interested student is referred to Bôcher, *Higher Algebra*, Chapter IV.

There are two cases depending on whether a pair of the three equations have a single or an infinite number of solutions.

Case I. Suppose the first two equations have a single solution; *i.e.*,

$$x = -\frac{\begin{vmatrix} c_1 & b_1 \\ c_2 & b_2 \end{vmatrix}}{\begin{vmatrix} a_1 & b_1 \\ a_2 & b_2 \end{vmatrix}}, \quad y = -\frac{\begin{vmatrix} a_1 & c_1 \\ a_2 & c_2 \end{vmatrix}}{\begin{vmatrix} a_1 & b_1 \\ a_2 & b_2 \end{vmatrix}}, \quad \text{provided} \quad \begin{vmatrix} a_1 & b_1 \\ a_2 & b_2 \end{vmatrix} \neq 0$$

For the equations to be consistent these values must satisfy the third equation, *i.e.*,

$$-a_3 \begin{vmatrix} c_1 & b_1 \\ c_2 & b_2 \end{vmatrix} - b_3 \begin{vmatrix} a_1 & c_1 \\ a_2 & c_2 \end{vmatrix} + c_3 \begin{vmatrix} a_1 & b_1 \\ a_2 & b_2 \end{vmatrix} = 0$$

or

$$\begin{vmatrix} a_1 & b_1 & c_1 \\ a_2 & b_2 & c_2 \\ a_3 & b_3 & c_3 \end{vmatrix} = 0$$

Case II. Suppose the first two equations have an infinite number of solutions. Then

$$\frac{a_1}{a_2} = \frac{b_1}{b_2} = \frac{c_1}{c_2}$$

Hence by Corollary I, Theorem V, the value of the determinant

$$\begin{vmatrix} a_1 & b_1 & c_1 \\ a_2 & b_2 & c_2 \\ a_3 & b_3 & c_3 \end{vmatrix} \text{ is zero}$$

Hence for three linear equations in two unknowns to have a common solution, it is *necessary* that the determinant of the coefficients of the unknowns and the known terms vanish. This result is readily extended to n linear equations in $n - 1$ unknowns.

The vanishing of the determinant is only a *necessary* and not a sufficient condition that the equations be consistent. For example, the system

$$\begin{aligned} x + 2y - 1 &= 0 \\ x + 2y + 5 &= 0 \\ 2x + 4y - 3 &= 0 \end{aligned}$$

gives

$$\Delta = \begin{vmatrix} 1 & 2 & -1 \\ 1 & 2 & 5 \\ 2 & 4 & -3 \end{vmatrix} = 0$$

but the equations are inconsistent.

EXERCISES

Find if the following systems of equations are consistent:

1. $3x - y - 1 = 1$
$2x + y = 3$
$x - 2y + 1 = 0$

2. $3x + y = 2$
$x - y = 5$
$x - y = 1$

3. $2x + y = 1$
$4x + y = 2$
$3x - 2y = 5$

4. $4x + 3z = 5$
$2x - 5z = -1$
$x + z = 4$

5. $x + y = -1$
$2x - y = 10$
$3x + 2y = 1$

6. $3w - 2z = 19$
$2w - z = 12$
$w + z = 3$

7. Find k so that the following equations will be consistent:

$$\begin{aligned} 3x - y &= 2 \\ x + y &= k \\ 2x + y &= 3 \end{aligned}$$

8. Find k so that the following equations will be consistent:

$$\begin{aligned} 2x - y &= k \\ 3x + y &= 0 \\ x - 2y &= 1 \end{aligned}$$

9. Find k so that the following equations will be consistent:

$$\begin{aligned} x + y &= k \\ 2x - w &= 3 \\ y + w &= 2 \\ 2y + w &= 4 \end{aligned}$$

10. Find k so that the following equations are consistent:

$$\begin{aligned} y + z + w &= k \\ 2y - z &= -2 \\ y + z - w &= 0 \\ y - z &= -3 \end{aligned}$$

MISCELLANEOUS EXERCISES

1. Show: $\begin{vmatrix} 0 & x & y \\ x & 0 & z \\ y & z & 0 \end{vmatrix} = 2\,xyz$

2. Prove: $\begin{vmatrix} b+c & a & a \\ b & a+c & b \\ c & c & a+b \end{vmatrix} = 4\,abc$

3. Solve for x, y, and z by means of determinants:

$$\begin{aligned} 2\,x + 3\,y - z &= 6 \\ 4\,x - y + 3\,z &= 6 \\ x - 2\,y + z &= 4 \end{aligned}$$

4. Evaluate: $\begin{vmatrix} 32 & 25 & 21 \\ 18 & 20 & 28 \\ 16 & 15 & 35 \end{vmatrix}$

5. Evaluate: $\begin{vmatrix} 2 & 4 & -5 & 6 \\ 3 & -3 & 4 & 9 \\ 4 & 2 & 5 & 7 \\ 5 & 2 & 7 & -3 \end{vmatrix}$

6. Prove: $\begin{vmatrix} a+2\,b & a+4\,b & a+6\,b \\ a+3\,b & a+5\,b & a+7\,b \\ a+4\,b & a+6\,b & a+8\,b \end{vmatrix} = 0$

7. Expand: $\begin{vmatrix} 1 & x & x & x \\ 1 & y & x & x \\ 1 & x & y & x \\ 1 & x & x & y \end{vmatrix}$

8. Expand: $\begin{vmatrix} 0 & a & b & c \\ a & 0 & c & b \\ b & c & 0 & a \\ c & b & a & 0 \end{vmatrix}$

MASTERY TEST

1. Solve by determinants:

$$\begin{aligned} 2\,x + y - z &= 4 \\ x + 3\,y + z &= 5 \\ 3\,x - 2\,y - 3\,z &= -2 \end{aligned}$$

2. Prove: $\begin{vmatrix} 6 & 12 & 8 & -4 \\ -1 & 3 & 0 & -1 \\ 1 & -4 & -2 & 5 \\ -3 & 2 & -1 & 2 \end{vmatrix} = -234$

3. Prove: $\begin{vmatrix} a-b-c & 2a & 2a \\ 2b & b-c-a & 2b \\ 2c & 2c & c-b-a \end{vmatrix} = (a+b+c)^3$

4. Solve by determinants:

$$\begin{aligned} x + y + z &= 1 \\ ax + by + cz &= k \\ a^2x + b^2y + c^2z &= k^2 \end{aligned}$$

5. Evaluate: $\begin{vmatrix} 3 & -2 & 3 & 7 \\ 4 & 5 & -3 & -2 \\ 5 & -2 & 5 & 8 \\ 6 & -4 & 2 & 3 \end{vmatrix}$

6. Evaluate: $\begin{vmatrix} 1 & 1 & 0 & 1 & 3 \\ 2 & 3 & 2 & 3 & 2 \\ 3 & 2 & 3 & 2 & 2 \\ 2 & 2 & 2 & -2 & 2 \\ 2 & 2 & 2 & 4 & 2 \end{vmatrix}$

7. Solve for z by determinants:

$$\begin{aligned} x + y + z &= a + b + c \\ ax + by + cz &= ab + ac + bc \\ bx + cy + az &= a^2 + b^2 + c^2. \end{aligned}$$

8. Prove: $\begin{vmatrix} a^2 & ab & b^2 \\ 2a & a+b & 2b \\ 1 & 1 & 1 \end{vmatrix} = (a-b)^3$

9. Evaluate: $\begin{vmatrix} 1 & 1 & 1 & 1 \\ a & -a & b & b \\ -a & -a & -a & b \\ b & -b & -b & a \end{vmatrix}$

10. Find k so that the lines whose equations are

$$\begin{aligned} kx + 4y &= 5 \\ 3x - 5y &= 4 \end{aligned}$$

are parallel.

11. Show that $Ax^2 + By^2 + 2\,Hxy + 2\,Gx + 2\,Fy + C$ can be factored if and only if

$$\begin{vmatrix} A & H & G \\ H & B & F \\ G & F & C \end{vmatrix} = 0$$

12. Using the result of ex. 11, determine if

$$6\,x^2 - xy + 9\,y - 2\,y^2 - 3\,x - 5$$

can be factored.

13. Determine if the following equations are consistent:

$$\begin{aligned} x - y - 2 &= 0 \\ x - y &= -7 \\ 3\,x &= 2 - y \end{aligned}$$

14. Find k so that the following equations are consistent:

$$\begin{aligned} 2\,x - 3\,y - 4 &= 0 \\ 2\,x + 5\,y &= 2 \\ x + y + k &= 0 \end{aligned}$$

15. Factor: $\begin{vmatrix} a & a^2 & bc \\ b & b^2 & ca \\ c & c^2 & ab \end{vmatrix}$

16. Prove: $\begin{vmatrix} 1 & \omega & \omega^2 & 1 \\ \omega & \omega^2 & 1 & 1 \\ \omega^2 & 1 & 1 & \omega \\ 1 & 1 & \omega & \omega^2 \end{vmatrix} = 3\sqrt{3}\,i$, where ω = an imaginary cube root of 1.

17. Evaluate: $\begin{vmatrix} a & y & b & x \\ x & y & b & a \\ x & b & y & a \\ a & b & y & x \end{vmatrix}$

18. Solve by determinants for z:

$$\begin{aligned} ax + by + cz &= d \\ a^2x + b^2y + c^2z &= d^2 \\ a^3x + b^3y + c^3z &= d^3 \end{aligned}$$

19. Solve for x: $\begin{vmatrix} 2+x & 2 & 3 \\ 3-x & 5 & -1 \\ 4 & 2 & 3 \end{vmatrix} = 0$

20. Factor: $\begin{vmatrix} 0 & 1 & 1 & 1 \\ 1 & 0 & a^2 & b^2 \\ 1 & a^2 & 0 & c^2 \\ 1 & b^2 & c^2 & 0 \end{vmatrix}$

CHAPTER XIX

Scale of Notation

Writing a number to any base

In our number system we use the digits 0, 1, 2, 3, 4, 5, 6, 7, 8, 9. Thus, the number 27983 means

$$2 \times 10^4 + 7 \times 10^3 + 9 \times 10^2 + 8 \times 10 + 3$$

The number 10 is called the *base* or *radix* of the system.

Obviously, any positive integer greater than 1 can be used as a base. For example, if the base is r any positive integer N can be written in the form

$$N = a_n r^n + a_{n-1} r^{n-1} + \cdot \cdot \cdot + a_1 r + a_0$$

or with detached coefficients we write

$$N = (a_n a_{n-1} \cdot \cdot \cdot a_0 a_1)_r$$

Thus, for example, $(213)_4$ means $2 \times 4^2 + 1 \times 4 + 3 = 39$.

EXERCISES

1. Write the first 10 numbers in the system whose base is 8.

2. Write the first 15 numbers in the system whose base is 4.

Write the following numbers in the decimal system; *i.e.*, in the system whose base is 10.

3. $(425)_6$ **5.** $(783)_9$ **7.** $(10121)_5$

4. $(1233)_4$ **6.** $(5011)_8$ **8.** $(1111)_2$

Changing a number from base 10 to any other base

This is the converse of our last problem. The method is just as easy but not quite so obvious. If the number is not too large, we can solve the example by inspection. Thus, suppose we wish to express $(31)_{10}$ to base or radix 7.

Now $(31)_{10} = 4 \times 7 + 3$
Hence $(31)_{10} = (43)_7$

In general, to write the number $N = (a_n a_{n-1} \cdots a_1 a_0)_r$ to the base 10, we have merely to find the values of $a_0, a_1, \cdots a_n$ in the polynomial

$$a_n r^n + a_{n-1} r^{n-1} + \cdots + a_1 r + a_0$$

If we divide N by r, the remainder is a_0; and the quotient is $a_n r^{n-1} + a_{n-1} r^{n-2} + \cdots + a_2 r + a_1$. If this quotient is divided by r, the remainder is a_1. If this process is continued until there are no further quotients, the coefficients $a_0, a_1, \cdots a_n$ will be determined.

EXAMPLE. Express $(3467)_{10}$ to base 4.

$$\begin{array}{rll} 4\,|\,3467 & & \\ 4\,|\,866 + 3 & & 3 = a_0 \\ 4\,|\,216 + 2 & & 2 = a_1 \\ 4\,|\,54 + 0 & & 0 = a_2 \\ 4\,|\,13 + 2 & & 2 = a_3 \\ 4\,|\,3 + 1 & & 1 = a_4 \\ 0 + 3 & & 3 = a_5 \end{array}$$

Therefore $(3467)_{10} = (312023)_4$.

EXERCISES

Express each of the following numbers to the base indicated:

1. $(200)_{10}$ base 4
2. $(1567)_{10}$ base 7
3. $(45672)_9$ base 8
4. $(45610)_{10}$ base 6
5. $(1010101)_6$ base 5
6. $(75)_8$ base 2
7. $(21453)_{10}$ base 11 (use t for 10)
8. $(44565)_{10}$ base 12 (use t and e to represent 10 and 11)
9. $(33333)_{10}$ base 3
10. $(7070707)_{10}$ base 7

Fundamental operations of arithmetic in scales other than ten

Addition and subtraction.

EXAMPLE. Add $(356)_7$ and $(234)_7$.

Let us first write our numbers as polynomials and see what happens when we add them.

Solution.

$$(356)_7 = 3 \times 7^2 + 5 \times 7 + 6$$
$$(234)_7 = 2 \times 7^2 + 3 \times 7 + 4$$

Hence $$(356)_7 + (234)_7 = 5 \times 7^2 + 8 \times 7 + 10$$

As in the case when the base is 10, we must "carry to the next column" when the sum is equal to or greater than the base. Hence the right-hand member can be written

$$6 \times 7^2 + 2 \times 7 + 3 \text{ and the sum is } (623)_7$$

Therefore, to add $(356)_7$ and $(234)_7$ we obtain

$$\begin{array}{r} 356 \\ \underline{234} \\ 623 \end{array}$$

The addition of the right-hand column gives 10 or 7 + 3. We write the 3 and "carry" 1. Adding the next column gives 5 + 3 + 1 or 9. This is 7 + 2. Hence we write 2 and "carry" 1. Adding the last column gives 3 + 2 + 1 or 6. Hence the sum is $(623)_7$.

EXAMPLE 2. Subtract $(234)_7$ from $(623)_7$.

Solution.

$$\begin{array}{r} 623 \\ \underline{234} \\ 356 \end{array}$$

Since we cannot subtract 4 from 3, we must borrow 1 from the next column. But 1 borrowed from the second column is the same as 7 in the first column. Hence we have 3 + 7 − 4 or 6. Since we borrowed 1 from the second column, we are now trying to subtract 3 from 1. Hence we must borrow 1 from the third column. Therefore, we have 1 + 7 − 3 = 5 for the difference. The last column difference is 5 − 2 or 3. Hence,

$$(623)_7 - (234)_7 = (356)_7$$

EXERCISES

Perform the following additions and subtractions:

1. $(472)_8 + (412)_8$
2. $(222)_3 - (111)_3$
3. $(412)_5 + (443)_5$
4. $(652)_7 + (345)_7$
5. $(756)_8 + (257)_8$
6. $(1818)_9 + (3724)_9$
7. $(42156)_7 - (21546)_7$
8. $(7654321)_8 - (1234567)_8$
9. $(204060)_7 - (122134)_7$
10. $(12\,t\,e\,41)_{12} + (421\,t\,e\,4)_{12}$

Multiplication and division.

EXAMPLE 1. Multiply $(3245)_6$ by $(215)_6$.

Solution.

```
    3245
     215
   -----
   25201
   3245
  10534
 -------
 1155451
```

Thus $5 \times 5 = 25 = 4 \times 6 + 1$. Hence, we put down 1 and "carry" 4. Now $4 \times 5 + 4 = 24 = 6 \times 4 + 0$. Hence, we put down 0 and "carry" 4, and so on.

EXAMPLE 2. Divide $(1155451)_6$ by $(215)_6$.

Solution.

```
215 | 1155451 | 3245
      1053
      ----
       1024
        434
       ----
        1505
        1312
        ----
         1531
         1531
         ----
```

EXERCISES

Find the product of each of the following pairs of numbers. Divide the product found by the first number and show that the quotient is the second number.

1. $(243)_5 \times (412)_5$
2. $(112)_3 \times (211)_3$
3. $(5252)_8 \div (116)_8$
4. $(345)_7 \times (652)_7$
5. $(156)_8 \times (723)_8$
6. $(145)_6 \times (543)_6$
7. $(114201)_5 \div (1222)_5$
8. $(10403)_6 \div (2121)_6$
9. $(23125)_7 \div (1462)_7$
10. $(1231)_8 \times (4777)_8$

Radix fractions

In our decimal system .23 means $\frac{2}{10} + \frac{3}{10^2}$. Likewise, if our base or radix is 7, then .23 means $\frac{2}{7} + \frac{3}{7^2}$. In general $(0.b_1b_2 \cdots b_n)_r$ means $F = \frac{b_1}{r} + \frac{b_2}{r^2} + \cdots + \frac{b_n}{r^n}$.

Our problem is to determine the values of b_1, b_2, etc. If we multiply both sides of the equation by r, we have

$$Fr = b_1 + \frac{b_2}{r} + \cdots + \frac{b_n}{r^{n-1}}$$

Hence, b_1 is the integral part of Fr. If we denote the fractional part of F by F_1, then $F_1 = \frac{b_2}{r} + \cdots + \frac{b_n}{r^{n-1}}$.

Multiplying by r gives

$$F_1r = b_2 + \frac{b_3}{r} + \cdots + \frac{b_n}{r^{n-2}}$$

and b_2 is the integral part of F_1r. By continuing this process the values of all the digits, $b_1, b_2, \cdots, b_n$ can be found.

EXAMPLE. Express $\frac{7}{8}$ as a radix fraction in scale 6.

Solution. $\frac{7}{8} \times 6 = \frac{42}{8} = 5 + \frac{2}{8}$
$\frac{2}{8} \times 6 = \frac{12}{8} = 1 + \frac{4}{8}$
$\frac{4}{8} \times 6 = \frac{24}{8} = 3$

Therefore the required fraction is

$$\frac{5}{6} + \frac{1}{6^2} + \frac{3}{6^3} \text{ or } .513$$

EXERCISES

Express the following fractions as radix fractions in the scales indicated:

1. $\frac{3}{5}$ (6)
2. $\frac{7}{8}$ (5)
3. $\frac{13}{16}$ (7)
4. $\frac{3}{4}$ (8)
5. $\frac{7}{8}$ (20)
6. $\frac{5}{11}$ (5)

MASTERY TEST

1. By the remainder theorem, find a value of k for which

$$x^3 + 5\,kx^2 - 7\,x - 3$$

is divisible by $x - 2$.

2. Draw the graph of $y = x(x - 2)(x + 1)^2(x - 3)^3$.

3. If the equation $f(x) = 0$ has real coefficients and is of odd degree, prove that the equation has an odd number of real roots.

4. Find the rational roots of $3\,x^3 + 8\,x^2 + x - 2 = 0$.

5. The sum of two roots of $2\,x^3 + 3\,x^2 - 98\,x - 147 = 0$ is zero. Find all the roots.

6. Prove that one root of $x^3 + 9\,x^2 + 24\,x + 17 = 0$ lies between -4 and -5. Find the value of this root to the nearest hundredth.

7. Find all the roots of $x^4 - 4\,x^3 + 6\,x^2 - 5\,x + 2 = 0$.

8. Transform $x^5 + \frac{1}{2}\,x^4 - \frac{1}{3}\,x^3 + \frac{11}{24}\,x^2 - \frac{17}{162}\,x + \frac{23}{144} = 0$ into another equation having only integral coefficients.

9. Prove that the equation $x^7 + 2\,x^5 - 5\,x^2 - 4 = 0$ has one positive real root and six complex roots.

10. Construct the graph of $\frac{1}{8}\,x^3 - x + 2$ from $x = -4$ to $x = 4$.

11. Determine n so that one root of $x^3 - 7\,x^2 + nx - 8 = 0$ is the double of another root. Solve the equation.

12. Determine m and n so that two of the roots of

$$x^3 + 7\,x^2 + mx + n = 0$$

shall be 1 and 2.

13. Determine p and q so that the roots of $x^3 - 3\,x^2 + px + q = 0$ shall form an A.P. with a common difference of 2.

14. Find the rational roots of $6\,x^3 - 29\,x^2 + 14\,x + 24 = 0$.

15. Form the equation whose roots are $3, -4, \frac{3}{4}, \frac{2}{3}$.

16. Find the roots of $x^4 - 6\,x^3 + 17\,x^2 - 28\,x + 20 = 0$.

17. The width of the strongest beam one can cut from a log 12 inches in diameter is given by the positive irrational root of the equation $x^3 - 144\,x + 665 = 0$. Find the width to the nearest hundredth of an inch.

18. Determine the number of positive, negative, and imaginary roots of $x^6 + 7\,x^2 + 4\,x - 9 = 0$.

19. Solve by Horner's method to two places of decimals, $x = \sqrt[3]{3\,x + 4}$.

20. Solve $2\,x^4 + x^3 + x + 2 = 6\,x^2$.

21. The equation $3\,x^4 - 25\,x^3 + 50\,x^2 - 50\,x + 12 = 0$ has two roots whose product is 2. Find all the roots.

22. Construct the graph of $\frac{1}{2}(x^3 - 19x + 30)$ from $x = -6$ to $x = 4$.

23. Show that the equation $x^9 + 7x^7 + 5x^5 - 3x^4 - 2 = 0$ has one positive root and eight imaginary roots.

24. Find the equation whose roots are 8, 2, -3, $\pm\sqrt{-7}$.

25. Solve the equation $6x^4 - 13x^3 - 35x^2 - x + 3 = 0$ if one root is $2 - \sqrt{3}$.

26. Transform the equation $x^3 - 5x^2 + 4x - 3 = 0$ into an equation whose roots are 3 greater than those of the given equation.

27. The cube of a number plus six times the number equals 2; find the number to the nearest hundredth.

28. If p, q, and m are the roots of the equation

$$x^3 + ax^2 + bx + c = 0$$

what are the roots of the equation

$$x^3 - akx^2 + bk^2x - ck^3 = 0$$

29. What condition must be satisfied by the coefficients of the equation

$$x^3 + ax^2 + bx + c = 0$$

if the three roots form an A.P.?

30. The product of two roots of $x^4 - 10x^3 + px^2 + qx + 24 = 0$ is 2, and the sum of the other two roots is 7. Find the values of p and q and the four roots.

31. Evaluate

$$\begin{vmatrix} a & b & c & d \\ b & a & d & c \\ c & d & a & b \\ d & c & b & a \end{vmatrix}$$

32. If $2^{x+y} = 16$ and $2^{x-y} = 64$, find x and y.

33. Simplify $(\frac{9}{4})^{\frac{3}{2}} - 1^x + 4^{-\frac{1}{2}}$.

34. The sum of three numbers in G.P. is 70. If we multiply the first number by 4, the second by 5, and the third by 4, the resulting numbers are in A.P. Find the three original numbers.

35. Evaluate $\log_8 96 + \log_8 \frac{2}{3}$.

36. Evaluate $\log_{81} \frac{3}{4} + \log_{81} 108$.

37. Using logarithms find x, if $3^x = 5$.

38. Express $\frac{(2+i)^2}{3+i}$ in the form $a + bi$.

39. Express in the form $a + bi$ the value of $\frac{2z+1}{z^2 - 4z + 3}$ if $z = 1 + 2i$.

40. Find k so that $x^3 - 3x^2 + kx + 5$ is divisible by $x + 2$.

41. If $f(x) = x^4 - 2x^2 + 1$, find $f(-1)$; $f(0)$; $f(-3)$.

42. If k is a root of $x^3 + ax^2 + ax + 1 = 0$, prove that $\frac{1}{k}$ is also a root.

43. What is the sum and the product of the roots of

$$5x^4 - 3x^3 + 7x^2 - x + 1 = 0?$$

44. Given that the roots of $48x^3 = 74x^2 - 37x + 6$ are in G.P. Find the roots.

45. Prove that all of the roots of $x^4 + x^2 + 1 = 0$ are imaginary. What is their sum?

46. In how many ways can 10 children form a ring by joining hands?

47. In a bag are 13 balls marked from 1 to 13. If two balls are drawn at random, find the probability that the numbers on the balls are—

a) one even, one odd.
b) both even.
c) both odd.

48. If the roots of $5x^3 - 8x^2 + 7x - 1 = 0$ are a, b, and c, write the equation whose roots are—

a) $\frac{1}{a}, \frac{1}{b}, \frac{1}{c}$

b) $-\frac{1}{a}, -\frac{1}{b}, -\frac{1}{c}$

c) $a + 1, b + 1, c + 1$

d) $a - 2, b - 2, c - 2$

49. Transform $x^3 - 9x^2 + 2x - 1 = 0$ into an equation in which the second degree term is missing.

50. How many odd numbers of four digits each not starting with 9 or ending with 9 can be formed with the digits 2, 3, 5, 7, 9, 0, repetition of digits being allowed?

51. Given the equation $2x^3 - 4x^2 - x + 3 = 0$. If the roots are a, b, and c, find the value of—

a) abc

b) $\frac{1}{a} + \frac{1}{b} + \frac{1}{c}$

c) $\frac{1}{ab} + \frac{1}{bc} + \frac{1}{ac}$

d) $\frac{1}{2a} + \frac{1}{2b} + \frac{1}{2c}$

e) $\frac{ab + ac + bc}{5abc}$

f) $\frac{(a+1)(b+1) + (a+1)(c+1) + (b+1)(c+1)}{(a+1)(b+1)(c+1)}$

52. Find k if the following equations have a unique solution:

$$\begin{aligned} 3x + 2y &= 5 \\ 4x - y &= 3 \\ kx + 3y &= 1 \end{aligned}$$

53. Find a set of values for a, b, and c if the equation $ax + by + c = 0$ is satisfied by $x = 4$, $y = 3$, and $x = 2$, $y = 1$.

54. For what value of k has the following system of equations no solution?

$$\begin{aligned} kx + 2y &= 5 \\ 3x - y &= 2 \end{aligned}$$

55. Solve for z by determinants:

$$\begin{aligned} 3x + y - z &= 2 \\ x + y - w &= -1 \\ x + z - 2w &= -4 \\ 3x - z &= 0 \end{aligned}$$

56. Evaluate: $\begin{vmatrix} x & y & y & x \\ y & x & x & y \\ x & x & y & y \\ 0 & x & y & y \end{vmatrix}$

57. Write 943 in the scale 6.

58. Multiply $(28)_9$ by $(35)_9$.

59. Solve for x by determinants the equations $x - 2y + 3z = 0$, $3x + ay - z = 1$, $2x + z = 1 - ay$. For what value of a does the system have no solution?

60. Is $y - 2 + i$ a factor of $y^3 - 3y^2 + y + 5$?

61. If the roots of $x^3 - bx^2 + cx - d = 0$ are p, q, and r, show that

$$\begin{vmatrix} p & q & r \\ r & p & q \\ q & r & p \end{vmatrix} = b(b^2 - 3c)$$

62. Given $\dfrac{8}{1+i} = x + yi + 2i$. If x and y are real, find their value.

63. Solve the equation $4x^3 - 12x^2 + 11x - 3 = 0$, knowing that the roots are in arithmetic progression.

64. In how many ways can the first seven letters of the alphabet be arranged in which the vowels precede the consonants?

65. How many diagonals are there in a dodecagon?

66. Solve the simultaneous equations $x^2 - y^2 = 9$, $x^2 + y^2 = 16$. Draw the graphs of the equations and give the co-ordinates of their points of intersection.

67. Find x if $\begin{vmatrix} 1 & 1 & 1 & 1 \\ x & x & x & 4 \\ 2 & 4 & 7 & 1 \\ -1 & 2 & 3 & 4 \end{vmatrix} = 0$

68. If $l = ar^{n-1}$ and $s = \dfrac{a - ar^n}{1 - r}$, prove that $l = \dfrac{a + rs - s}{r}$.

69. John and Tom run a mile. If John gives Tom a start of 11 yd., he can beat him by 57 seconds. If John gives Tom a start of $1\frac{7}{20}$ minutes, he is beaten by 88 yd. How long does it take each man to run a mile?

70. What is the price of eggs if 2 less for 24 cents raises the price 2 cents per dozen?

71. As an army 1 mile long began a march, a courier left the rear for the front. He returned, reaching the rear after the army had traveled a mile. How far did the courier travel?

72. A hare takes 6 leaps to a dog's 5, and 7 of the dog's leaps are equivalent to 9 of the hare's. The hare has a start of 50 of her own leaps. How many leaps will the hare take before she is caught?

73. Decompose into partial fractions: $\dfrac{3x - 4}{(x^2 - 1)(x^2 + 1)}$

74. Solve: $\sqrt{x + 1} + \sqrt{2x + 3} = \sqrt{8x + 1}$

75. Factor: $\begin{vmatrix} 0 & x & y \\ x & 0 & y \\ x & y & 0 \end{vmatrix}$

76. The volume of a rectangular box is 30 cu. in. Find the dimensions of the box if the length and width are 1 in. and 3 in., respectively, greater than the height.

77. Resolve into partial fractions: $\dfrac{2x - 5}{x^2(x^2 + 1)}$

78. Find the 5th roots of $1 + i$. Do they lie on a circle?

79. A circle has its center at the origin, and a diameter with one extremity at $2 + 2i$. Find the numbers which represent the extremities of the diameter which is perpendicular to the given diameter. What is the length of a diameter?

80. Solve: $xy + y^2 = 18,\ x^2 - 2xy = 21$

81. Prove by mathematical induction:

$$4^0 + 4^1 + 4^2 + \cdots + 4^{n-1} = \tfrac{1}{3}(4^n - 1)$$

82. Find all the solutions of the following system of equations:

$$\begin{aligned} x + y + z &= 0 \\ 5x - 3y - 19z &= 0 \\ x + 2y + 4z &= 0 \end{aligned}$$

83. Solve the equation $x^4 + 2x^3 - 3x^2 + 14x + 4 = 0$ if one root is $1 - \sqrt{3}\,i$.

84. Find the rational roots of $6x^4 + 17x^3 + 7x^2 + x - 10 = 0$.

85. According to Kepler's Third Law, the squares of the times of rotation of two planets about the sun are proportional to the cubes of their distances from the sun. If Neptune takes 165 years to make a complete revolution about the sun, how does its distance from the sun compare with the earth's distance from the sun?

86. Using the binomial theorem, find the value of $(.99)^7$ correct to 4 significant figures.

87. The coefficients of the $(2k + 1)$th and $(k + 5)$th terms of $(x + y)^{25}$ are equal. Find k.

88. By Horner's method find to two decimal places the positive root of $x^3 + x^2 + x - 20 = 0$.

89. The roots of $x^3 - 11x^2 = 36 - 36x$ are in harmonic progression. Find them.

90. The roots of $x^3 + ax + b = 0$ are p, $q + ir$, $q - ir$. Prove that $q = -\frac{p}{2}$.

91. If $f(n) = n!$, prove that $(n + 1)f(n) = f(n + 1)$.

92. To decide partners in a game of tennis, four players toss their rackets. The 2 "smooths" and the 2 "roughs" are to be partners. What are the odds against the choice being made on the first throw?

93. Find to the nearest hundredth the root of $x^3 + 50 = 3x(x + 5)$ that lies between -3 and -4.

94. Draw the graph of

$$y = \tfrac{1}{12}(3x^4 + 4x^3 - 12x^2 + 24)$$

95. Resolve into partial fractions:

$$\frac{x^2 + 2x + 1}{x^2(x^2 + 1)(x - 1)}$$

96. Add graphically $7 + 12i$ and $\frac{2 - 3i}{1 - i}$.

97. Find the values of k and m if

$$2x^3 - 3x^2 + kx + m \text{ is divisible by } x - 2 \text{ and } x - 3$$

98. Find all the roots of $12x^3 - 4x^2 - 3x + 1 = 0$.

99. Solve $x^4 - mx^3 + 5x^2 + 5x - 6 = 0$ if one root is 1.

100. If $x = \frac{2 - i}{3}$, express $\frac{1}{x + 3} + i^3$ in the form $a + bi$.

101. If a, b, and c are the roots of $2x^3 - 5x + 1 = 0$, find the value of $\frac{ab + ac + bc}{5abc}$.

102. Solve $48x^3 + 74x^2 + 37x + 6 = 0$ if the roots are in G.P.

103. Without expanding, find the two roots of the equation:

$$\begin{vmatrix} x^2 & 1 & 9 \\ 2x & 2 & 6 \\ 1 & 1 & 1 \end{vmatrix} = 0$$

104. If the roots of $x^3 + x^2 + 1 = 0$ are a, b, and c, what is the value of

$$\begin{vmatrix} ab & bc & ac \\ bc & ac & ab \\ ac & ab & bc \end{vmatrix}$$

105. In how many ways can ten men be seated in a row if among them there are one German, one Frenchman, one Englishman, and seven Americans, provided no two foreigners sit together?

106. Solve for x, $\frac{1}{12}(x + 3)(x - 1)(x - 2) = 1$.

107. Find k if $3a + m = 6$, $2a - m = 1$, $3ka + 2m = 1$.

108. I am twice as old as you were when I was as old as you now are. When you get to be as old as I am now, together our ages will be 63. How old are we now?

109. Prove that an equation which involves only even powers of x with positive coefficients cannot have a positive or a negative root.

110. Prove that if a cubic equation with rational coefficients has a multiple root, this root must be rational.

N	N^2	N^3	$\sqrt{N}$	$\sqrt[3]{N}$	N	N^2	N^3	$\sqrt{N}$	$\sqrt[3]{N}$
1	1	1	1.000	1.000	51	2 601	132 651	7.141	3.708
2	4	8	1.414	1.260	52	2 704	140 608	7.211	3.733
3	9	27	1.732	1.442	53	2 809	148 877	7.280	3.756
4	16	64	2.000	1.587	54	2 916	157 464	7.348	3.780
5	25	125	2.236	1.710	55	3 025	166 375	7.416	3.803
6	36	216	2.449	1.817	56	3 136	175 616	7.483	3.826
7	49	343	2.646	1.913	57	3 249	185 193	7.550	3.849
8	64	512	2.828	2.000	58	3 364	195 112	7.616	3.871
9	81	729	3.000	2.080	59	3 481	205 379	7.681	3.893
10	100	1 000	3.162	2.154	**60**	3 600	216 000	7.746	3.915
11	121	1 331	3.317	2.224	61	3 721	226 981	7.810	3.936
12	144	1 728	3.464	2.289	62	3 844	238 328	7.874	3.958
13	169	2 197	3.606	2.351	63	3 969	250 047	7.937	3.979
14	196	2 744	3.742	2.410	64	4 096	262 144	8.000	4.000
15	225	3 375	3.873	2.466	65	4 225	274 625	8.062	4.021
16	256	4 096	4.000	2.520	66	4 356	287 496	8.124	4.041
17	289	4 913	4.123	2.571	67	4 489	300 763	8.185	4.062
18	324	5 832	4.243	2.621	68	4 624	314 432	8.246	4.082
19	361	6 859	4.359	2.668	69	4 761	328 509	8.307	4.102
20	400	8 000	4.472	2.714	**70**	4 900	343 000	8.367	4.121
21	441	9 261	4.583	2.759	71	5 041	357 911	8.426	4.141
22	484	10 648	4.690	2.802	72	5 184	373 248	8.485	4.160
23	529	12 167	4.796	2.844	73	5 329	389 017	8.544	4.179
24	576	13 824	4.899	2.884	74	5 476	405 224	8.602	4.198
25	625	15 625	5.000	2.924	75	5 625	421 875	8.660	4.217
26	676	17 576	5.099	2.962	76	5 776	438 976	8.718	4.236
27	729	19 683	5.196	3.000	77	5 929	456 533	8.775	4.254
28	784	21 952	5.292	3.037	78	6 084	474 552	8.832	4.273
29	841	24 389	5.385	3.072	79	6 241	493 039	8.888	4.291
30	900	27 000	5.477	3.107	**80**	6 400	512 000	8,944	4.309
31	961	29 791	5.568	3.141	81	6 561	531 441	9.000	4.327
32	1 024	32 768	5.657	3.175	82	6 724	551 368	9.055	4.344
33	1 089	35 937	5.745	3.208	83	6 889	571 787	9.110	4.362
34	1 156	39 304	5.831	3.240	84	7 056	592 704	9.165	4.380
35	1 225	42 875	5.916	3.271	85	7 225	614 125	9.220	4.397
36	1 296	46 656	6.000	3.302	86	7 396	636 056	9.274	4.414
37	1 369	50 653	6.083	3.332	87	7 569	658 503	9.327	4.431
38	1 444	54 872	6.164	3.362	88	7 744	681 472	9.381	4.448
39	1 521	59 319	6.245	3.391	89	7 921	704 969	9.434	4.465
40	1 600	64 000	6.325	3.420	**90**	8 100	729 000	9.487	4.481
41	1 681	68 921	6.403	3.448	91	8 281	753 571	9.539	4.498
42	1 764	74 088	6.481	3.476	92	8 464	778 688	9.592	4.514
43	1 849	79 507	6.557	3.503	93	8 649	804 357	9.644	4.531
44	1 936	85 184	6.633	3.530	94	8 836	830 584	9.695	4.547
45	2 025	91 125	6.708	3.557	95	9 025	857 375	9.747	4.563
46	2 116	97 336	6.782	3.583	96	9 216	884 736	9.798	4.579
47	2 209	103 823	6.856	3.609	97	9 409	912 673	9.849	4.595
48	2 304	110 592	6.928	3.634	98	9 604	941 192	9.899	4.610
49	2 401	117 649	7.000	3.659	99	9 801	970 299	9.950	4.626
50	2 500	125 000	7.071	3.684	**100**	10 000	1 000 000	10.000	4.642

N	0	1	2	3	4	5	6	7	8	9
10	0000	0043	0086	0128	0170	0212	0253	0294	0334	0374
11	0414	0453	0492	0531	0569	0607	0645	0682	0719	0755
12	0792	0828	0864	0899	0934	0969	1004	1038	1072	1106
13	1139	1173	1206	1239	1271	1303	1335	1367	1399	1430
14	1461	1492	1523	1553	1584	1614	1644	1673	1703	1732
15	1761	1790	1818	1847	1875	1903	1931	1959	1987	2014
16	2041	2068	2095	2122	2148	2175	2201	2227	2253	2279
17	2304	2330	2355	2380	2405	2430	2455	2480	2504	2529
18	2553	2577	2601	2625	2648	2672	2695	2718	2742	2765
19	2788	2810	2833	2856	2878	2900	2923	2945	2967	2989
20	3010	3032	3054	3075	3096	3118	3139	3160	3181	3201
21	3222	3243	3263	3284	3304	3324	3345	3365	3385	3404
22	3424	3444	3464	3483	3502	3522	3541	3560	3579	3598
23	3617	3636	3655	3674	3692	3711	3729	3747	3766	3784
24	3802	3820	3838	3856	3874	3892	3909	3927	3945	3962
25	3979	3997	4014	4031	4048	4065	4082	4099	4116	4133
26	4150	4166	4183	4200	4216	4232	4249	4265	4281	4298
27	4314	4330	4346	4362	4378	4393	4409	4425	4440	4456
28	4472	4487	4502	4518	4533	4548	4564	4579	4594	4609
29	4624	4639	4654	4669	4683	4698	4713	4728	4742	4757
30	4771	4786	4800	4814	4829	4843	4857	4871	4886	4900
31	4914	4928	4942	4955	4969	4983	4997	5011	5024	5038
32	5051	5065	5079	5092	5105	5119	5132	5145	5159	5172
33	5185	5198	5211	5224	5237	5250	5263	5276	5289	5302
34	5315	5328	5340	5353	5366	5378	5391	5403	5416	5428
35	5441	5453	5465	5478	5490	5502	5514	5527	5539	5551
36	5563	5575	5587	5599	5611	5623	5635	5647	5658	5670
37	5682	5694	5705	5717	5729	5740	5752	5763	5775	5786
38	5798	5809	5821	5832	5843	5855	5866	5877	5888	5899
39	5911	5922	5933	5944	5955	5966	5977	5988	5999	6010
40	6021	6031	6042	6053	6064	6075	6085	6096	6107	6117
41	6128	6138	6149	6160	6170	6180	6191	6201	6212	6222
42	6232	6243	6253	6263	6274	6284	6294	6304	6314	6325
43	6335	6345	6355	6365	6375	6385	6395	6405	6415	6425
44	6435	6444	6454	6464	6474	6484	6493	6503	6513	6522
45	6532	6542	6551	6561	6571	6580	6590	6599	6609	6618
46	6628	6637	6646	6656	6665	6675	6684	6693	6702	6712
47	6721	6730	6739	6749	6758	6767	6776	6785	6794	6803
48	6812	6821	6830	6839	6848	6857	6866	6875	6884	6893
49	6902	6911	6920	6928	6937	6946	6955	6964	6972	6981
50	6990	6998	7007	7016	7024	7033	7042	7050	7059	7067
51	7076	7084	7093	7101	7110	7118	7126	7135	7143	7152
52	7160	7168	7177	7185	7193	7202	7210	7218	7226	7235
53	7243	7251	7259	7267	7275	7284	7292	7300	7308	7316
54	7324	7332	7340	7348	7356	7364	7372	7380	7388	7396

N	0	1	2	3	4	5	6	7	8	9
55	7404	7412	7419	7427	7435	7443	7451	7459	7466	7474
56	7482	7490	7497	7505	7513	7520	7528	7536	7543	7551
57	7559	7566	7574	7582	7589	7597	7604	7612	7619	7627
58	7634	7642	7649	7657	7664	7672	7679	7686	7694	7701
59	7709	7716	7723	7731	7738	7745	7752	7760	7767	7774
60	7782	7789	7796	7803	7810	7818	7825	7832	7839	7846
61	7853	7860	7868	7875	7882	7889	7896	7903	7910	7917
62	7924	7931	7938	7945	7952	7959	7966	7973	7980	7987
63	7993	8000	8007	8014	8021	8028	8035	8041	8048	8055
64	8062	8069	8075	8082	8089	8096	8102	8109	8116	8122
65	8129	8136	8142	8149	8156	8162	8169	8176	8182	8189
66	8195	8202	8209	8215	8222	8228	8235	8241	8248	8254
67	8261	8267	8274	8280	8287	8293	8299	8306	8312	8319
68	8325	8331	8338	8344	8351	8357	8363	8370	8376	8382
69	8388	8395	8401	8407	8414	8420	8426	8432	8439	8445
70	8451	8457	8463	8470	8476	8482	8488	8494	8500	8506
71	8513	8519	8525	8531	8537	8543	8549	8555	8561	8567
72	8573	8579	8585	8591	8597	8603	8609	8615	8621	8627
73	8633	8639	8645	8651	8657	8663	8669	8675	8681	8686
74	8692	8698	8704	8710	8716	8722	8727	8733	8739	8745
75	8751	8756	8762	8768	8774	8779	8785	8791	8797	8802
76	8808	8814	8820	8825	8831	8837	8842	8848	8854	8859
77	8865	8871	8876	8882	8887	8893	8899	8904	8910	8915
78	8921	8927	8932	8938	8943	8949	8954	8960	8965	8971
79	8976	8982	8987	8993	8998	9004	9009	9015	9020	9025
80	9031	9036	9042	9047	9053	9058	9063	9069	9074	9079
81	9085	9090	9096	9101	9106	9112	9117	9122	9128	9133
82	9138	9143	9149	9154	9159	9165	9170	9175	9180	9186
83	9191	9196	9201	9206	9212	9217	9222	9227	9232	9238
84	9243	9248	9253	9258	9263	9269	9274	9279	9284	9289
85	9294	9299	9304	9309	9315	9320	9325	9330	9335	9340
86	9345	9350	9355	9360	9365	9370	9375	9380	9385	9390
87	9395	9400	9405	9410	9415	9420	9425	9430	9435	9440
88	9445	9450	9455	9460	9465	9469	9474	9479	9484	9489
89	9494	9499	9504	9509	9513	9518	9523	9528	9533	9538
90	9542	9547	9552	9557	9562	9566	9571	9576	9581	9586
91	9590	9595	9600	9605	9609	9614	9619	9624	9628	9633
92	9638	9643	9647	9652	9657	9661	9666	9671	9675	9680
93	9685	9689	9694	9699	9703	9708	9713	9717	9722	9727
94	9731	9736	9741	9745	9750	9754	9759	9763	9768	9773
95	9777	9782	9786	9791	9795	9800	9805	9809	9814	9818
96	9823	9827	9832	9836	9841	9845	9850	9854	9859	9863
97	9868	9872	9877	9881	9886	9890	9894	9899	9903	9908
98	9912	9917	9921	9926	9930	9934	9939	9943	9948	9952
99	9956	9961	9965	9969	9974	9978	9983	9987	9991	9996

n	1%	1½%	2%	2½%	3%	4%	5%	6%
1	1.0100	1.0150	1.0200	1.0250	1.0300	1.0400	1.0500	1.0600
2	1.0201	1.0302	1.0404	1.0506	1.0609	1.0816	1.1025	1.1236
3	1.0303	1.0457	1.0612	1.0769	1.0927	1.1249	1.1576	1.1910
4	1.0406	1.0614	1.0824	1.1038	1.1255	1.1699	1.2155	1.2625
5	1.0510	1.0773	1.1041	1.1314	1.1593	1.2167	1.2763	1.3382
6	1.0615	1.0934	1.1262	1.1597	1.1941	1.2653	1.3401	1.4185
7	1.0721	1.1098	1.1487	1.1887	1.2299	1.3159	1.4071	1.5036
8	1.0829	1.1265	1.1717	1.2184	1.2668	1.3686	1.4775	1.5938
9	1.0937	1.1434	1.1951	1.2489	1.3048	1.4233	1.5513	1.6895
10	1.1046	1.1605	1.2190	1.2801	1.3439	1.4802	1.6289	1.7908
11	1.1157	1.1779	1.2434	1.3121	1.3842	1.5395	1.7103	1.8983
12	1.1268	1.1956	1.2682	1.3449	1.4258	1.6010	1.7959	2.0122
13	1.1381	1.2136	1.2936	1.3785	1.4685	1.6651	1.8856	2.1329
14	1.1495	1.2318	1.3195	1.4130	1.5126	1.7317	1.9799	2.2609
15	1.1610	1.2502	1.3459	1.4483	1.5580	1.8009	2.0789	2.3966
16	1.1726	1.2690	1.3728	1.4845	1.6047	1.8730	2.1829	2.5404
17	1.1843	1.2880	1.4002	1.5216	1.6528	1.9479	2.2920	2.6928
18	1.1961	1.3073	1.4282	1.5597	1.7024	2.0258	2.4066	2.8543
19	1.2081	1.3270	1.4568	1.5987	1.7535	2.1068	2.5270	3.0256
20	1.2202	1.3469	1.4859	1.6386	1.8061	2.1911	2.6533	3.2071
21	1.2324	1.3671	1.5157	1.6796	1.8603	2.2788	2.7860	3.3996
22	1.2447	1.3876	1.5460	1.7216	1.9161	2.3699	2.9253	3.6035
23	1.2572	1.4084	1.5769	1.7646	1.9736	2.4647	3.0715	3.8197
24	1.2697	1.4295	1.6084	1.8087	2.0328	2.5633	3.2251	4.0489
25	1.2824	1.4509	1.6406	1.8539	2.0938	2.6658	3.3864	4.2919
26	1.2953	1.4727	1.6734	1.9003	2.1566	2.7725	3.5557	4.5494
27	1.3082	1.4948	1.7069	1.9478	2.2213	2.8834	3.7335	4.8223
28	1.3213	1.5172	1.7410	1.9965	2.2879	2.9987	3.9201	5.1117
29	1.3345	1.5400	1.7758	2.0464	2.3566	3.1187	4.1161	5.4184
30	1.3478	1.5631	1.8114	2.0976	2.4273	3.2434	4.3219	5.7435
31	1.3613	1.5865	1.8476	2.1500	2.5001	3.3731	4.5380	6.0881
32	1.3749	1.6103	1.8845	2.2038	2.5751	3.5081	4.7649	6.4534
33	1.3887	1.6345	1.9222	2.2589	2.6523	3.6484	5.0032	6.8406
34	1.4026	1.6590	1.9607	2.3153	2.7319	3.7943	5.2533	7.2510
35	1.4166	1.6839	1.9999	2.3732	2.8139	3.9461	5.5160	7.6861
36	1.4308	1.7091	2.0399	2.4325	2.8983	4.1039	5.7918	8.1473
37	1.4451	1.7348	2.0807	2.4933	2.9852	4.2681	6.0814	8.6361
38	1.4595	1.7608	2.1223	2.5557	3.0748	4.4388	6.3855	9.1543
39	1.4741	1.7872	2.1647	2.6196	3.1670	4.6164	6.7048	9.7035
40	1.4889	1.8140	2.2080	2.6851	3.2620	4.8010	7.0400	10.2857
41	1.5038	1.8412	2.2522	2.7522	3.3599	4.9931	7.3920	10.9029
42	1.5188	1.8688	2.2972	2.8210	3.4607	5.1928	7.7616	11.5570
43	1.5340	1.8969	2.3432	2.8915	3.5645	5.4005	8.1497	12.2505
44	1.5493	1.9253	2.3901	2.9638	3.6715	5.6165	8.5572	12.9855
45	1.5648	1.9542	2.4379	3.0379	3.7816	5.8412	8.9850	13.7646
46	1.5805	1.9835	2.4866	3.1139	3.8950	6.0748	9.4343	14.5905
47	1.5963	2.0133	2.5363	3.1917	4.0119	6.3178	9.9060	15.4659
48	1.6122	2.0435	2.5871	3.2715	4.1323	6.5705	10.4013	16.3939
49	1.6283	2.0741	2.6388	3.3533	4.2562	6.8333	10.9213	17.3775
50	1.6446	2.1052	2.6916	3.4371	4.3839	7.1067	11.4674	18.4202

n	1%	1½%	2%	2½%	3%	4%	5%	6%
1	.99010	.98522	.98039	.97561	.97087	.96154	.95238	.94340
2	.98030	.97066	.96117	.95181	.94260	.92456	.90703	.89000
3	.97059	.95632	.94232	.92860	.91514	.88900	.86384	.83962
4	.96098	.94218	.92385	.90595	.88849	.85480	.82270	.79209
5	.95147	.92826	.90573	.88385	.86261	.82193	.78353	.74726
6	.94205	.91454	.88797	.86230	.83748	.79031	.74622	.70496
7	.93272	.90103	.87056	.84127	.81309	.75992	.71068	.66506
8	.92348	.88771	.85349	.82075	.78941	.73069	.67684	.62741
9	.91434	.87459	.83676	.80073	.76642	.70259	.64461	.59190
10	.90529	.86167	.82035	.78120	.74409	.67556	.61391	.55839
11	.89632	.84893	.80426	.76214	.72242	.64958	.58468	.52679
12	.88745	.83639	.78849	.74356	.70138	.62460	.55684	.49697
13	.87866	.82403	.77303	.72542	.68095	.60057	.53032	.46884
14	.86996	.81185	.75788	.70773	.66112	.57748	.50507	.44230
15	.86135	.79985	.74301	.69047	.64186	.55526	.48102	.41727
16	.85282	.78803	.72845	.67362	.62317	.53391	.45811	.39365
17	.84438	.77639	.71416	.65720	.60502	.51337	.43630	.37136
18	.83602	.76491	.70016	.64117	.58739	.49363	.41552	.35034
19	.82774	.75361	.68643	.62553	.57029	.47464	.39573	.33051
20	.81954	.74247	.67297	.61027	.55368	.45639	.37689	.31180
21	.81143	.73150	.65978	.59539	.53755	.43883	.35894	.29416
22	.80340	.72069	.64684	.58086	.52189	.42196	.34185	.27751
23	.79544	.71004	.63416	.56670	.50669	.40573	.32557	.26180
24	.78757	.69954	.62172	.55288	.49193	.39012	.31007	.24698
25	.77977	.68921	.60953	.53939	.47761	.37512	.29530	.23300
26	.77205	.67902	.59758	.52623	.46369	.36069	.28124	.21981
27	.76440	.66899	.58586	.51340	.45019	.34682	.26785	.20737
28	.75684	.65910	.57437	.50088	.43708	.33348	.25509	.19563
29	.74934	.64936	.56311	.48866	.42435	.32065	.24295	.18456
30	.74192	.63976	.55207	.47674	.41199	.30832	.23138	.17411
31	.73458	.63031	.54125	.46511	.39999	.29646	.22036	.16425
32	.72730	.62099	.53063	.45377	.38834	.28506	.20987	.15496
33	.72010	.61182	.52023	.44270	.37703	.27409	.19987	.14619
34	.71297	.60277	.51003	.43191	.36604	.26355	.19035	.13791
35	.70591	.59387	.50003	.42137	.35538	.25342	.18129	.13011
36	.69892	.58509	.49022	.41109	.34503	.24367	.17266	.12274
37	.69200	.57644	.48061	.40107	.33498	.23430	.16444	.11579
38	.68515	.56792	.47119	.39128	.32523	.22529	.15661	.10924
39	.67837	.55953	.46195	.38174	.31575	.21662	.14915	.10306
40	.67165	.55126	.45289	.37243	.30656	.20829	.14205	.09722
41	.66500	.54312	.44401	.36335	.29763	.20028	.13528	.09172
42	.65842	.53509	.43530	.35448	.28896	.19257	.12884	.08653
43	.65190	.52718	.42677	.34584	.28054	.18517	.12270	.08163
44	.64545	.51939	.41840	.33740	.27237	.17805	.11686	.07701
45	.63905	.51171	.41020	.32917	.26444	.17120	.11130	.07265
46	.63273	.50415	.40215	.32115	.25674	.16461	.10600	.06854
47	.62646	.49670	.39427	.31331	.24926	.15828	.10095	.06466
48	.62026	.48936	.38654	.30567	.24200	.15219	.09614	.06100
49	.61412	.48213	.37896	.29822	.23495	.14634	.09156	.05755
50	.60804	.47500	.37153	.29094	.22811	.14071	.08720	.05429

n	1%	$1\frac{1}{2}$%	2%	$2\frac{1}{2}$%	3%	4%	5%	6%
1	1.0000	1.0000	1.0000	1.0000	1.0000	1.0000	1.0000	1.0000
2	2.0100	2.0150	2.0200	2.0250	2.0300	2.0400	2.0500	2.0600
3	3.0301	3.0452	3.0604	3.0756	3.0909	3.1216	3.1525	3.1836
4	4.0604	4.0909	4.1216	4.1525	4.1836	4.2465	4.3101	4.3746
5	5.1010	5.1523	5.2040	5.2563	5.3091	5.4163	5.5256	5.6371
6	6.1520	6.2296	6.3081	6.3877	6.4684	6.6330	6.8019	6.9753
7	7.2135	7.3230	7.4343	7.5474	7.6625	7.8983	8.1420	8.3938
8	8.2857	8.4328	8.5830	8.7361	8.8923	9.2142	9.5491	9.8975
9	9.3685	9.5593	9.7546	9.9545	10.1591	10.5828	11.0266	11.4913
10	10.4622	10.7027	10.9497	11.2034	11.4639	12.0061	12.5779	13.1808
11	11.5668	11.8633	12.1687	12.4835	12.8078	13.4864	14.2068	14.9716
12	12.6825	13.0412	13.4121	13.7956	14.1920	15.0258	15.9171	16.8699
13	13.8093	14.2368	14.6803	15.1404	15.6178	16.6268	17.7130	18.8821
14	14.9474	15.4504	15.9739	16.5190	17.0863	18.2919	19.5986	21.0151
15	16.0969	16.6821	17.2934	17.9319	18.5989	20.0236	21.5786	23.2760
16	17.2579	17.9324	18.6393	19.3802	20.1569	21.8245	23.6575	25.6725
17	18.4304	19.2014	20.0121	20.8647	21.7616	23.6975	25.8404	28.2129
18	19.6147	20.4894	21.4123	22.3863	23.4144	25.6454	28.1324	30.9057
19	20.8109	21.7967	22.8406	23.9460	25.1169	27.6712	30.5390	33.7600
20	22.0190	23.1237	24.2974	25.5447	26.8704	29.7781	33.0660	36.7856
21	23.2392	24.4705	25.7833	27.1833	28.6765	31.9692	35.7193	39.9927
22	24.4716	25.8376	27.2990	28.8629	30.5368	34.2480	38.5052	43.3923
23	25.7163	27.2251	28.8450	30.5844	32.4529	36.6179	41.4305	46.9958
24	26.9735	28.6335	30.4219	32.3490	34.4265	39.0826	44.5020	50.8156
25	28.2432	30.0630	32.0303	34.1578	36.4593	41.6459	47.7271	54.8645
26	29.5256	31.5140	33.6709	36.0117	38.5530	44.3117	51.1135	59.1564
27	30.8209	32.9867	35.3443	37.9120	40.7096	47.0842	54.6691	63.7058
28	32.1291	34.4815	37.0512	39.8598	42.9309	49.9676	58.4026	68.5281
29	33.4504	35.9987	38.7922	41.8563	45.2189	52.9663	62.3227	73.6398
30	34.7849	37.5387	40.5681	43.9027	47.5754	56.0849	66.4388	79.0582
31	36.1327	39.1018	42.3794	46.0003	50.0027	59.3283	70.7608	84.8017
32	37.4941	40.6883	44.2270	48.1503	52.5028	62.7015	75.2988	90.8898
33	38.8690	42.2986	46.1116	50.3540	55.0778	66.2095	80.0638	97.3432
34	40.2577	43.9331	48.0338	52.6129	57.7302	69.8579	85.0670	104.1838
35	41.6603	45.5921	49.9945	54.9282	60.4621	73.6522	90.3203	111.4348
36	43.0769	47.2760	51.9944	57.3014	63.2759	77.5983	95.8363	119.1209
37	44.5076	48.9851	54.0343	59.7339	66.1742	81.7022	101.6281	127.2681
38	45.9527	50.7199	56.1149	62.2273	69.1594	85.9703	107.7095	135.9042
39	47.4123	52.4807	58.2372	64.7830	72.2342	90.4091	114.0950	145.0585
40	48.8864	54.2679	60.4020	67.4026	75.4013	95.0255	120.7998	154.7620
41	50.3752	56.0819	62.6100	70.0876	78.6633	99.8265	127.8398	165.0477
42	51.8790	57.9231	64.8622	72.8398	82.0232	104.8196	135.2318	175.9505
43	53.3978	59.7920	67.1595	75.6608	85.4839	110.0124	142.9933	187.5076
44	54.9318	61.6889	69.5027	78.5523	89.0484	115.4129	151.1430	199.7580
45	56.4811	63.6142	71.8927	81.5161	92.7199	121.0294	159.7002	212.7435
46	58.0459	65.5684	74.3306	84.5540	96.5015	126.8706	168.6852	226.5081
47	59.6263	67.5519	76.8172	87.6679	100.3965	132.9454	178.1194	241.0986
48	61.2226	69.5652	79.3535	90.8596	104.4084	139.2632	188.0254	256.5645
49	62.8348	71.6087	81.9406	94.1311	108.5406	145.8337	198.4267	272.9584
50	64.4632	73.6828	84.5794	97.4843	112.7969	152.6671	209.3480	290.3359

n	1%	1½%	2%	2½%	3%	4%	5%	6%
1	.9901	.9852	.9804	.9756	.9709	.9615	.9524	.9434
2	1.9704	1.9559	1.9416	1.9274	1.9135	1.8861	1.8594	1.8334
3	2.9410	2.9122	2.8839	2.8560	2.8286	2.7751	2.7232	2.6730
4	3.9020	3.8544	3.8077	3.7620	3.7171	3.6299	3.5460	3.4651
5	4.8534	4.7826	4.7135	4.6458	4.5797	4.4518	4.3295	4.2124
6	5.7955	5.6972	5.6014	5.5081	5.4172	5.2421	5.0757	4.9173
7	6.7282	6.5982	6.4720	6.3494	6.2303	6.0021	5.7864	5.5824
8	7.6517	7.4859	7.3255	7.1701	7.0197	6.7327	6.4632	6.2098
9	8.5660	8.3605	8.1622	7.9709	7.7861	7.4353	7.1078	6.8017
10	9.4713	9.2222	8.9826	8.7521	8.5302	8.1109	7.7217	7.3601
11	10.3676	10.0711	9.7868	9.5142	9.2526	8.7605	8.3064	7.8869
12	11.2551	10.9075	10.5753	10.2578	9.9540	9.3851	8.8633	8.3838
13	12.1337	11.7315	11.3484	10.9832	10.6350	9.9856	9.3936	8.8527
14	13.0037	12.5434	12.1062	11.6909	11.2961	10.5631	9.8986	9.2950
15	13.8651	13.3432	12.8493	12.3814	11.9379	11.1184	10.3797	9.7122
16	14.7179	14.1313	13.5777	13.0550	12.5611	11.6523	10.8378	10.1059
17	15.5623	14.9076	14.2919	13.7122	13.1661	12.1657	11.2741	10.4773
18	16.3983	15.6726	14.9920	14.3534	13.7535	12.6593	11.6896	10.8276
19	17.2260	16.4262	15.6785	14.9789	14.3238	13.1339	12.0853	11.1581
20	18.0456	17.1686	16.3514	15.5892	14.8775	13.5903	12.4622	11.4699
21	18.8570	17.9001	17.0112	16.1845	15.4150	14.0292	12.8212	11.7641
22	19.6604	18.6208	17.6580	16.7654	15.9369	14.4511	13.1630	12.0416
23	20.4558	19.3309	18.2922	17.3321	16.4436	14.8568	13.4886	12.3034
24	21.2434	20.0304	18.9139	17.8850	16.9355	15.2470	13.7986	12.5504
25	22.0232	20.7196	19.5235	18.4244	17.4131	15.6221	14.0939	12.7834
26	22.7952	21.3986	20.1210	18.9506	17.8768	15.9828	14.3752	13.0032
27	23.5596	22.0676	20.7069	19.4640	18.3270	16.3296	14.6430	13.2105
28	24.3164	22.7267	21.2813	19.9649	18.7641	16.6631	14.8981	13.4062
29	25.0658	23.3761	21.8444	20.4535	19.1885	16.9837	15.1411	13.5907
30	25.8077	24.0158	22.3965	20.9303	19.6004	17.2920	15.3725	13.7648
31	26.5423	24.6461	22.9377	21.3954	20.0004	17.5885	15.5928	13.9291
32	27.2696	25.2671	23.4683	21.8492	20.3888	17.8736	15.8027	14.0840
33	27.9897	25.8790	23.9886	22.2919	20.7658	18.1476	16.0025	14.2302
34	28.7027	26.4817	24.4986	22.7238	21.1318	18.4112	16.1929	14.3681
35	29.4086	27.0756	24.9986	23.1452	21.4872	18.6646	16.3742	14.4982
36	30.1075	27.6607	25.4888	23.5563	21.8323	18.9083	16.5469	14.6210
37	30.7995	28.2371	25.9695	23.9573	22.1672	19.1426	16.7113	14.7368
38	31.4847	28.8051	26.4406	24.3486	22.4925	19.3679	16.8679	14.8460
39	32.1630	29.3646	26.9026	24.7303	22.8082	19.5845	17.0170	14.9491
40	32.8347	29.9158	27.3555	25.1028	23.1148	19.7928	17.1591	15.0463
41	33.4997	30.4590	27.7995	25.4661	23.4124	19.9931	17.2944	15.1380
42	34.1581	30.9941	28.2348	25.8206	23.7014	20.1856	17.4232	15.2245
43	34.8100	31.5212	28.6616	26.1664	23.9819	20.3708	17.5459	15.3062
44	35.4555	32.0406	29.0800	26.5038	24.2543	20.5488	17.6628	15.3832
45	36.0945	32.5523	29.4902	26.8330	24.5187	20.7200	17.7741	15.4558
46	36.7272	33.0565	29.8923	27.1542	24.7754	20.8847	17.8801	15.5244
47	37.3537	33.5532	30.2866	27.4675	25.0247	21.0429	17.9810	15.5890
48	37.9740	34.0426	30.6731	27.7732	25.2667	21.1951	18.0772	15.6500
49	38.5881	34.5247	31.0521	28.0714	25.5017	21.3415	18.1687	15.7076
50	39.1961	34.9997	31.4236	28.3623	25.7298	21.4822	18.2559	15.7619

Age	Number living	Number dying	Age	Number living	Number dying	Age	Number living	Number dying
10	100,000	749	**40**	78,106	765	**70**	38,569	2,391
11	99,251	746	41	77,341	774	71	36,178	2,448
12	98,505	743	42	76,567	785	72	33,730	2,487
13	97,762	740	43	75,782	797	73	31,243	2,505
14	97.022	737	44	74,985	812	74	28,738	2,501
15	96,285	735	45	74,173	828	75	26,237	2,476
16	95,550	732	46	73,345	848	76	23,761	2,431
17	94,818	729	47	72,497	870	77	21,330	2,369
18	94,089	727	48	71,627	896	78	18,961	2,291
19	93,362	725	49	70,731	927	79	16,670	2,196
20	92,637	723	**50**	69,804	962	**80**	14,474	2,091
21	91,914	722	51	68,842	1,001	81	12,383	1,964
22	91,192	721	52	67,841	1,044	82	10,419	1,816
23	90,471	720	53	66,797	1,091	83	8,603	1,648
24	89,751	719	54	65,706	1,143	84	6,955	1,470
25	89,032	718	55	64,563	1,199	85	5,485	1,292
26	88,314	718	56	63,364	1,260	86	4,193	1,114
27	87,596	718	57	62,104	1,325	87	3,079	933
28	86,878	718	58	60,779	1,394	88	2,146	744
29	86,160	719	59	59,385	1,468	89	1,402	555
30	85,441	720	**60**	57,917	1,546	**90**	847	385
31	84,721	721	61	56,371	1,628	91	462	246
32	84,000	723	62	54,743	1,713	92	216	137
33	83,277	726	63	53,030	1,800	93	79	58
34	82,551	729	64	51,230	1,889	94	21	18
35	81,822	732	65	49,341	1,980	95	3	3
36	81,090	737	66	47,361	2,070			
37	80,353	742	67	45,291	2,158			
38	79,611	749	68	43,133	2,243			
39	78,862	756	69	40,890	2,321			

Index